Longman

Higher Science 1

for GCSE

Mark Levesley

Jackie Hardie

Richard O'Regan

Sarah Pitt

Nicky Thomas

Bob Wakefield

with additional material by

Richard Grime, Penny Johnson,
Silvia Newton, Mike O'Neill,
Gary Philpott

Contents for Higher Science

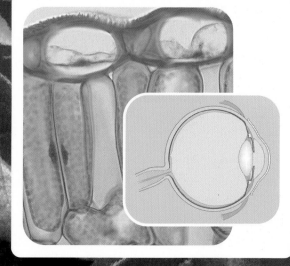

Matching chart for AQA Dual Award Specification

Name of module	AQA specification number	Higher Science module
Humans as Organisms	01	A (Book 1)
Maintenance of Life	02	B (Book 1)
Environment	03	G (Book 2)
Inheritance and Evolution	04	H (Book 2)
Metals	05	C (Book 1)
Earth materials	06	D (Book 1)
Patterns of Chemical Change	07	I (Book 2)
Structures and Bonding	08	J (Book 2)
Energy	09	E (Book 1)
Electricity	10	F (Book 1)
Forces	11	K (Book 2)
Waves and Radiation	12	L (Book 2)

Full topic by topic matching charts are available on the companion web site
www.higherscience.co.uk

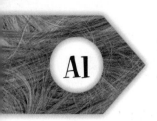

What is life?

What makes something alive?

We all know what it feels like to be alive, but it is hard to explain what life is.

Living things are called **organisms** and include all the plants and animals on Earth. Every living organism must carry out the seven life processes to keep itself alive.

Respiration
Living things get energy from food (often by using oxygen).

Movement
Living things can move all or part of themselves.

Reproduction
Living things can produce offspring.

Nutrition
All living things feed. Plants use energy from light to help them make food. Animals eat plants or other animals.

Excretion
Living things get rid of the waste substances they produce.

Sensitivity
Living things can sense and respond to changes in their surroundings.

Growth
Living things can increase the size of their bodies by adding mass and (often) new cells.

? 1 List the seven life processes.

A *The seven life processes.*

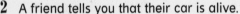

? 2 A friend tells you that their car is alive.
  a) Give three reasons why your friend is wrong.
  b) Give three ways in which a car is similar to something that is alive.

All organisms are made of **cells**. Cells are very small. About 40 cells from the inside of your cheek would fit into a line 1 mm long.

? 3 What are all organisms made from?

A cell is separated from its surroundings by a **cell membrane**. It controls which substances can get into and out of the cell.

The **nucleus** controls the chemical reactions that take place in the cytoplasm.

The **cytoplasm** is where many chemical reactions take place.

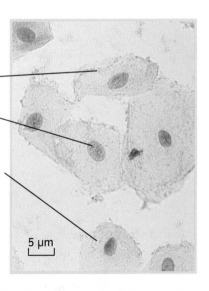

5 μm

B *Human cheek cells seen with a light microscope. Magnification ×1000.*

Looking at cells

Although cells can look different, they all have the same basic structure. They contain smaller structures called **organelles** (e.g. the nucleus) which carry out the different processes necessary for life.

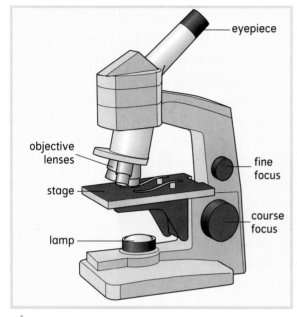

C   *A light microscope.*

! The sizes of microscopic things are measured in micrometres, written µm.

One µm is 1/1000 of a millimetre.

P   You can look at some human cells with a microscope. How could you measure the size of these cells with a microscope?

? **8** Which parts of a cell can be seen using an electron microscope?

9 Why are there are a lot of mitochondria in muscle cells?

10 Look at photographs B and D. Work out the actual sizes of:
- **a)** the nucleus
- **b)** the mitochondrion.

? **4** Look at photograph B. Use it to draw a diagram of a cheek cell. Label your diagram.

5 What separates a cell from its surroundings?

6 What controls the cell?

7 Where do the chemical reactions happen in a cell?

Light microscopes can magnify up to 1000 times (×1000). However, some parts of a cell are too small to be seen with a light microscope.

An **electron microscope** can magnify up to 500 000 times (×500 000). Electron microscopes use a beam of electrons instead of light. The image shows up on a fluorescent screen, and can be photographed. Using an electron microscope, organelles called **mitochondria** can be seen in the cytoplasm of a cell. Respiration takes place inside mitochondria.

D   *A mitochondrion as seen with an electron microscope. Magnification ×350 000.*

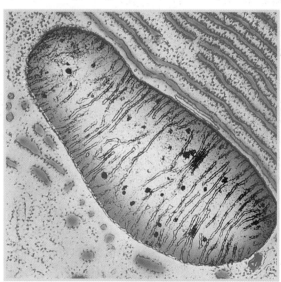

Summary

Write sentences in your own words to explain the following words:

cell   cell membrane   cytoplasm
mitochondria   nucleus   organism
respiration

Cells, tissues and organs

How are cells adapted to carry out their functions?

Your body is made of millions of cells. Cells come in different shapes and sizes. They all have jobs to do and their shapes help them to do their jobs. We say that the cells are **adapted** to their **functions** (jobs).

Your **white blood cells** can change shape, so they can move, and surround and destroy microbes.

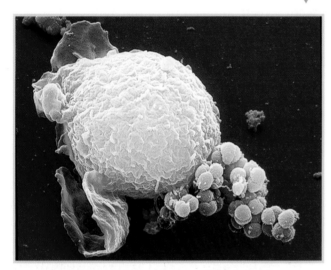

Nerve cells have lots of fine threads on their surface so they can make connections with lots of other nerve cells. This means they can pass electrical messages (called **impulses**) from one cell to another.

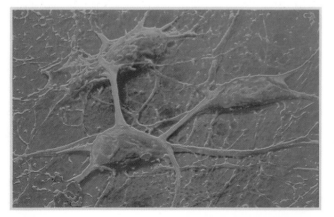

Muscle cells are long and thin. These cells can **contract** (get shorter). When groups of muscle cells contract they move part of your body.

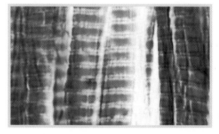

? 1 Why do cells have different shapes?

2 How is a white blood cell adapted to its job of killing bacteria?

3 How do muscle cells move parts of your body?

Tissues, organs and systems

Cells are often grouped together with other cells of the same type to do one job. A group of cells like this is called a **tissue**. For example, epithelial cells cover the surfaces of your body and form **epithelial** tissue.

D Epithelial tissue.

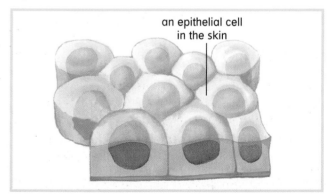

an epithelial cell in the skin

4 a) What is a tissue?
b) Name one part of the body that contains epithelial tissue.

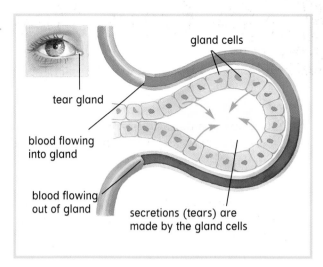

Gland cells are grouped together to form **glandular** tissue. Gland cells work to make fluids called **secretions**, which leave the cells and go to other parts of the body. For example, in your eyes the cells of your tear glands make the secretions we call tears. These tears pass out from the gland cells and are used to clean the surfaces of your eyes.

5 a) What does glandular tissue produce?
b) Write down the name of one gland.

A group of different tissues all working together is called an **organ**. Your eyes, stomach and heart are all organs. Each organ has one main job. Your stomach is made of muscle, nerve and glandular tissue. Your stomach's main job is to mix the food you swallow with secretions from its glandular tissue. The muscle tissue in the stomach walls contracts and so the food inside it is mixed with the secretions.

Organs often work together in **organ systems**. Your mouth, gullet, stomach, intestines, pancreas and liver are all organs that are found in the **digestive system** which breaks down the food that you swallow.

6 Write down the names of three tissues found in the stomach.

7 What is the difference between a tissue and an organ?

8 Draw an outline of your body on A4 paper. Draw in the places where you would find your brain, heart, stomach, lungs, liver and kidneys.

9 a) Find out the functions of red blood cells, ciliated epithelial cells and sperm cells.
b) Explain how these three cells are adapted to their functions.

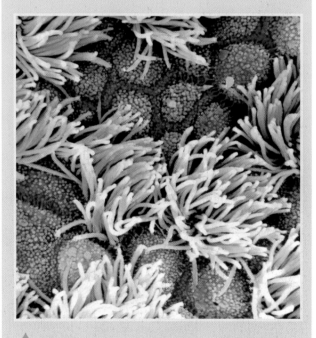

F   *Ciliated epithelial cells.*

Summary

Make up a 'fill in the gaps' exercise to describe how different cells are adapted to their functions. Provide a 'filled in' version as well. Then give the blank one to a friend to see if they can complete it.

Food

Why do we need to eat?

Nutrition means eating food to keep us healthy and to keep our cells alive. We eat food that comes from animals and from plants. What you eat is called your **diet**.

You need food to:

- give your body energy
- supply substances that can be used for growth and repairing your body
- supply substances that are needed to keep you healthy.

1 Write down three things your body needs food for.

All foods contain water and other chemicals called **nutrients**. These nutrients can be divided into five groups: **proteins**, **carbohydrates**, **fats**, **vitamins** and **minerals**. To stay healthy you need to eat the right amounts of these nutrients. You also need to eat foods containing **fibre**, and you also need **water**.

2 **a)** List the five kinds of nutrients that your body needs.
b) What other substances does your body need?

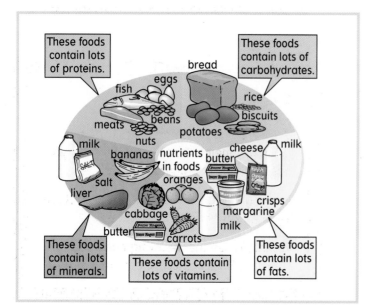

A *People in different countries eat different types of food.*

About 75% of your body is water. It is used to dissolve other substances and carry them around your body. Water also helps you get rid of waste chemicals.

Most of every cell in your body is made of **protein**. Protein is needed in your diet to keep your body growing and to help replace cells that have worn out. Protein is also needed for repairing cells that are damaged.

Proteins are giant molecules made up of long chains of smaller molecules. These smaller molecules are called **amino acids**.

3 **a)** Look at diagram B. Which foods have protein in them?
b) Why does the body need protein?

B *Different foods contain different amounts of nutrients.*

Carbohydrates are needed for energy. **Sugars** are carbohydrates, and so is **starch**. Starch is a giant molecule (polymer) made up of long chains of smaller sugar molecules.

Sucrose is the sugar found in fruits and in the stems of plants like sugar cane. Another sugar is **glucose**. Glucose is the fuel used by cells for respiration. Sugars dissolve in water and taste sweet. Starch is found in some plant leaves, wheat, potatoes, and rice. Starch does not taste sweet. It is **insoluble** in water.

The cell walls in plants are made of **cellulose** which is also called **fibre**. Cellulose is also made out of long chains of sugar molecules but it cannot be digested by your body. However, it gives the muscles of your intestines something to squeeze against. This means your intestines get exercise and keep fit!

Fats can be liquid, like olive oil, or solid like the fat on meat. Fats do not dissolve in water. There is a fat layer underneath your skin which helps to keep your body warm. Fat around delicate organs, like your kidneys, protects them from damage. Fat is needed to make cell membranes and can also be used as an energy store.

Minerals and **vitamins** are needed in very small quantities to help the body to work properly.

P How could you find out if foods contain starch, glucose or protein?

C

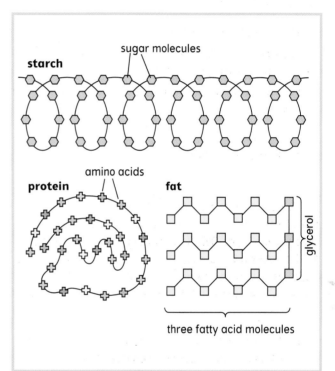

D *Different food substances have different structures.*

Summary

Draw up a table listing the following nutrients, their food sources and why you need each nutrient for a healthy diet:

carbohydrates   fats   fibre   proteins
vitamins and minerals   water

You could use the following headings: Nutrient, Food source, Use in the body.

The digestive system

What happens to food as it travels down your gut?

Your gut is all the tubes in your digestive system. It is not a straight tube. It is coiled up so that the 6.5 metres of your gut can be fitted inside your body. Your gut is made of several tissues, including muscular and glandular tissues. The nutrients in your food must dissolve so that they can move through the wall of the small intestine and into your blood. Proteins, starch and fats are insoluble. They have to be split into smaller, soluble units which do dissolve. The splitting of the molecules is called **digestion**.

1 What is digestion?

2 Why is digestion necessary?

Inside the gut, food is mixed with **enzymes** and other substances to help digest the food. Some of these substances are produced by organs like the liver and pancreas. Your gut and all the organs needed to digest your food are called the **digestive system**. Useful products are **absorbed** through the wall of the small intestine into your bloodstream.

! You can swallow food when you are upside down. Astronauts can swallow their food because muscles in the gullet push the food to their stomach, whatever position they are in!

Digestion begins in your mouth. When you chew food you chop it into smaller pieces. The food is mixed with **saliva**, which contains **enzymes** and also a slimy substance called **mucus** which helps food slip down your **gullet**. Your tongue shapes the food into a small ball that is easy to swallow.

? **3** How is food changed in your mouth?

Muscles of the gullet push the ball of food towards the stomach. This is called **peristalsis**.

Your **stomach** is a bag with lots of muscle in its walls. There are rings of muscle at each end of the stomach which work like elastic bands, so food can be held in your stomach for a couple of hours.

Your stomach muscles work to squeeze on the food. This mixes the food with a **digestive juice** made by the glandular tissue in the stomach lining. This **secretion** is called **gastric juice**. After several hours, your meal becomes a soup-like liquid. The liquid is squirted into the next part of your gut, the **small intestine**.

? **4 a)** How long is food kept in the stomach?
    b) What keeps the food in the stomach?

5 What do the stomach muscles do?

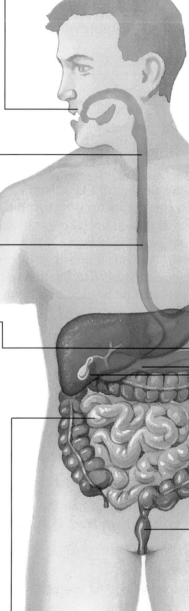

A The human digestive system.

In the small intestine, digestive juices are secreted by the glandular tissue in your **pancreas** and the wall of the small intestine. **Bile** is also added. Bile is made in the **liver** and stored in the **gall bladder** until it is needed.

After digestion, the dissolved nutrients move across the wall of the small intestine and into the blood. This is called **absorption**.

Some parts of your food cannot be digested and absorbed. The cell walls of plants are made of cellulose, which you cannot digest. The cellulose (called **fibre**), makes the food bulky, and gives the muscles something to squeeze against as the food continues its journey through the gut.

6 Name two substances that are added to the food in the small intestine.

The undigested remains of your meal move into the **large intestine**, where water is absorbed into the blood.

In the last part, called the **rectum**, the remains are formed into solid waste (**faeces**) and stored. When you go to the toilet they are passed out through the **anus**.

7 What is absorbed in the large intestine?

Alexis St Martin was shot through the stomach in 1822. The hole did not heal because of the acid in gastric juice. He allowed doctors to insert pieces of meat through the hole to find out about digestion.

P If you add a blue chemical called DCPIP to fruit juice, the vitamin C in the fruit juice turns the DCPIP colourless. How would you find out which fruit juices contained the most vitamin C?

B

8 What does the liver make that helps digestion?

9 Why is cellulose present in faeces?

10 How is food moved along the gut?

11 Why is there mucus in saliva?

12 Find out how food is prevented from entering the windpipe (trachea).

Summary

Copy and complete the table to show what happens to food as it passes along your gut from the mouth.

Part of gut	What happens to food
mouth	

Breaking down food

What substances help digestion?

The food that goes into your mouth is changed as it goes through you. The journey through your body takes between 24 and 48 hours.

1 List all the organs which are involved in the digestion of food.

2 How long does food take to go from your mouth to your anus?

Digestive juices and other substances are added to your food as it goes through your digestive system. These substances all have particular functions to break up your food into smaller particles so that nutrients can be absorbed. Digestive juices contain **enzymes**. These are chemicals that speed up the breakdown of large insoluble food molecules into smaller ones.

3 List three organs that produce amylase enzymes.

4 List three organs that produce protease enzymes.

5 List two organs that produce lipase enzymes.

Each kind of enzyme digests one type of nutrient:

- amylase enzymes digest carbohydrates such as starch
- protease enzymes digest protein
- lipase enzymes digest fats.

6 Where in the digestive system is starch digested?

7 Where are proteins digested?

8 Where are fats digested?

Chemicals are added to your food as it goes through your gut. Your gut is all the organs labelled here in red.

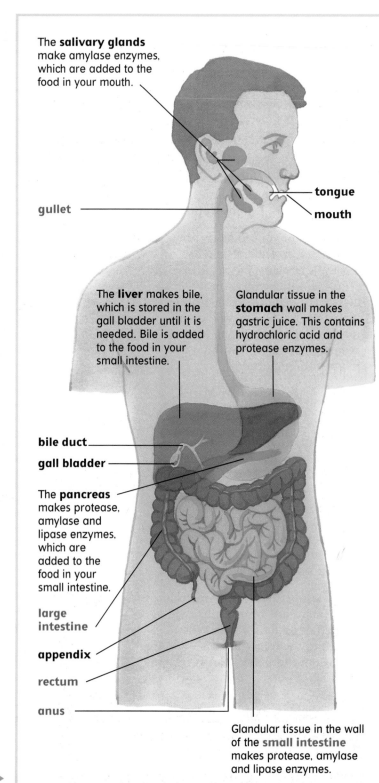

The **salivary glands** make amylase enzymes, which are added to the food in your mouth.

tongue

mouth

gullet

The **liver** makes bile, which is stored in the gall bladder until it is needed. Bile is added to the food in your small intestine.

Glandular tissue in the **stomach** wall makes gastric juice. This contains hydrochloric acid and protease enzymes.

bile duct

gall bladder

The **pancreas** makes protease, amylase and lipase enzymes, which are added to the food in your small intestine.

large intestine

appendix

rectum

anus

Glandular tissue in the wall of the **small intestine** makes protease, amylase and lipase enzymes.

The stomach produces **hydrochloric acid** because the protease enzymes in the stomach work best in acidic conditions. The acid also kills most of the micro-organisms (or microbes) that may be in your food.

9 How does the acid in your stomach protect you?

Bile is added to your food when it gets to the small intestine. The bile **neutralises** hydrochloric acid and makes the partly digested food slightly alkaline. This is because the enzymes that digest the food in the small intestine work best in **alkaline** conditions.

Bile also helps lipase enzymes to digest fat. It splits large drops of fat into smaller droplets. This is called **emulsification**. Many little droplets have a much larger surface area than one big drop. This gives the lipase enzymes more chance to break down the fats.

10 a) Where is bile made?
  b) Where is bile stored?

11 Describe two ways that bile helps enzymes to digest fats.

12 Suggest a reason why a piece of food will be broken down more rapidly by digestive enzymes if it is chewed first.

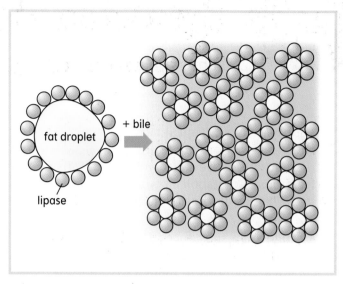

B When a large fat droplet is split into little droplets, there is more surface area for lipase enzymes to get to the fat and digest it.

C If you shake up a mixture of oil and water, it does not stay mixed for very long. If you put some bile in as well, the oil breaks up into tiny droplets and stays mixed up with the water. This is called an **emulsion**.

Summary

You eat a chicken sandwich and drink a glass of milk. Describe the journey of this meal through your gut, explaining which enzymes or other substances are added at each stage, and where the different nutrients are digested.

P Chew a piece of bread for about 3 minutes to mix it with saliva in your mouth.

- What happens to the taste of the bread?
- Can you predict what is happening to the starch in the bread?
- How would you find out if saliva contains an enzyme which digests starch?

More about enzymes

What are enzymes?

Your body is a chemical factory. At any one time hundreds of chemical reactions are taking place inside every cell. Together these reactions are called your **metabolism**. The chemical reactions of metabolism would go very slowly, or not at all, if our bodies did not contain enzymes.

A catalyst is a substance that speeds up chemical reactions. Since enzymes speed up (**catalyse**) chemical reactions in living cells, they are sometimes called **biological catalysts**.

Some enzymes speed up reactions involving the breaking down of large molecules into smaller ones. This type of reaction is important in digestion, where large food molecules are broken down into smaller molecules. Other enzymes speed up the **synthesis** (building up) of large molecules from smaller ones, for example when the body makes proteins from amino acids.

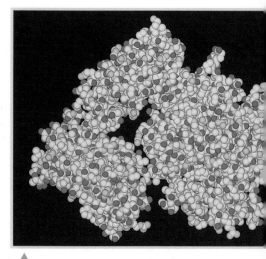

A   *A molecular model of an enzyme.*

> **!** An enzyme helps energy to be transferred from food to a molecule called ATP during respiration. ATP is used by the body to store energy until it is needed.

?
1   Name a reaction that involves breaking down large molecules into smaller ones.

2   Which of the seven life processes rely on synthesis reactions?

How an enzyme works

A molecule that an enzyme works on is called its **substrate**. The part of the enzyme surface which catalyses the reaction is called the **active site**. The active site of an enzyme will only fit onto a substrate with the correct shape; in other words they fit like a 'lock and key'. Enzymes can be used over and over again as they are unchanged at the end of the reaction.

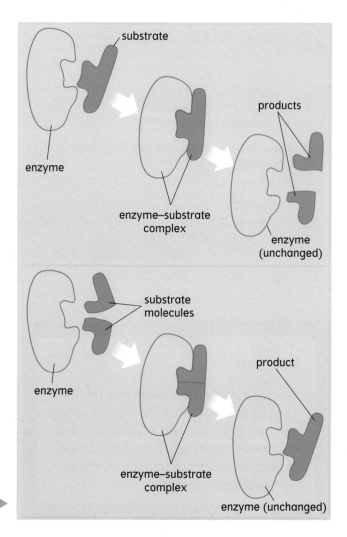

B

Enzymes are affected by temperature. Most human enzymes work best at about 37 °C. This is said to be their **optimum temperature**. At lower temperatures enzymes work more slowly. At higher temperatures (above about 45 °C) the shape of the active site of the enzyme is changed and the substrate no longer fits. We say the enzyme has been **denatured** and it no longer works.

> Amylase enzymes from the bacterium *Bacillus stearothermophilus*, which are used in biological washing powders, are only denatured at 75 °C.

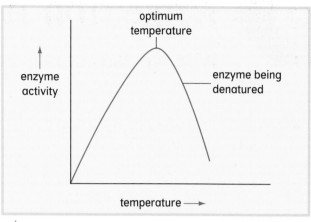

C *Effect of temperature on enzyme activity.*

Each enzyme works best at a certain pH. Most human enzymes work best at around pH7, but there are some exceptions. For instance, the protease enzymes in your stomach work best at around pH1 to pH2 (strong acid). If the pH changes, the shape of the active site is changed and the enzyme stops working. It becomes denatured.

Enzymes have the following properties:

- They are made of protein.
- They speed up (**catalyse**) reactions but are not changed themselves.
- They are **specific**, which means that they work on one type of substrate only.
- They work best within a small pH range, which is different for each enzyme.
- They work fastest when warm, but are denatured at high temperatures.

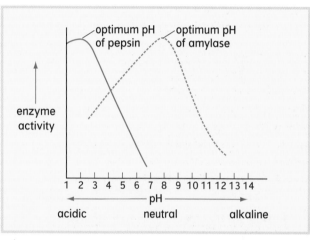

D *Effect of pH on enzyme activity.*

3 What happens to the active site of many enzymes if they are heated above 45 °C?

4 An amylase is produced in the mouth. It works best in neutral conditions. Write a sentence to explain why this amylase will not work in the stomach.

5 What is an enzyme made of?

6 Why is only a small amount of enzyme needed to speed up a reaction?

7 Biological washing powders contain protein-digesting enzymes.
  a) What advice would you put on the container on how to get the best results with a biological washing powder?
  b) Explain your advice.

Summary

A Using the idea of the active site, draw labelled diagrams to show why an enzyme works on only one substrate.

B Draw a diagram to explain why a denatured enzyme does not work. Explain how an enzyme could be denatured.

Digestion and absorption

Why does food need to be digested?

When nutrients are **absorbed**, they go through the wall of your small intestine into your blood. Only small, soluble molecules can pass through. Proteins, starch and fats are large, insoluble molecules. They have to be split into smaller molecules which do dissolve. Vitamins and minerals are soluble, so they are able to pass through the walls of the small intestine and do not need to be digested.

1 **a)** What is digestion?
   b) Name two nutrients that do not need to be digested.

2 Explain why most food has to be digested before it can be absorbed into the body.

Enzymes help to speed up or **catalyse** digestion. Enzymes are found in **digestive juices**, which are made in glandular tissue in different parts of the digestive system.

3 What is glandular tissue? (*Hint*: see page 9.)

4 How do digestive juices help digestion?

Each different kind of enzyme catalyzes the digestion of a different kind of nutrient. The name of an enzyme tells you the nutrient it digests.

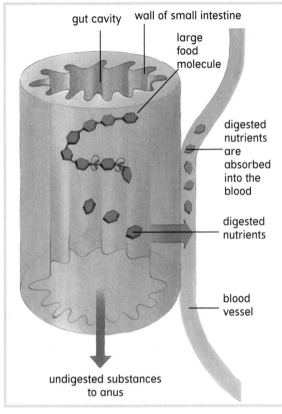

A *Part of the small intestine.*

The names of enzymes always end in -ase. **B**

Nutrient		Enzyme	Product	
	starch	Amylases found in digestive juices from the salivary glands, the pancreas and the small intestine.	glucose (a sugar)	
	proteins	Proteases found in digestive juices from the stomach, the pancreas and the small intestine.	amino acids	
	fats	Lipases found in digestive juices from the pancreas and the small intestine.	fatty acids and glycerol	

5 Look at table B.
 a) What is the name of an enzyme that works on starch?
 b) What are the products of fat digestion?
 c) What are proteins digested into?

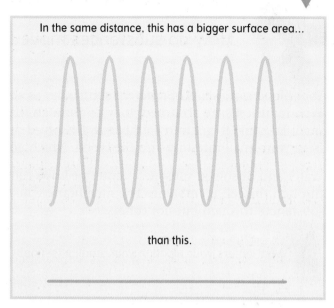

In the same distance, this has a bigger surface area...

than this.

Digested nutrients are absorbed into the blood through the walls of the small intestine. More nutrients can be absorbed faster if there is a large **surface area**. The surface area of something can be made larger if it is folded.

The inside lining of your small intestine has about 5 million tiny finger-like projections on it, so the total surface area is very large. Each projection is called a **villus** and is about 1 mm long. The plural of villus is **villi**.

D

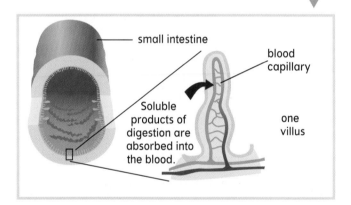

small intestine

blood capillary

Soluble products of digestion are absorbed into the blood.

one villus

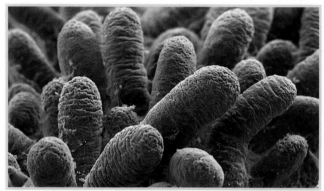

E *Photomicrograph of villi in the small intestine ×62.*

The small intestine is well adapted for the absorption of nutrients because it is very long and has:

- very thin walls
- a large surface area
- a good blood supply.

6 What is a villus?

7 How is the small intestine adapted for the absorption of nutrients?

8 Why do you think the small intestine is very long?

9 Explain why the small intestine has a large surface area.

Summary

Draw a concept map to summarise what you have learned about the digestion and absorption of food. Include the words:

amylase, lipase, mouth, pancreas, protease, small intestine, soluble, stomach, villi.

Start your map like this:

food

amylase

mouth

digests starch

Diffusion and active transport

How do substances move from one place to another?

Your blood carries lots of different substances around your body. When nutrients are **absorbed**, they go through the wall of the small intestine to get into your blood. Dissolved nutrients go from your small intestine into the blood, which goes to your liver.

Water and dissolved substances enter or leave cells by passing through the cell membrane. The membrane will allow some substances through but not others.

? 1 What enters your blood in your small intestine?

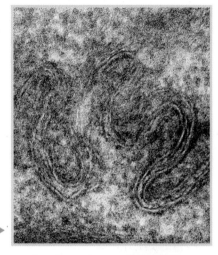

Cell membrane
× 1 000 000.
A

Look at picture B. There is a lot of the purple chemical in the middle of the tank.

There is a **high concentration** of the purple chemical here.

There is a **low concentration** of the purple chemical here.

B *The purple chemical has just been put into the tank.*

C *After a few hours, the purple chemical has spread out to fill the tank.*

The particles which make up all substances are moving all the time. Look at picture C. After a few hours, the particles of the purple chemical have moved around and spread out. This spreading movement is called **diffusion**. We say the particles have moved along a **concentration gradient**.

When there is a big difference in concentration, diffusion happens quickly.

? 2 What is diffusion?

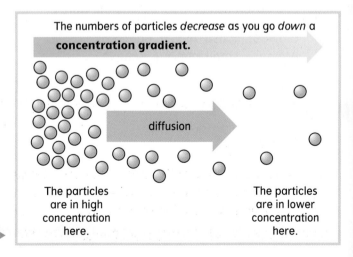

The numbers of particles *decrease* as you go *down* a **concentration gradient.**

diffusion

The particles are in high concentration here.

The particles are in lower concentration here.

D

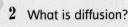

Substances move into and out of cells in your body by diffusion. There is a high concentration of dissolved nutrients inside your small intestine, and a low concentration in the blood. Nutrients diffuse through the walls of the villi in the small intestine into the blood. The walls of the villi are thin which allows diffusion to happen faster than if they were thicker. The villi have a good blood supply so that nutrients are carried away quickly.

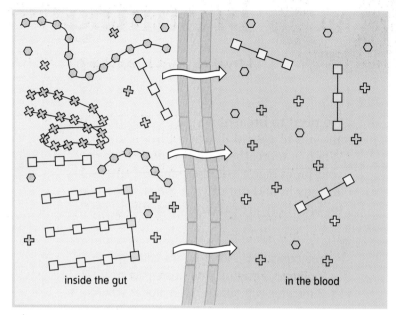

inside the gut   in the blood

 Nutrients diffuse into the blood.

? **3** How do nutrients from food get into your blood?

4 How is the small intestine adapted to help nutrients diffuse into the blood?

Active transport

In diffusion, substances move along a concentration gradient from a high to a low concentration. Cells can take up some substances in the opposite direction, against a concentration gradient. They do this using **active transport**. Glucose is absorbed from the small intestine by active transport. Active transport requires energy, which is provided by respiration in the cell. Cells involved in active transport contain a lot of mitochondria.

Active transport.

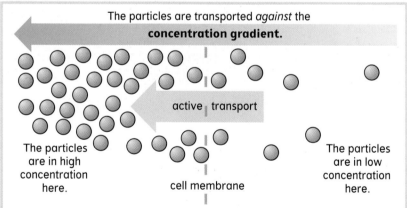

The particles are transported *against* the **concentration gradient.**

active transport

The particles are in high concentration here.

cell membrane

The particles are in low concentration here.

? **5** What is active transport?

6 Where in the body is glucose absorbed by active transport?

7 Why do villi have very thin walls?

8 Explain how a good blood supply to the villi speeds up diffusion.

9 a) When you breathe, oxygen diffuses from the air in your lungs into your blood. Where is the concentration of oxygen highest?
b) Which other gas moves by diffusion in the lungs?

10 Poisons like cyanide stop respiration in cells. What effect do you think this would have on:
a) diffusion
b) active transport?

Summary

Describe the similarities and differences between active transport and diffusion. Include the words concentration gradient and energy in your answer.

21

Breathing

How do we breathe?

We need to **breathe** to get oxygen from the air, and to get rid of waste carbon dioxide. When you breathe, muscles move to make your lungs bigger and then smaller. This makes air flow in and out of your lungs. The organs for breathing are called the **breathing system**.

You can survive for 3 weeks without food and 3 days without water but only 3 minutes without air. So in places where there is no air, humans take it with them!

A

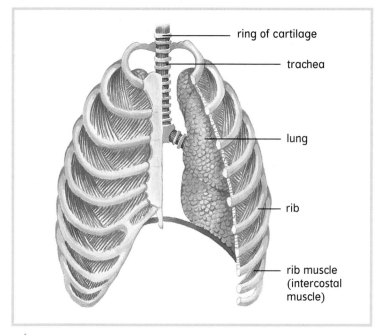

B *Your lungs are protected by your ribs and muscles* C

Your lungs are in your **thorax** (chest). The **diaphragm** is a sheet of muscle that separates your thorax from your **abdomen** (the lower part of your body). Your lungs are protected by your ribs. There are muscles between your ribs that can move them.

1 What is the thorax?
2 What is the diaphragm?

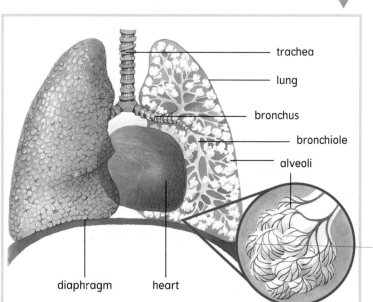

From your nose and mouth, air goes into your windpipe or **trachea**. The trachea is kept open by tough rings of gristle called **cartilage**. The trachea divides into two **bronchi**. Each bronchus divides into smaller tubes (**bronchioles**) in your lungs.

3 Air travels from your nose to the alveoli. List the parts it goes through in order.

At the tips of the smallest branches are tiny pockets (**alveoli**). These alveoli have thin walls and are surrounded by a network of very tiny blood vessels, called **capillaries**, which have blood in them.

When you breathe, the diaphragm and the muscles between your ribs (intercostal muscles) can make your thorax bigger or smaller.

When you breathe in, or **inhale**:

- intercostal muscles contract, pulling the ribcage upwards and out
- the diaphragm muscles contract, pulling the diaphragm down.

These movements of the ribs and diaphragm increase the volume of your thorax. This reduces the air pressure inside your lungs and air flows in.

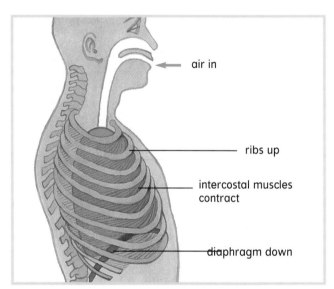

air in

ribs up

intercostal muscles contract

diaphragm down

 Inhalation.

The movement of air in and out of your lungs is called **ventilation**.

! You cannot breathe and swallow at the same time. When you swallow, a small flap moves over the opening to your trachea. This flap is your epiglottis. It makes sure food does not go down the wrong way and get into your breathing tubes. If some food lands on the flap, you cough and splutter to jerk the food away.

4 Which muscles move to change the size of your thorax?

When you breathe out, or **exhale**:

- intercostal muscles relax, and the ribcage falls down
- the diaphragm muscles relax so the diaphragm moves up.

These movements decrease the volume of your thorax. This increases the air pressure and air flows out of the lungs.

Exhalation.

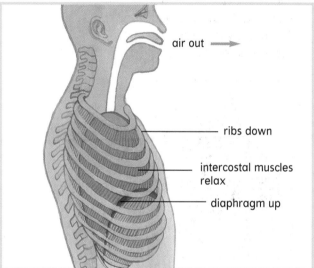

air out

ribs down

intercostal muscles relax

diaphragm up

5 What is ventilation?

6 What type of tissue is the diaphragm made of?

7 What is the function of:
   a) the diaphragm
   b) the intercostal muscles?

8 Explain why air flows into the lungs during inhalation.

Summary

A Write a paragraph to explain how you ventilate your lungs.

B Why is ventilation vital for life?

Inside the lungs

What happens to the air that you breathe in?

Air is moved in and out of the lungs when you breathe. This is **ventilation**. Oxygen from the air needs to get into your blood so that it can be taken to the other cells in your body. Waste carbon dioxide needs to be removed from the blood so you can breathe it out.

If your lungs are to work properly, they must be kept clean. Air enters and leaves your body through your nose and mouth. When you breathe in through your nose, the air passes over the warm, moist lining in your nostrils. The lining is covered in tiny hairs which work like a filter and trap any dust particles that are in the air.

 1 How does your nose help to clean the air you breathe in?

Air moves down the trachea and bronchi into the lungs. There are gland cells in the lining of these tubes. The gland cells make a sticky liquid called **mucus** which traps dust. Other cells (called **ciliated epithelial cells**) have tiny, moving hairs called **cilia**, which move the mucus towards your throat. You swallow this mucus. The mucus you blow out of your nose comes from your nose not your trachea.

 2 Which liquid traps dust?

3 How is the dust moved out of the breathing tubes?

4 How are ciliated epithelial cells adapted to their function?

 There are about 700 million alveoli in your lungs. If they were spread out they would cover the area of a tennis court!

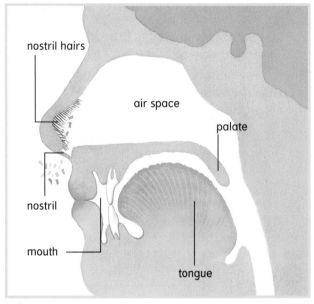

A

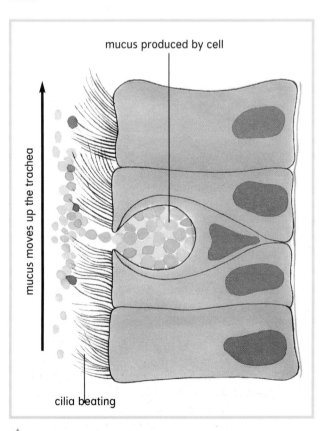

B *Ciliated epithelial cells.*

When the air is in the alveoli, oxygen has to **diffuse** into the blood. Your lungs are adapted for exchanging gases.

- The millions of alveoli provide a very large surface area.
- The moist walls of the alveoli allow gases to dissolve, so they can pass through the alveoli walls by diffusion.
- The walls of the alveoli and the walls of the capillaries are only one cell thick, so substances like oxygen have only a short distance to diffuse from one place to another.
- The alveoli are covered by capillaries to transport gases to and from the lungs.

Oxygen is at a higher concentration in the alveoli than in the blood, so it diffuses into the blood. The blood carries the oxygen away, so that the blood around the alveoli always has a low concentration of oxygen.

The blood brought to the lungs from the rest of the body contains waste carbon dioxide, which is at a higher concentration in the blood than in the air in the alveoli. The carbon dioxide diffuses from the blood into the alveoli.

The shape of the alveoli gives the lungs a very large surface area. This helps a lot of oxygen and carbon dioxide to diffuse into and out of the blood quickly. The diffusion of these gases in the lungs is called **gaseous exchange**.

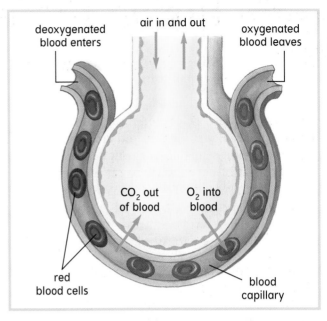

C Inside an alveolus.

5 Explain how the shape of the alveoli helps the diffusion of gases.

6 a) Why do alveoli have thin walls?
   b) Why are the alveoli surrounded by many blood capillaries?

7 Explain why:
   a) oxygen diffuses into the blood in the capillaries surrounding the alveoli
   b) carbon dioxide diffuses out of the blood.

8 It is possible to measure the differences between the air you breathe in and the air you breathe out. How would you expect the following to be different in the two samples? Explain your answers.
   a) oxygen   b) carbon dioxide
   c) water vapour   d) temperature.

P What would you predict about the temperature and amount of carbon dioxide in the air you breathe in compared with the air you breathed out?

- Will the air stay at the same temperature?
- Will there be the same amount of carbon dioxide?
- How would you find out?

D

Summary

Describe how the lungs are adapted to their function of gas exchange and how the breathing system cleans the air you breathe in.

Blood

What is blood and what does it do?

Blood looks like a thick, red liquid but it is really a yellow liquid (**plasma**) with lots of red coloured cells in it. Blood travels around your body in tubes called **blood vessels**. The smallest blood vessels are called **capillaries**, which have very thin walls. The blood vessels take the plasma and cells round and round your body, collecting and delivering chemicals. There are 4–5 litres of blood in an adult woman and 5–6 litres in an adult man.

Apart from red blood cells, the plasma also carries white blood cells and platelets. These all have different functions.

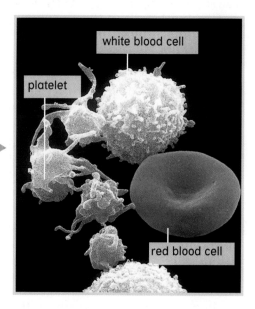

A

	Red blood cell	White blood cell	Platelet
number in 1 mm³ blood	5 000 000	7 000	250 000
nucleus	no	yes	no
life span	120 days	up to 40 years	variable
function	carries oxygen	protection	blood clotting

B

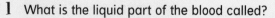

1 What is the liquid part of the blood called?

2 What is a capillary?

Red blood cells are very tiny. They are red because they contain a red chemical called **haemoglobin**. When blood flows through the capillaries in the lungs, oxygen attaches itself to haemoglobin forming **oxyhaemoglobin**. The blood carries the oxyhaemoglobin to the cells of your body. Oxygen leaves the oxyhaemoglobin and enters the cells that need it. Your cells use the oxygen to get energy from nutrients such as glucose by respiration. Nutrients from your digested food are dissolved in the plasma.

Respiration produces carbon dioxide as a waste product. The carbon dioxide leaves your cells and goes into your blood. It is dissolved in the plasma. The carbon dioxide is taken back to the lungs where it passes through the capillary walls into the alveoli and you breathe it out.

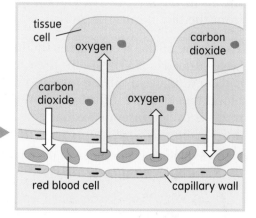

C

Red blood cells do not have a nucleus. A red blood cell survives for about 120 days, so you need to replace them all the time. In the hollow centres of some of your bones there is a substance called bone marrow. This is where your new red blood cells are made.

3 What do red blood cells do?

White blood cells are bigger than red blood cells. Your blood has far fewer white blood cells than red blood cells. All white blood cells have a nucleus. These cells can move and squeeze between the cells in the wall of a capillary. The white blood cells help protect you from disease. Some of them can destroy bacteria.

4 What do white blood cells do?

5 Give two differences between red blood cells and white blood cells.

Platelets are bits of cells. Platelets do not have a nucleus. The cells they come from are in the bone marrow. The platelets help blood to clot, so that cuts can heal.

6 What do platelets do?

7 Where are platelets formed?

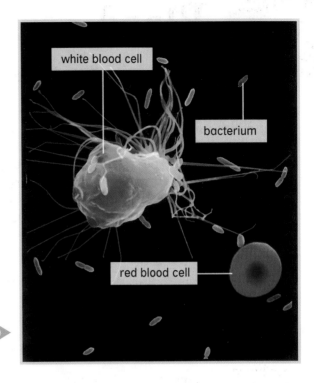

8 Write down three things that the plasma transports.

9 Name a waste chemical that is taken from your liver to your kidneys by the plasma.

10 Capillaries have thin walls. Why do you think this is important?

11 Red blood cells are packed with haemoglobin. Why do you think they have no nucleus?

12 People who don't have enough iron in their diet cannot make haemoglobin and become anaemic. Explain why people who are anaemic often feel tired and have fewer red blood cells.

A blood clot. E

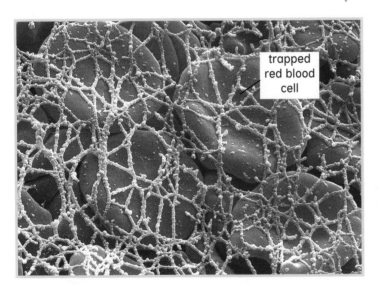

Plasma is mainly water. Dissolved substances and blood cells are transported around your body in the plasma. Nutrients like glucose and amino acids from the small intestine dissolve in plasma and are supplied to the rest of your body. Carbon dioxide leaves your cells and goes into the blood, where it dissolves in the plasma. The plasma carries it back to your lungs. Your liver breaks down amino acids that your body does not need. This produces waste called **urea**. The urea is dissolved in the plasma and is carried to the kidneys where it is excreted in the urine.

Summary

Produce a leaflet for a blood donor centre describing the structure and functions of red blood cells, white blood cells, platelets and plasma.

Blood vessels

Why do you have different kinds of blood vessels?

Your **heart** is an organ that pumps blood through tubes called **blood vessels**. The blood vessels and your heart form the **circulation system**. The system is in two parts: one part goes to the lungs and one part goes to all the other organs of your body. Blood is pumped from the right side of your heart to the lungs, where it collects oxygen and gets rid of carbon dioxide. This blood then comes back to the left side of the heart, where it is pumped to the rest of the body.

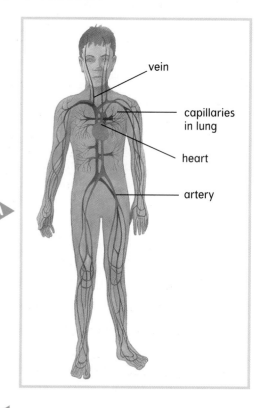

A

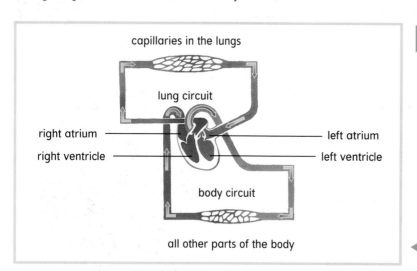

capillaries in the lungs

lung circuit

right atrium

right ventricle

left atrium

left ventricle

body circuit

all other parts of the body

B

There are three different types of blood vessels: **arteries**, **veins** and **capillaries**.

Arteries are tubes that take blood away from your heart. Your main artery (the aorta) carries the blood away from the left side of your heart. It is over 2.5 cm wide and branches many times, forming smaller arteries that go to the organs of your body. Another artery leaves the right side of your heart. It divides into two, and one branch goes to your right lung, the other to the left lung. Blood in these arteries picks up oxygen in the lungs and goes back to the left side of the heart. From there the blood goes around your body carrying oxygen to your different organs.

C

?

1   What are the three different kinds of blood vessel?

2   Where do arteries carry blood from?

Arteries have thick, muscular, elastic walls. The blood in the arteries is under very high pressure, so the artery walls stretch as the blood flows through. The muscles in the walls then contract, making the channel in the artery narrower and helping to push the blood along. Blood cells and plasma cannot get through the wall of an artery.

artery

Thick wall of elastic muscle. Arteries carry blood away from the heart.

vein

Thin wall of muscle. Veins carry blood back towards the heart.

capillary

Very thin wall. Capillaries allow substances to pass in and out of the bloodstream.

Veins carry blood back to the heart. The blood pressure in the veins is low, so veins have thinner walls than arteries. Blood cells and plasma cannot get through the wall of a vein.

Gravity helps blood get back to your heart from your head. However the blood from your legs has to go upwards against the force of gravity. To stop blood flowing the wrong way, veins often have **valves** in them.

Capillaries are the smallest blood vessels, about the thickness of a hair. In an organ, an artery branches into a network of capillaries. The capillaries pass close to all the cells in your organs. The walls of capillaries are very thin. This is so that substances such as glucose and oxygen carried in the blood can diffuse through them and reach the cells. Waste substances produced by the cells (like carbon dioxide) diffuse into the blood through the capillary walls. The capillaries link up to form a vein which takes blood back to the heart.

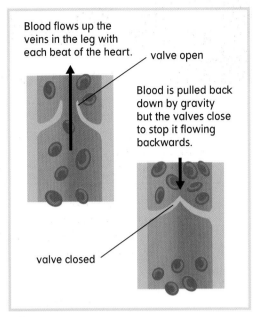

Blood flows up the veins in the leg with each beat of the heart.

valve open

Blood is pulled back down by gravity but the valves close to stop it flowing backwards.

valve closed

 Vein valves.

A model showing capillaries in a kidney.

3 What is the difference between the wall of an artery and the wall of a vein? Explain why are they different.

4 Where do you find capillary networks?

5 List four substances that are exchanged through the walls of the capillaries.

6 Give two ways in which capillaries are adapted to their function.

P If you had a piece of artery and a piece of vein, how would you find out which was most elastic (stretchy)?

! Your body contains enough capillaries to stretch around the world one and a half times!

7 List in order the organs and types of blood vessel the blood flows through as it goes around your body from your right leg and back again to your right leg.

8 What do you think are the advantages of having two separate circulation systems, one to the lungs and one to all the other organs of your body?

Summary

Draw up a table to show the differences between arteries, veins and capillaries. Include information about the walls of the blood vessels, blood pressure, valves, the direction of blood flow, and the amount of oxygen in the blood.

The heart and its beat

What is your heart and why does it beat?

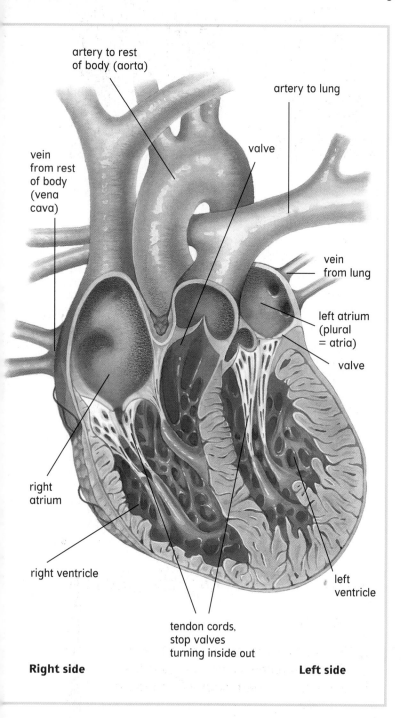

- artery to rest of body (aorta)
- artery to lung
- vein from rest of body (vena cava)
- valve
- vein from lung
- left atrium (plural = atria)
- valve
- right atrium
- right ventricle
- left ventricle
- tendon cords, stop valves turning inside out

Right side   **Left side**

 A *Diagrams of the heart are always drawn as if the person were facing you.*

 Your heart beats about 100 000 times each day.

Your heart is held in place inside your chest by strong threads. The heart is made of a special type of muscle which never gets tired. The muscle **contracts** (gets shorter) and pushes blood out of the heart into arteries. When the heart muscle **relaxes** (goes back to its original size) the heart fills with blood from the veins. Each time the muscle contracts, it is called a **heart beat**.

When a heart is cut open you see a thick wall down the middle. A heart has a right side and a left side; it is two pumps working side by side. Each pump has an upper space called an **atrium**, which receives blood from the veins. Each atrium then contracts and forces blood into a **ventricle**. The ventricles then contract to pump blood out of the heart into the arteries.

?

1 What are the two upper spaces in a heart called?

2 What are the two lower spaces in a heart called?

The two muscular pumps of the heart work together to push blood around your body. The right side pumps blood to your lungs to pick up oxygen and the left side pumps this blood to the rest of your body. Blood travels back to the heart through the veins and the journey round the body begins again.

?

3 Where does the right side of the heart pump blood to?

4 Where does the left side of the heart pump blood to?

An adult heart beats about 70 times every minute. The number of beats each minute is the **heart beat rate**. If you start to move or do any kind of exercise your heart beats faster. This is because during exercise your cells need more oxygen and nutrients. Your heart must work harder to get the blood carrying oxygen and nutrients to your cells quickly.

P How would you find out if your heart beat rate changes when your body is in different positions or doing different activities?

Body position or activity	Pulse rate			mean (average)
	Try 1	Try 2	Try 3	

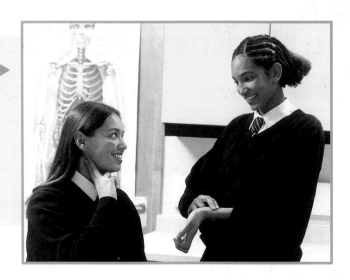

B

Blood is always pushed out of the heart in the correct direction because there are tough **heart valves** between the atria and the ventricles. These valves stop blood flowing back the wrong way.

? **5** What stops blood from going the wrong way?

P How would you find a way of listening to someone's heart? The sounds you hear are the heart valves slamming shut.

C

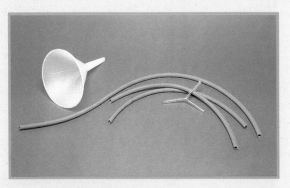

! Your heart does not take nutrients and oxygen from the blood passing through it. It has its own blood supply. The coronary arteries supply the heart muscle with oxygen and food. Waste is taken away in coronary veins. If a coronary artery gets blocked, then the heart muscle won't get the oxygen and nutrients it needs. The person will have a heart attack.

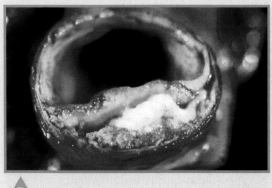

D *A partly blocked artery.*

? **6 a)** What happens to the heart beat rate when a person exercises?
b) Explain why this change takes place.

7 Explain what would happen if a coronary artery was blocked.

8 The left half of the heart has a thicker wall than the right half. Suggest a reason for this.

9 Before birth, a baby gets oxygen from the mother through the placenta. Sometimes a baby is born with a 'hole in the heart' between the two ventricles. Explain why these babies look blue.

Summary

Draw a flow chart to describe how blood circulates round the body. Include the lungs in your chart. Start your diagram like this:

left atrium → [ ] → [ ]
    ↑
[ ]

31

Respiration

Why does your body need oxygen?

Cells need energy to stay alive. Cells get energy by **respiration**.

The energy from respiration is used:

- to make your muscles contract to allow you to move
- to keep you warm
- to help you grow by building up larger molecules from smaller ones.

A *You use up energy even when you are asleep.*

? 1 What does your body need energy for?

Aerobic respiration is a chemical reaction that goes on all the time in the **mitochondria** of every cell of your body. **Glucose**, a sugar from digested food, combines with oxygen to release energy. It is called aerobic respiration because it needs oxygen from the *air*. The glucose and oxygen are used up inside the cells and two chemical products are made, carbon dioxide and water. The carbon dioxide is carried away from your cells to your lungs and you breathe it out. Some of the water may be used by the cells.

This is the **word equation** for respiration. Energy is put in brackets because it is not a substance.

glucose + oxygen $\longrightarrow$ carbon dioxide + water (+ energy)

P When you exercise, what will happen to the number of breaths you take each minute and the size of those breaths? How would you measure the size of your breaths? **B**

? 2 Where does respiration take place?

3 a) What substances are needed for aerobic respiration?
b) How does your body get these substances?

4 What substances are produced during aerobic respiration?

Your muscle cells need glucose and oxygen. When you exercise you need more energy, so your cells need more oxygen and glucose. You breathe faster and deeper to get more air into your lungs so that more oxygen can get into your blood. Your heart beats faster to pump more blood around your body, so that more oxygen and glucose can be carried to your muscles.

During vigorous exercise, **anaerobic respiration** happens because your muscle cells need more oxygen than they can get from your blood. Anaerobic respiration does not need oxygen. A waste product called **lactic acid** is produced.

The word equation is:

glucose $\longrightarrow$ lactic acid (+ energy)

If there is a lot of lactic acid, then your muscles stop contracting properly and start to ache. After exercise, you breathe deeply for a few minutes. This gets extra oxygen into your blood. The extra oxygen is used to oxidise the lactic acid to carbon dioxide and water. The amount of oxygen needed is called the **oxygen debt**.

Anaerobic respiration produces much less energy than aerobic respiration. Not all of the energy is released from the glucose and so a lot of energy remains in the molecules of lactic acid.

C This sprinter used anaerobic respiration during her race. She has an oxygen debt.

5   What is anaerobic respiration?

6   **a)** When is lactic acid produced?
    b) What does lactic acid do to your muscles?

7   What is the oxygen debt?

8   Why do you pant or take very deep breaths after exercise?

9   What is the difference between ventilation and respiration?

10 Copy and complete the table below to compare aerobic and anaerobic respiration.

	Aerobic Respiration	Anaerobic Respiration
Where does it take place?		
Is oxygen needed?		
What are the products?		
How much energy is released?		

11 Explain why aerobic respiration releases more energy than anaerobic respiration.

12 Explain why a 100 m runner has a bigger oxygen debt than a marathon runner.

Summary

Imagine you are commentating on the 100 metre race at an athletics meeting. You need to use up a few minutes before the race and decide to explain why the runners are 'out of breath' by the end of the race. Write down your commentary.

Microbes and disease

What are the causes of disease?

When a person has a disease their body is not working properly. There are signs that a doctor can see or find out using instruments or by doing a test. These signs or **symptoms** include things like a high temperature, a skin rash or the wrong sort of chemicals in the urine.

Some diseases are caused by not eating properly. Some diseases are linked to growing old, and others may be passed on by our parents. A large number of diseases are caused by **microbes** (short for **micro-organisms**). Microbes are tiny organisms that can only be seen with the help of powerful microscopes.

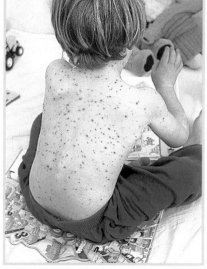

A   *Chickenpox.*

? 1   What is a symptom?

Bacteria (singular: bacterium) are single cells that can only be seen through a microscope. The cells have cytoplasm and a cell membrane surrounded by a cell wall. These cell walls do not contain cellulose and are flexible – unlike the cell walls in plant cells.

Bacteria have a coiled up strand of genetic material (**DNA**) which contains **genes**. The genes are not in a nucleus. Bacteria reproduce when a single cell splits into two new ones.

We use bacteria in many ways; for example, we mix them with milk to make yoghurt. A few bacteria are harmful and cause disease either by destroying our cells or making poisons called **toxins**.

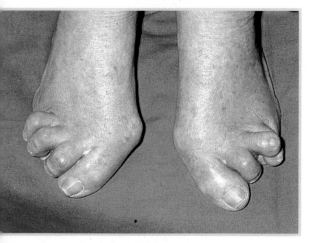

B   *Arthritis.*   *AIDS.*   **C**

? 2   How do bacteria reproduce?

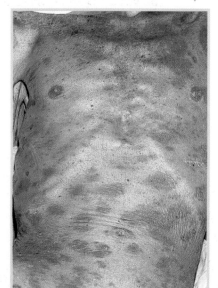

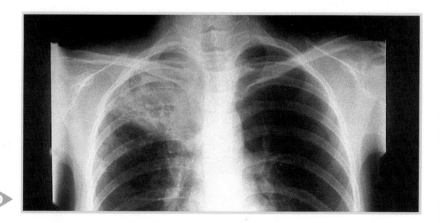

Tuberculosis.   **D**

Disease caused by bacterium	Symptoms
tuberculosis	coughing up blood
impetigo	red patches on skin
cholera	fever, diarrhea and thirst

tuberculosis bacterium

impetigo bacterium

cholera bacterium

0.001 mm

E

Viruses are microbes that are much smaller than bacteria. Viruses can only live and reproduce inside another living cell and so they damage the cells they live in. A virus has a layer of protein on the outside — a **protein coat**. Inside this is a short strand of genetic material (often made of DNA) containing a few genes.

G

Disease caused by virus	Symptoms
mumps	salivary glands swell
chickenpox	small spots forming a rash on the skin
AIDS	may stop the immune system from working, so the person gets other diseases

mumps virus

chickenpox virus

AIDS virus (HIV)

0.00001 mm

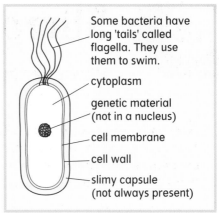

Some bacteria have long 'tails' called flagella. They use them to swim.

cytoplasm

genetic material (not in a nucleus)

cell membrane

cell wall

slimy capsule (not always present)

F *General structure of a bacterium.*

General structure of a virus. **H**

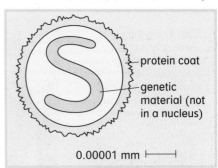

protein coat

genetic material (not in a nucleus)

0.00001 mm

In the right conditions, a bacterium can divide once every 20 minutes. So in one day, a simple bacterium could produce 1000 million, million, million offspring! There are more bacteria in your body than there are people on earth, yet they could all be packed into a soup tin.

Summary

Write the text for a leaflet for a doctor's waiting room, describing some causes of diseases. Add labelled diagrams to illustrate your descriptions.

3 Where do viruses reproduce?

4 Which is bigger, a virus or a bacterium?

5 Write down the names of:
   a) two diseases caused by bacteria
   b) two diseases caused by viruses.

6 How are bacteria useful to us?

7 What is the job of the flagellum of a bacterium?

8 Give three differences between a bacterium and a virus.

9 Why do you think people with AIDs are more likely to get colds and suffer from tuberculosis?

Stopping microbes

How does your body protect itself from microbes?

Your body is a battleground. Microbes settle on it and some try to break in, but your body usually fights back and protects you from disease.

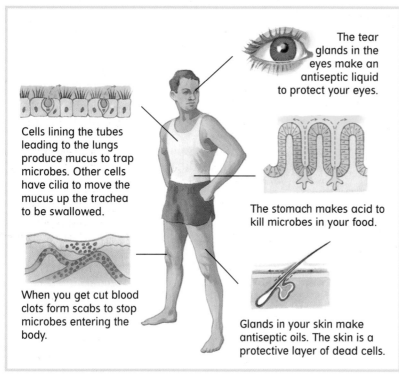

The tear glands in the eyes make an antiseptic liquid to protect your eyes.

Cells lining the tubes leading to the lungs produce mucus to trap microbes. Other cells have cilia to move the mucus up the trachea to be swallowed.

The stomach makes acid to kill microbes in your food.

When you get cut blood clots form scabs to stop microbes entering the body.

Glands in your skin make antiseptic oils. The skin is a protective layer of dead cells.

Your skin protects you. It keeps out microbes. But cuts and grazes can open the way for microbes to get in. Some parts of your body, like your eyes, are not protected by skin. Tear glands produce an **antiseptic** liquid that kills microbes. Sweat and saliva also contain these chemicals.

Your throat is a direct route into your body and you swallow microbes with your food. Cells in your stomach make hydrochloric acid and this kills most microbes.

Your nose is a direct route into your body. Cells lining the breathing tubes produce sticky **mucus** which traps most microbes. The **ciliated epithelial cells** in the lining of the breathing tubes sweep the mucus and trapped microbes up the trachea to be swallowed. The acid in your stomach kills the microbes.

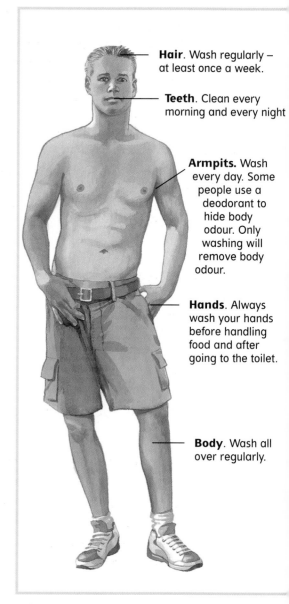

Hair. Wash regularly – at least once a week.

Teeth. Clean every morning and every night

Armpits. Wash every day. Some people use a deodorant to hide body odour. Only washing will remove body odour.

Hands. Always wash your hands before handling food and after going to the toilet.

Body. Wash all over regularly.

B *Simple hygiene rules.*

You can cut down the chances of becoming infected by taking care of your body as shown in diagram B.

? **1** How are your eyes protected from infection?
2 What happens to microbes you swallow with your food?

? **3** Why is it important to wash your hands after going to the toilet?

The food we prepare for ourselves can also be food for microbes. Some of these microbes are harmless. Some can cause a disease, like **food poisoning**, if they enter our bodies. One common form of food poisoning is caused by a bacterium called *Salmonella*. People often get *Salmonella* food poisoning from chicken or eggs that are not properly cooked.

! Botulism is the most dangerous type of food poisoning. It is caused by a bacterium called *Clostridium botulinum*. This microbe makes a toxin that is the most poisonous substance known. Two or three spoonfuls would be enough to kill 100 million people!

If someone has a disease caused by a virus or a bacterium, they are **infected**. They can pass the disease on to other people. Different diseases spread in different ways. Some are spread by touching an infected person, or by breathing in microbes.

Microbes from infected people or animals can get into drinking water. If the water is not cleaned properly, people who drink it can catch the disease.

?

4 Write down three hygiene rules for both men and women.

5 Write down two ways that you can catch a disease from an infected person.

6 a) Why should you not drink water out of a river?
  b) How could you make the river water safe to drink?

7 Explain why it is important to cook chicken properly.

8 Why do you think people who work in schools and offices get colds more frequently than usual?

9 In 1848, Dr John Snow was working in London during an outbreak of cholera. Suggest why there were no more cases of cholera after he removed the handle from a water pump in one street.

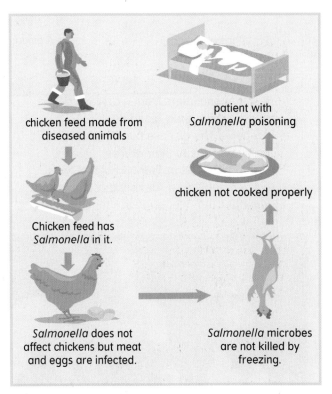

chicken feed made from diseased animals

patient with *Salmonella* poisoning

Chicken feed has *Salmonella* in it.

chicken not cooked properly

Salmonella does not affect chickens but meat and eggs are infected.

Salmonella microbes are not killed by freezing.

D *How food poisoning spreads.*

Summary

Draw up a table to describe how the body protects itself from microbes. Include one column to describe the protection mechanism and another column to explain how we can help our natural protection mechanisms.

Healing cuts

How does your body heal cuts?

When you bleed, the flow of blood helps to wash away any microbes that get into the cut. A wound is sealed by a **blood clot**, which also stops more microbes getting in and blood getting out. The clot of blood dries, forming a **scab**. New skin grows under the scab to seal the cut permanently.

 1 What is a scab?

A blood clot. **A**

! If someone suffers from a disease called haemophilia, their blood does not clot properly. The disease can be passed on by parents to their children. Alexis, the son of Russian Tsar Nicholas II, was a haemophiliac. If Alexis was cut, his wounds bled a lot and for a long time. **B**

Alexis

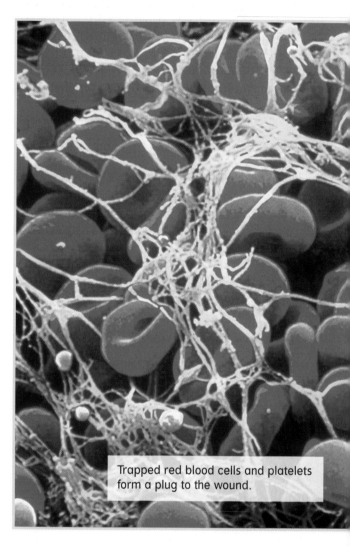

Trapped red blood cells and platelets form a plug to the wound.

If microbes get through the body's defences, the microbes will be in a warm place. In warm conditions the microbes multiply quickly and attack the cells or put **toxins** (poisons) into the blood. Your body can identify these dangerous microbes and destroy them without damaging your own cells. This is the job of the **immune system**. The white blood cells are the most important part of this system.

 2 What is the job of the immune system?

Some white blood cells destroy microbes by surrounding them. A white cell is said to **ingest** the microbe. Once inside the white blood cell, enzymes are released to digest the microbe. At a cut or a 'spot', there may be many white cells fighting the infection. These cells and the dead microbes form a yellow **pus**.

Pus from an infected toe.

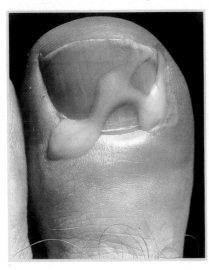

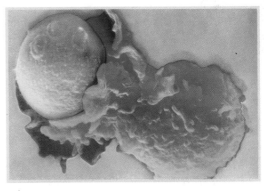

C *A white blood cell surrounding a yeast cell.*

Other white blood cells make **antitoxins**. These are chemicals which cancel out the toxins made by microbes. White blood cells also make **antibodies** to destroy some bacteria and viruses.

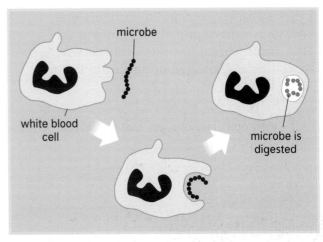

E *A white blood cell surrounding and digesting a microbe.*

? 3 Give three ways in which white blood cells protect you.

4 What is pus?

5 What are antitoxins?

6 Explain why there may be pus in a spot.

7 Why do you think that blood donated to blood banks is stored at a temperature just above freezing?

8 People who have had a kidney transplant need to be given drugs to prevent white blood cells attacking the cells of the transplanted organ. Why do you think these people are more likely to get diseases caused by microbes?

9 Find out why some people need to have blood transfusions.

! When someone is badly injured they can lose a lot of blood. Blood is made inside the body to replace what is lost, but this takes time. Blood can be taken from a healthy person (a donor) and given to an injured one in a blood transfusion. Doctors must check that the blood of the donor matches the blood of the person who needs it.

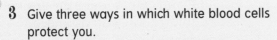

Summary

Describe what happens when you cut yourself and some microbes get into the body. Present your answer as a flow chart.

A18 Immunity

Why do we catch some diseases and not others?

Lots of children catch diseases like measles, mumps, chickenpox and whooping cough. Adults rarely get them. Other diseases are found in animals but not humans. These differences are due to the way our **immune systems** work.

Some microbes cause diseases in animals. For example, one virus that attacks cattle causes a disease called 'foot and mouth' disease. This virus cannot grow inside human cells. This means we cannot catch this disease. We are naturally protected or **naturally immune**.

Animals with 'foot and mouth' disease have to be killed and burned to stop the disease from spreading. **A**

? 1 Why don't humans get 'foot and mouth' disease?

B

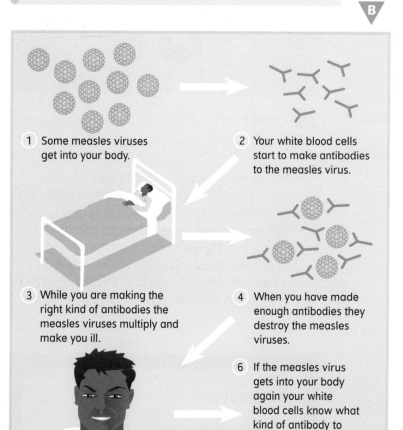

1 Some measles viruses get into your body.

2 Your white blood cells start to make antibodies to the measles virus.

3 While you are making the right kind of antibodies the measles viruses multiply and make you ill.

4 When you have made enough antibodies they destroy the measles viruses.

6 If the measles virus gets into your body again your white blood cells know what kind of antibody to make to destroy it quickly before you get ill – you are now immune to measles.

5 The measles viruses are destroyed and you get better.

The first time that measles viruses get into your body, you get measles. Your white blood cells take time to recognise the measles virus. Once they have recognised the virus, some of them produce **antibodies**. Antibodies destroy the measles virus. If the measles virus gets into your body again, your white blood cells already have a 'plan of action' and can produce the antibodies very quickly. They do not need to spend time recognising the measles virus. This is why you can only get measles once. Once you have had measles, you have become **immune** to the disease. The measles antibody works only against measles, it does not protect you against other microbes. White blood cells have to produce specific antibodies for each disease.

? 2 What is an antibody?

3 What does being immune to measles mean?

4 A measles antibody will not protect you from mumps. Why not?

Doctors can help to protect you from diseases. When you have a 'jab' or injection a small dose of a mild or dead microbe is put in your body. The small dose makes your white blood cells produce the antibodies that fight the infection. Later you may be given another jab that causes your body to make even more antibodies. This is the booster jab. You will be protected for a long time against the disease. Injections like this are called **vaccinations**. The mild or dead microbe you are given is called a **vaccine**. As a vaccine makes you immune to a disease, having a vaccination means you are **immunised** against a disease.

5 If you have measles once, you are unlikely to catch it again. Explain why.

6 Explain why a second, or booster, jab is needed to protect you against tetanus for a long time.

7 Explain why vaccines may contain live organisms, but do not cause disease.

8

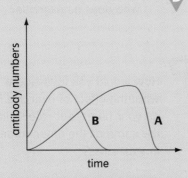

Two people, A and B, contract a disease. Look at graph D.
a) Which person has had the disease before? How can you tell?
b) Person C has been vaccinated against the disease. Would a graph of their cell count resemble A or B?

9 Find out about the work of Alexander Fleming and antibiotics.

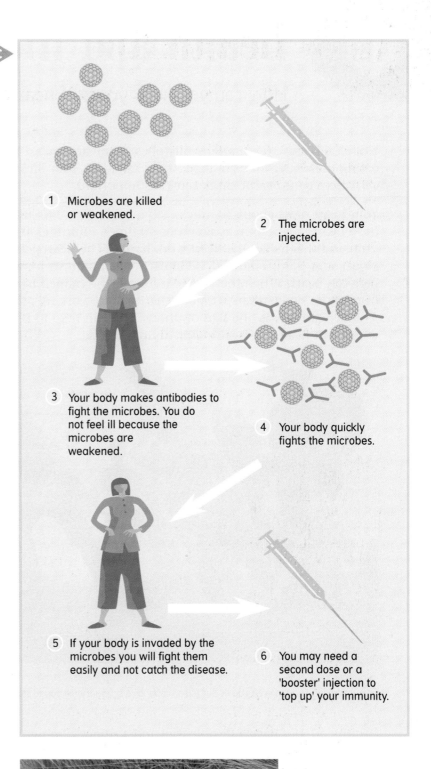

1 Microbes are killed or weakened.

2 The microbes are injected.

3 Your body makes antibodies to fight the microbes. You do not feel ill because the microbes are weakened.

4 Your body quickly fights the microbes.

5 If your body is invaded by the microbes you will fight them easily and not catch the disease.

6 You may need a second dose or a 'booster' injection to 'top up' your immunity.

Summary

Produce a leaflet for parents to explain how their children can be protected against a disease like measles by having a vaccination.

Health and lifestyle

How can you keep yourself healthy?

Not all diseases are caused by microbes. Some are caused by eating the wrong kinds of food, or by smoking. Your lifestyle can affect your health, and exercise is important.

Your heart beats about 70 times each minute. Some fit athletes have hearts that pump as slowly as 40 times a minute. Athletes train and this makes the heart work harder. The heart gets bigger so it pumps more blood at each beat and rests longer between beats. When the athlete is at rest, the trained heart beats more slowly than normal – but it is still working properly. A slow heart rate is one sign of fitness. You can help to keep your heart healthy by getting plenty of exercise.

Athletes have to be very fit. **A**

 1 How can you keep your heart healthy?

2 How might the heart of a trained athlete differ from that of a person who does no exercise?

B *Playing sports keeps you fit but even walking to school helps you to stay healthy.*

P How would you investigate what the effect of exercise is on your heartbeat rate? Is it the same as the other students in your class? **C**

Healthy arteries have a flexible wall and a smooth lining. In some people, the arteries change as they get older. A fatty substance, called cholesterol, starts to stick to the lining. Then the artery walls become thicker and harder. This means the blood supply to an organ will be less. If this organ is the heart, a person may have chest pains when they try to run. If the arteries become blocked, it causes a heart attack and possibly death.

Cholesterol is found in red meat, eggs and milk. You need some cholesterol to stay healthy, but too much leads to **heart disease** (when some of the heart muscle cells die). You can keep your arteries healthy by eating the right kind of diet.

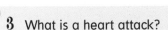
D *This meal contains a lot of cholesterol.*

This meal still contains cholesterol, but not as much. **E**

! You would expect someone with a diet of milk and meat to have a lot of cholesterol in their blood and so run the risk of having a heart attack. The Masai people of Kenya have a diet like this and yet they stay healthy. This is because they eat a plant that contains chemicals called saponins. These have been found in soya beans and chick peas. Saponins stop cholesterol moving across the gut wall into the blood. **F**

? **3** What is a heart attack?

4 How can you protect yourself against having a heart attack?

Sometimes a lump of cholesterol forms a clot inside a blood vessel. If a clot gets stuck in an artery or vein it will stop the flow of blood. A clot in the brain cuts down the blood supply to the brain. This lowers the amount of oxygen reaching the brain cells and can damage the cells or even kill the person. This is called a **stroke**.

? **5** What is a stroke?

Smoking is also bad for you. Chemicals in tobacco smoke can cause lung cancer. The chemicals also affect your blood vessels, and can lead to heart attacks or strokes.

? **6** Why is smoking bad for your health?

You can keep yourself healthy by having a healthy lifestyle.

? **7** Some people have a tendency to form blood clots inside their blood vessels. How can regular exercise help to prevent these blood clots?

8 People who work in offices often go out for a walk in the fresh air at lunchtime. Why do they usually feel much better for the exercise?

9 During a heart attack, the coronary arteries which supply blood to the heart muscle are blocked. What effect does this have on the heart muscle?

Summary

Design a leaflet to tell people how they can change their lifestyle to keep them healthy. You could also include some information from topic A16 (page 36).

1 This diagram shows an animal cell.

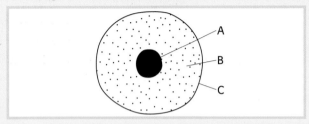

a) i) What is part A? **ii)** What does it do? (2)

b) i) What is part C? **ii)** What does it do? (2)

c) i) In which part do most chemical reactions occur?

ii) What substances catalyse these reactions? (2)

2 This diagram shows a ciliated epithelial cell.

a) What is the function of this kind of cell? (1)

b) Where in the body would you find this kind of cell? (1)

c) Describe *one* way in which this cell is adapted to its function. (1)

3 a) What is diffusion? (1)

b) How does active transport differ from diffusion? (2)

4 a) What is the function of glandular tissue? (1)

b) i) Name *three* organs in the digestive system. (3)

ii) What does the digestive system do? (2)

5 This diagram shows part of the digestive system.

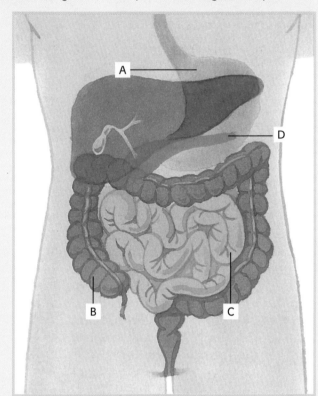

a) Write down the names of parts A, B, C and D (4)

b) i) In which of these parts are nutrients absorbed into the body? (1)

ii) How is the structure of this part adapted for the absorption of nutrients? (2)

c) i) What enzyme is added in part A? (1)

ii) What is the function of this enzyme? (1)

6 Various substances are added to your food as it moves through your digestive system. Describe the functions of each of these.

a) saliva (2)

b) acid in the stomach (2)

c) bile (2)

d) lipase enzymes (1)

7 a) When you breathe in, the air goes through all the following parts of your breathing system. Write them out in order, starting with your nose. (3)

> bronchi   alveoli   trachea
> nose   bronchiole

b) Explain how the inside of the lungs is adapted for gas exchange. (3)

8 Describe how the intercostal muscles and diaphragm work together to allow you to inhale air. (4)

9 This diagram shows a heart.

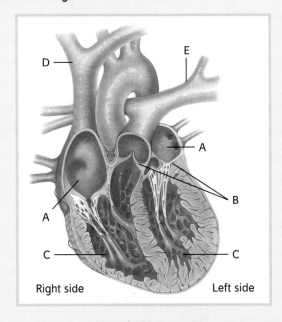

Right side   Left side

a) i) What are the spaces labelled A called?

ii) What are the spaces labelled C called? (2)

b) What is the function of the structures labelled B? (1)

c) i) Is blood vessel D an artery or a vein?

ii) Explain your answer. (2)

d) i) Which side of the heart will contain blood with a lot of oxygen in it?

ii) Explain your answer. (2)

e) Why is the wall of the left side of the heart thicker than the right side? (2)

10 a) Write out the word equation for aerobic respiration. (4)

b) Where in a cell does respiration take place? (1)

c) What is the energy released during respiration used for? (3)

d) i) What form of respiration happens in cells when they do not get enough oxygen?

ii) What is the waste product from this process?

iii) How does the amount of energy released in this process differ from the amount of energy released in aerobic respiration? (3)

e) What is the oxygen debt? (1)

11 Describe the functions of each of these parts of the blood.

a) white blood cells (2)

b) red blood cells (1)

c) plasma (1)

d) platelets (1)

12 Read the passage and then answer the questions.

You can protect yourself against infections by washing your hands before preparing food, by storing and cooking food properly, and by getting vaccinated against common diseases like measles and tetanus.

You can keep your body healthy by getting plenty of exercise, by eating a healthy diet, and not smoking.

a) Name *two* kinds of microbe that can cause infections. (2)

b) Why is it important to cook food properly? (1)

c) Describe *two* ways that your body protects itself against microbes. (4)

d) What is a vaccination, and how does it protect you against infection? Explain as fully as you can. (3)

e) Name the *five* kinds of nutrient that humans need. (5)

f) Describe *one* harmful effect that an unhealthy diet can have. (1)

Plant structure

What are the features of flowering plants?

Plants provide many useful substances for us, including food. The main parts of a plant are called **plant organs** and each organ has a particular function (job).

1 a) Write down the names of four plant organs.

  b) Which organ on your list makes food for the plant?

Plants which have flowers are known as **flowering plants**. Flowers produce **seeds** from which new plants will grow. The seeds of flowering plants are often contained in **fruits**. Any plant organ that is eaten and is not a fruit, is called a **vegetable**.

flower

The main organs of a flowering plant. **A**

B *Some flowers are not obvious. These are grass flowers.*

2 We can eat carrots, spinach, celery and broccoli. Write down which plant organ each vegetable is.

3 Picture C shows a tomato. Write down whether a tomato is a fruit or a vegetable. Explain your answer.

C

4 What do flowers do?

5 Why do you think plants die if they do not get any light?

Many plants have **flowers**. They make seeds from which new plants grow. They also contain the male and female **sex organs**.

The **leaf** is used to make food for the plant. Leaves use **photosynthesis** to do this. Photosynthesis needs light energy to make it work.

The **stem** helps to support the plant and hold the leaves in place. It also contains tubes which carry water and food around the plant.

The **roots** keep the plant in the ground and take in water and mineral salts from the soil. Mineral salts are important for healthy growth.

Plant cells

All living things are made out of smaller units called **cells**. Robert Hooke discovered cells in the middle of the 17th century. Using a **microscope** he looked at thin layers of cork and observed small boxes which he called cells.

D *Robert Hooke's drawing of cork cells from his book* Micrographia *published in 1665.*

Plant cells have some features that are different from animal cells and they look more like 'boxes' than animal cells.

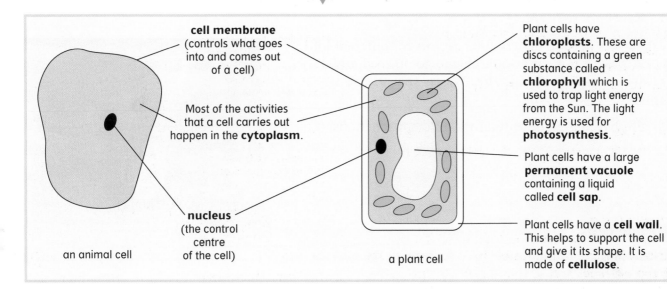

cell membrane (controls what goes into and comes out of a cell)

Most of the activities that a cell carries out happen in the **cytoplasm**.

nucleus (the control centre of the cell)

an animal cell

Plant cells have **chloroplasts**. These are discs containing a green substance called **chlorophyll** which is used to trap light energy from the Sun. The light energy is used for **photosynthesis**.

Plant cells have a large **permanent vacuole** containing a liquid called **cell sap**.

Plant cells have a **cell wall**. This helps to support the cell and give it its shape. It is made of **cellulose**.

a plant cell

6 a) Draw a plant cell and label the parts.
  b) On your drawing, draw a box around the labels for parts that *only* plant cells have.

7 a) Which part, normally found in plant cells, is not found in the onion cells in photograph F?
  b) Write down why you think this part is missing.

8 a) What substance do chloroplasts contain?
  b) What colour is this substance?
  c) What does this substance do?

9 a) What are cell walls made out of?
  b) From your knowledge of cell walls, name one property that this substance should have.

10 In 1882 Walther Flemming published a book describing cells in detail for the first time. What do you think Walther Flemming used to see cells more clearly?

11 When examining onion cells it is often easier to use red onions rather than the white ones. Why do you think this might be?

12 All animals depend on plants for their survival. Explain this statement.

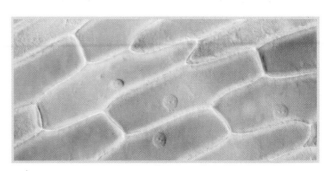

F *Onion cells as seen through a microscope. The cells have had a **stain** added to them so that the parts can be seen more easily.*

Summary

A Draw a diagram of a plant. Label the organs, and add notes to your diagram to describe the function of each organ.

B Draw up a table to show the functions of these parts of the cell: cell membrane, cell wall, chloroplasts, cytoplasm, nucleus, vacuole.

Use these column headings: Name of part, Function, Is it found in animal cells?, Is it found in plant cells?

Adaptations of plant cells

How are plant cells adapted to do certain jobs?

Car designers need to design different cars for different jobs. The function of this car is to be able to go off road and it has features to allow it to do this. We say that the car is **adapted** to its function.

Cells also have different features for different functions.

A

Palisade cells

Palisade cells are found near the top of leaves and so they get a lot of light from the Sun. They contain many chloroplasts to trap as much light energy as possible for photosynthesis.

Xylem cells

Many people like eating celery because it is crunchy. Its crunchiness is due to cells in the stem called **xylem cells**.

Xylem cells are dead cells that are adapted to carry water and mineral salts to where they are needed in the plant.

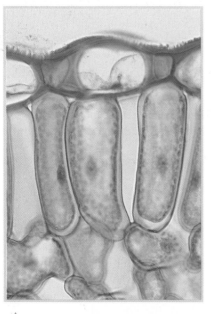

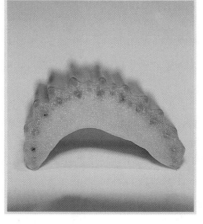

> A xylem cell is dead. The walls have rings of thickening to help to make the hollow tube stronger.

 C *This stem of celery has been left in a blue dye for a few hours. The dye has risen up through the xylem tubes.*   D

 B *The function of palisade cells is to produce food using photosynthesis. They are adapted to do this by having many chloroplasts.*

The dead xylem cells join together forming long tubes, like thin straws. When cells of the same type are found together, they are known as a **tissue**. So, xylem cells form **xylem tissue**.

 1 How are palisade cells adapted to their function?

 2 How is the structure of a xylem cell adapted to its function?

Root hair cells

The function of **root hair cells** is to take water and mineral salts out of the ground. They are adapted to this function by having 'root hairs'. A root hair increases the **surface area** through which water and mineral salts can enter the root.

Water moves from the soil into root hair cells by **osmosis**. The cell membrane is **partially permeable**, which means that water molecules can go through it but most larger molecules cannot.

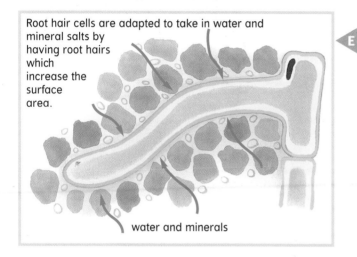
Root hair cells are adapted to take in water and mineral salts by having root hairs which increase the surface area.

water and minerals

When a little water contains lots of mineral salts, the solution of mineral salts is said to be **concentrated**. If there is a lot of water, the solution of mineral salts is said to be **dilute**. Water molecules move from a dilute solution to a concentrated solution through the partially permeable cell membrane. This is called **osmosis**.

The solution of mineral salts inside a cell is concentrated. In the soil the solution is dilute, so water moves from the soil into the plant. The cells nearer the xylem have more and more concentrated solutions in them and so water moves from cell to cell and into the xylem.

The arrows in diagram F show the movement of water from the soil into the xylem by osmosis. Root hair cells take in mineral salts by **active transport**. Active transport is the movement of substances *against* a **concentration gradient**, from a low to a high concentration. Active transport requires energy. This energy is provided by the respiration in the **mitochondria** of the cells.

3 Make a drawing of a root hair cell and label its parts.

4 a) Explain what is meant by surface area.

   b) Explain how a root hair cell is adapted to its function.

P How would you find out if increasing the surface area of a sponge helps it to soak up water more quickly?

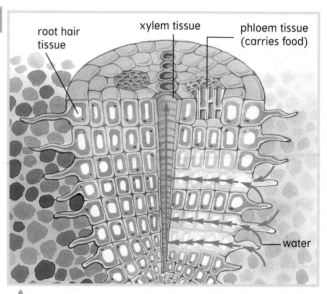
root hair tissue
xylem tissue
phloem tissue (carries food)
water

F The different tissues in a root.

5 What is active transport?

6 Explain how the mitochondria get what they need for respiration.

Summary

A Explain how palisade cells, xylem cells and root hairs cells are adapted for their functions.

B Explain how active transport is different from osmosis.

Plant tissues and organs

What are the tissues and organs in plants used for?

An **organ** contains different tissues, working together to do an important job. The root, stem and leaves are plant organs. Leaves contain **palisade tissue** that carries out photosynthesis. **Root hair tissue** takes water and mineral salts out of the soil. These are moved into **xylem tissue** by **osmosis**. The root, the stem and the leaves contain dead xylem tissue to carry water and mineral salts. They also contain strands of living cells (**phloem tissue**) that carry dissolved **nutrients**, such as sugars, from the leaves to all the other parts of the plant. A lot of nutrients are needed by the growing parts of plants. Nutrients are also needed by all plant tissues for respiration. The nutrients can also be moved into **storage organs** to be stored. Potatoes are storage organs.

 1 What is the function of:
  a) xylem tissue
  b) phloem tissue?

2 List two differences between xylem cells and phloem cells.

3 **a)** How does water get into the roots?
  b) How do mineral salts get into root hair cells?

 Some desert plants have very deep roots to reach water underground. Mesquite bushes have roots that can be over 30 m long.

Supporting the plant

The stem transports substances up and down the plant and helps to support the plant. Xylem tissue is mainly made out of **cellulose** which is very strong. Tall plants, like trees, have stems with a lot of xylem tissue in them.

4 Write down two functions of the stem.

5 Why do you think tall plants have stems containing a lot of xylem?

Veins carry substances into and out of the leaf. They contain **xylem tissue** and **phloem tissue**. The veins also help to support the leaf. However, water is also needed for support.

growing parts

Potatoes are storage organs.

A *A potato plant.*

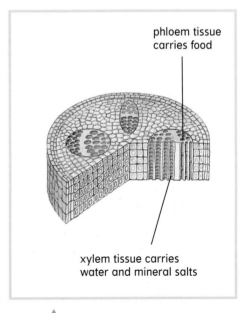

phloem tissue carries food

xylem tissue carries water and mineral salts

B *The different tissues in a stem.*

Water enters plant cells by osmosis. The water makes the cells swell and become firm (**turgid**) due to the increased pressure inside the cell. The vacuole swells and the cell contents push against the rigid cell walls. The cell wall is strong enough to withstand this pressure, so it does not burst. This pressure is called **turgor** and it keeps the cells rigid and provides support. When a plant does not have enough water it **wilts**. A plant wilts because the cells become soft or **flaccid** as they lose water. The vacuole is smaller and the pressure inside the cell is low so the cells do not push against each other to provide support.

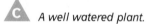
veins

C *A well watered plant.*

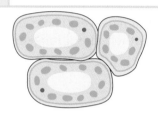

The **cell sap** in the **vacuole** helps to keep the cell's shape by pushing outwards, a bit like a balloon. These cells are **turgid**.

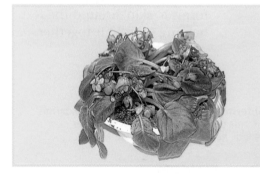

D *The plant has now wilted because it does not have enough water.*

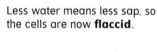

Less water means less sap, so the cells are now **flaccid**.

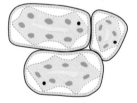

6 Name three plant organs that contain xylem cells.

7 Some plants have green stems. What would you expect to find in the cells of these stems?

8 Food is made in the leaves. Some of it needs to reach the roots.
 a) Explain why.
 b) How does it reach the roots?

9 How does water get into plant cells?

10 Write down two ways in which a leaf is supported.

11 The largest vein in the leaf runs down its centre. This is called the mid-rib.
 a) Draw a sketch of a leaf and label these parts: vein, mid-rib, stalk.
 b) All these parts have three functions. What are they?
 c) Write down the names of two tissues that are found in all of these parts.

12 Explain the following:
 a) Floppy lettuce can be made firm and crisp by putting it in cold water for a few minutes.
 b) Plants often wilt when the ground is frozen.
 c) If you put sugar on strawberries, the juice comes out of them.

Summary

What are the tissues in roots, stems and leaves used for? Include the following words in your answer.

xylem tissue   phloem tissue   turgid   flaccid
nutrients   mineral salts   support

51

Leaves

How is a leaf adapted to its function?

The function of the leaf is to produce food for the plant using **photosynthesis**. Leaves are adapted to help the plant photosynthesise as efficiently as possible. Light energy is needed for photosynthesis and so the more light energy a leaf gets, the more food it can produce. Many flowering plants have leaves with a large surface area to help them trap as much light energy as possible. Leaf stalks hold the leaves in the right position to trap as much light energy as possible.

Most plants that grow in the UK have many leaves. These are often arranged so that they do not shade each other. This arrangement is called a **leaf mosaic**.

A *The leaf mosaic in a rhododendron plant.*

1 **a)** What is the name of the process that plants use to make food?

b) What form of energy does a plant need to make this process happen?

c) How do leaf stalks help the process?

2 Beech trees have a very effective leaf mosaic. Why do you think very few plants grow beneath the trees in a beech wood?

The top surface of a leaf is covered in **cuticle** which makes the leaf waterproof and stops it drying out too much. The cells on the upper and lower sides of the leaf form **epidermis tissue**. This tissue forms a 'skin' around the leaf, helping to hold it together.

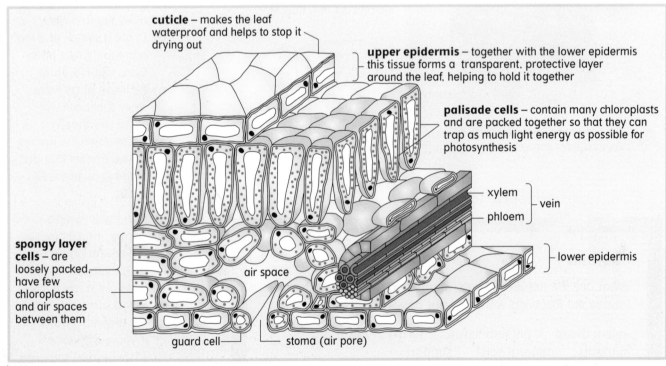

cuticle – makes the leaf waterproof and helps to stop it drying out

upper epidermis – together with the lower epidermis this tissue forms a transparent, protective layer around the leaf, helping to hold it together

palisade cells – contain many chloroplasts and are packed together so that they can trap as much light energy as possible for photosynthesis

xylem — } vein
phloem —

lower epidermis

spongy layer cells – are loosely packed, have few chloroplasts and air spaces between them

air space

guard cell

stoma (air pore)

B *The main tissues in a leaf.*

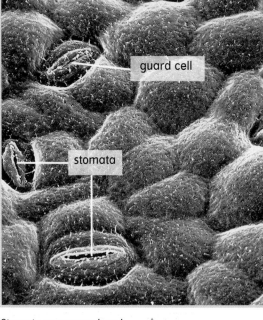

guard cell

stomata

Stomata are opened and closed by guard cells.

Photosynthesis needs two raw materials, carbon dioxide and water. The water comes from the roots and is carried in the xylem. The carbon dioxide comes from the air and gets into the leaf through small holes called **stomata**. (The singular is **stoma**). Each stoma has two **guard cells** which open and close it.

Water passes into the guard cells by osmosis during the day. This makes them bend so the stoma opens. At night, water passes out of the guard cells by osmosis. They straighten up so the stoma closes.

The air spaces make sure that all the cells get a supply of carbon dioxide if they need it. Leaves are often thin, so that the carbon dioxide does not have to go very far before reaching cells that need it. The carbon dioxide gets into the leaves and cells by **diffusion**. Diffusion means that a substance moves from where there is a lot of it to where there is less of it. In this case there is more carbon dioxide outside the leaf and less inside.

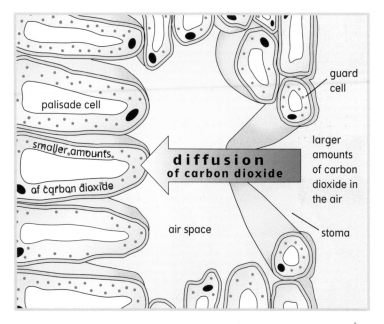

palisade cell

smaller amounts of carbon dioxide

diffusion of carbon dioxide

guard cell

larger amounts of carbon dioxide in the air

air space

stoma

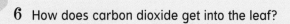

 If leaves are put into very hot water, gases bubble out of the stomata.

● How would you show where stomata are found in different leaves?

● Are stomata found in different places depending on where a plant lives?

D

6 How does carbon dioxide get into the leaf?

7 What is diffusion?

8 What are the raw materials for photosynthesis?

9 **a)** What are stomata?
  b) What are they used for?

10 The stomata close in hot, dry weather.
  a) Explain why this happens.
  b) What effect do you think this will have on photosynthesis?

Summary

A Describe how epidermis, palisade and spongy tissues are adapted to make the leaf efficient at photosynthesis.

B Explain why most leaves are thin, have veins and a large surface area.

B5 The transpiration stream

How do leaves get water for photosynthesis?

Water is very important for plants but many plants appear to waste a lot of it. When it is hot, about 700 litres of water will evaporate from the leaves of this oak tree each day.

The loss of water from leaves is called **transpiration** and it actually helps the plant because:

- it keeps the leaves cool
- it helps to suck up more water (containing mineral salts) from the roots. Mineral salts are needed to keep the plant healthy.

The passage of water from the roots, through the stem and out through the leaves is called the **transpiration stream**.

A   *An oak tree.*

 l a) What is transpiration?
    b) How does transpiration help the plant?

How transpiration works

As water evaporates from the cells, the cells take more water out of nearby cells, which in turn take more water out of the xylem. This creates a 'sucking' action which pulls more water from the xylem further down the plant.

B

These photographs show how guard cells change shape to open and close the stomata.

C

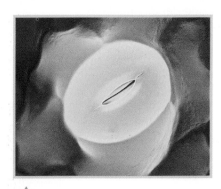

D

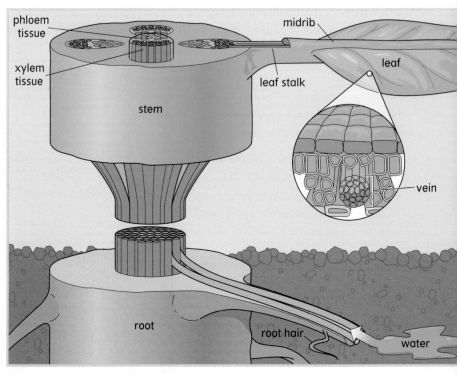

If the leaf is not getting enough water, the leaf tries to slow down transpiration by shutting the stomata. When there is plenty of water, the guard cells are **turgid** (full of water) and the stomata are open. When there is not enough water, the guard cells become soft and **flaccid** and the stomata close. This can help to stop a plant wilting.

Diagram labels: phloem tissue, xylem tissue, stem, midrib, leaf, leaf stalk, vein, root, root hair, water

2 How does water get into guard cells from the surrounding cells?

3 a) Which photograph (C or D) shows cells from a leaf that is running out of water?

b) Explain your answer.

Factors that affect transpiration

Transpiration is faster when:

- it is hot
- there is a lot of light
- it is windy
- there is not much water vapour in the air (low humidity).

P How could you find out which weather conditions cause the greatest amount of water loss from a leaf?

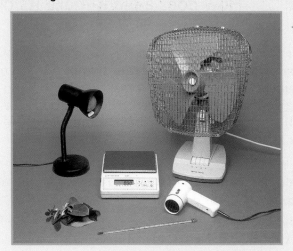

E

4 a) Which weather conditions make transpiration slower?

b) Explain your answer.

5 Graph F shows the mass of water lost by an oak tree during the course of two different days.

a) One set of results is from a day in summer and the other from a day in winter. Which is which?

b) Explain your answer to part a).

c) In the results for summer, what time do you think sunrise was?

d) Why do you think this?

F

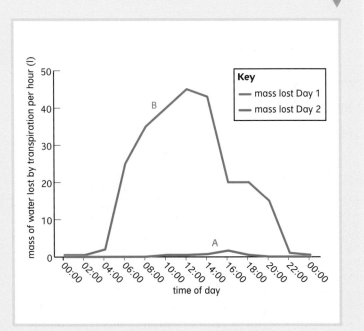

6 The stomata in desert plants only open at night. Why do you think this happens?

7 Look at the list of factors that affect transpiration. Explain why each of these factors affects transpiration.

8 Young seedlings are often grown in greenhouses and later transplanted into the garden. Suggest why:

a) transplanting is best done in the early evening

b) the seedling should be moved with a ball of soil around its roots.

Summary

A What is transpiration? Why is transpiration necessary for a plant?

B Write a short description of the route taken by a water molecule in the transpiration stream.

B6 Photosynthesis

How does a plant make its own food?

Animals would not exist if plants did not photosynthesise. The process that plants use to make their food also provides animals with food and oxygen. Photosynthesis is a series of **chemical reactions** which can be summarised and written down as a **word equation**.

carbon dioxide + water (+ light energy) ⟶ glucose + oxygen

reactants (raw materials)   products

1 What are the raw materials needed for photosynthesis?

2 What is the name of the substance that the plant makes for food?

The **reactants** are the **raw materials** needed for a chemical reaction. The **products** are the substances made by a chemical reaction. There are two more things that are needed to allow photosynthesis to happen: **chlorophyll** (a green substance found in **chloroplasts**) and **light energy** (normally from the Sun). The light energy goes in brackets in the word equation because it is not a substance, but it is needed to make the reaction happen.

3 Where do the reactants in photosynthesis come from?

4 In which part of the cell does photosynthesis take place?

5 What energy change takes place in photosynthesis?

The products of photosynthesis are **glucose** and **oxygen**. The oxygen **diffuses** out of the cells into the air spaces and out through the stomata. Since most of the oxygen is not needed it is often called a **by-product** of photosynthesis.

Some of the glucose is used by cells in **respiration**. Respiration happens in all living cells, all the time. Respiration is a chemical reaction which releases energy for the cell to use.

Some plants do not have green leaves but they still contain chlorophyll. It's just that other chemicals inside the leaf disguise the green colour of the chlorophyll. A large beech tree, like this one, produces enough oxygen each day to keep four people alive.

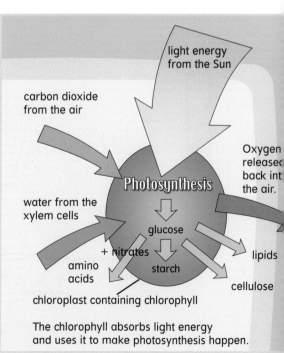

light energy from the Sun

carbon dioxide from the air

Oxygen released back into the air.

Photosynthesis

water from the xylem cells

glucose

+ nitrates

amino acids

starch

lipids

cellulose

chloroplast containing chlorophyll

The chlorophyll absorbs light energy and uses it to make photosynthesis happen.

The energy released in respiration is used to build up smaller molecules into larger molecules:

- Glucose is a small, **soluble** molecule. A lot of the glucose is turned into **starch** and stored. Starch is **insoluble**. It is a better way to store food since it will not dissolve, but stays where it is put!

- Some glucose is used to make **cellulose** for plant cell walls.

- Some glucose is combined with nitrogen from mineral salts called **nitrates** to make **amino acids**. The amino acids are built up into **proteins**. Plants need proteins for growth, and to make enzymes and chlorophyll.

- Some glucose is changed into **lipids** (**fats** or **oils**). Lipids are needed to make cell membranes and some are stored in seeds.

8 Why does the plant change glucose to starch for storage?

9 a) What gas is a by-product of photosynthesis?
b) How does it leave the leaf?

10 Look at the plant in picture D. For each lettered leaf, write down what colour you think it will turn when it is tested for starch. Explain each answser.

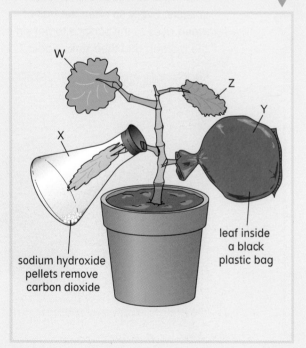

W

Z

Y

X

sodium hydroxide pellets remove carbon dioxide

leaf inside a black plastic bag

D

6 Most photosynthesis takes place in the leaves, so most of the glucose is made there. How does the glucose get to other parts of the plant?

7 What substances can glucose be converted into by plant cells?

P If you boil a leaf in water for a minute and then leave it in hot ethanol for 10 minutes, the chlorophyll is removed. You can test for starch in this leaf using iodine solution, which turns starch blue-black. How would you show that light and chlorophyll are needed for photosynthesis?

C

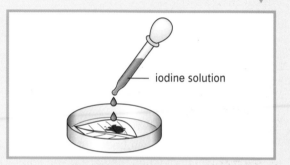

iodine solution

11 Plants need some oxygen for respiration. Plants that live underwater put the oxygen they produce into the water. They may also take oxygen out of the water.

Do you think the amount of oxygen in a river is highest during the day or at night? Explain your answer fully.

Summary

A Produce an A4 poster to describe how a carbon atom in carbon dioxide in the air could end up in the cell membrane of a root hair cell.

B Draw a concept map to summarise photosynthesis and how glucose is used by a plant.

**B7** # Rate of photosynthesis
What factors control the rate of photosynthesis?

In high mountain regions the air is 'thinner', which means that there are fewer air molecules. This means there is less carbon dioxide for photosynthesis. It is also colder. For these reasons, the plants grow slowly and many stay quite small.

The **rate** of photosynthesis is how fast it is happening. We can often measure this by finding out how much glucose or oxygen is produced in a certain time. The rate of photosynthesis is affected by the temperature, the amount of carbon dioxide and the amount of light. If there is not much of any one of these, it is said to be a **limiting factor**.

? **1** What are the three limiting factors in photosynthesis?

2 Why do you think plants grow slowly in high mountain regions?

P Cress leaves that have been cut in half and placed in a syringe will float when they are given light. This is because photosynthesis makes bubbles of oxygen which stick to the leaves.

How would you use this apparatus to compare how quickly photosynthesis happens when the cress leaves are given different strengths of light?

A *These plants are growing in the mountains.*

! The oxygen produced by most underwater plants bubbles into the water. However, some duckweeds form balls of weed in which the oxygen collects. Every so often the ball of weed rises to the surface to get rid of the oxygen and then sinks again.

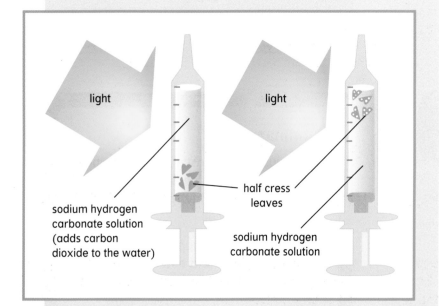

B

light

light

sodium hydrogen carbonate solution (adds carbon dioxide to the water)

half cress leaves

sodium hydrogen carbonate solution

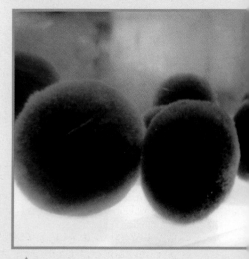

C

Graphs can show how some factors affect the rate of photosynthesis.

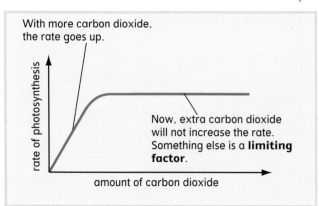

With more carbon dioxide, the rate goes up.

Now, extra carbon dioxide will not increase the rate. Something else is a **limiting factor**.

rate of photosynthesis

amount of carbon dioxide

A similar graph can be drawn for temperature. You can see in graph E that if the temperature gets too hot, photosynthesis stops completely. Photosynthesis is a series of reactions. Each reaction is controlled by a different **enzyme**. Enzymes are chemicals that speed up or **catalyse** chemical reactions in living cells. At high temperatures (above 45 °C) most enzymes are damaged or **denatured**, so they are no longer able to catalyse reactions. This causes photosynthesis to stop. At low temperatures the enzymes do not have enough energy so they work slowly. This slows down the rate of photosynthesis.

3 Look at graph D.

a) Explain what a limiting factor is.

b) Where the graph becomes level, something has become a limiting factor. Which of these could it be? (There are more than one.)

temperature   nitrogen   oxygen   sugar
carbon dioxide   glucose   light

4 a) What are enzymes?   **b)** What do they do?

5 In an experiment, the number of bubbles coming from some Canadian pondweed was counted each minute. The distance between a lamp and the pondweed was altered. Table F shows the results.

a) Plot these results on a line graph.

b) What is being used as a measure of the rate of photosynthesis?

c) What does your graph show (i.e. what is the relationship between the distance of the lamp and the number of bubbles)?

d) What was the maximum number of bubbles per minute?

e) How might the maximum number of bubbles be increased further?

f) At the end of the experiment, the bright lamp was left next to the pondweed by mistake. An hour later it was discovered that there were hardly any bubbles coming from the pondweed. Why do you think this happened?

E

rate of photosynthesis

5 10 15 20 25 30 35 40 45 50
temperature (°C)

F

Distance between lamp and pondweed (cm)	Number of bubbles per minute
1	65
5	65
10	63
15	59
20	54
25	47
30	35

6 Look at the plants in photograph A. Draw a graph like graph E for the enzymes in these plants. Explain your graph.

Summary

Sheila grows lettuces in greenhouses. She wants to grow as many big lettuces as possible. Using your knowledge of photosynthesis and limiting factors, suggest how she could increase the amount of photosynthesis in the lettuce leaves and so increase her crop yield.

Mineral ions

How do plants get the mineral ions they need to grow?

Many people think that venus fly trap plants eat food just like humans. This is *not* true. These plants grow in areas where there are very few nitrates in the soil. **Nitrates** are very important **mineral salts**. The plants catch insects and use them as a source of nitrates, *not* food. Like all plants, venus fly traps **photosynthesise** to make food.

 1 What process do venus fly trap plants use to make food?

A   *A venus fly trap.*

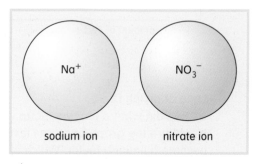

B   *Sodium nitrate (a mineral salt) is made of sodium ions and nitrate ions.*

Plants need elements from mineral salts for healthy growth. These elements are dissolved in soil water in the form of **mineral ions**. Ions are atoms or molecules that carry an electrical charge. Mineral ions are taken into the roots by two processes – **diffusion** and **active transport**.

2 a) Which part of the root takes in mineral ions?
   b) How is this part of the root adapted for absorbing mineral ions?

3 a) How does active transport differ from diffusion?
   b) Why are most minerals ions taken into plant roots by active transport?

C   *Fertilisers contain a mixture of different mineral ions.*

If the soil does not contain enough of these mineral ions, then farmers and gardeners can add **fertilisers**. The main mineral ions needed by plants are:

- **nitrates**, to synthesise (make) amino acids and proteins to grow leaves and shoots
- **phosphates**, which have an important role in respiration and photosynthesis reactions and are needed to make proteins and DNA
- **potassium**, to help the enzymes involved in respiration and photosynthesis reactions and to make flowers and fruits.

Other minerals, like magnesium, are needed in much smaller amounts. Magnesium is needed to make chlorophyll.

4 Explain why a plant in soil with too little magnesium would not grow properly.

If a plant is deprived of the mineral ions it needs, it develops **mineral deficiency symptoms**.

E *Plants grown without phosphates have poor root systems and small leaves. Their leaves also become purple as shown in the photograph.*

F *Plants grown without potassium have yellow leaves with dead patches.*

D *The plants on the left are growing in soil without nitrates. They are not as tall as they should be and have yellow leaves.*

5 Copy and complete the table to show the importance of the three main mineral elements needed for plant growth.

Nutrient	Function	Effect of deficiency
nitrate (N)		
phosphate (P)		
potassium (K)		

6 a) Which mineral ion(s) is especially important for growing **i)** tomatoes **ii)** lettuce?
   b) Explain why you chose this mineral ion(s).

Summary

Hydroponics is the growth of plants without soil. It can be used to grow plants in the desert.

Design an advertisement to promote a new brand of liquid fertiliser for growing plants without soil. Include the reasons why plants need fertilisers to help them grow.

Plant growth

How do plants know which way to grow?

When a new plant starts to grow, its shoot always grows upwards and its roots always grow downwards. It does not matter which way up the seed was planted.

Chemicals called **plant hormones** help to co-ordinate and control the growth of plants. **Auxin** is an example of a plant hormone. It is found in the tips of shoots and causes growth. Auxin is only found in the tip of a shoot. If the shoot tip is cut off, the shoot will not grow any further.

If a shoot grows sideways, the auxin is pulled by gravity to the underside of the shoot. It causes this part of the shoot to grow faster than the top side and so the shoot grows upwards.

 A

 1 **a)** What effect does auxin have in shoots?
   b) Why is this useful for the plant?

Auxin is also found in root tips where it has the *opposite effect*. The auxin slows down growth in the growing root.

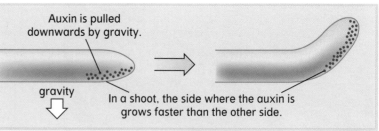

Auxin is pulled downwards by gravity.

gravity

In a shoot, the side where the auxin is grows faster than the other side.

B   C

 2 **a)** What effect does auxin have in roots?
   b) Why is this useful for the plant?

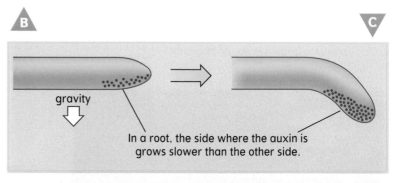

gravity

In a root, the side where the auxin is grows slower than the other side.

Plant shoots also grow towards the light. This is also due to the effects of auxin. The auxin moves to the part of the shoot tip in the shade. This again makes that part of the shoot grow faster.

D

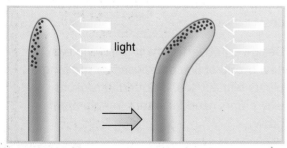

light

Response to light. E

Moisture in the soil causes auxin to move to the part of the root nearest the moisture. Again, in the root auxin slows down growth on that side of the root causing the root to grow towards the moisture.

3 Why do you think it is important that roots grow towards moisture?

P How would you find out whether shoots can still move towards light if the tip of the shoot is either covered in kitchen foil or cut off?

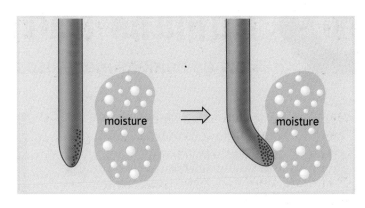

F *Response to water.*

4 Draw what you think would happen to the root and shoot in each of the experiments shown in picture G. Each drawing shows what the plant looked like at the start of the experiment.

G

a)
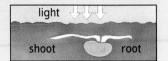
light
soil surface
shoot   root

b)

light

c)
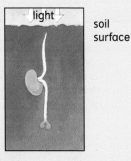
light
soil surface

d)
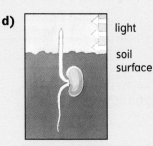
light
soil surface

e)
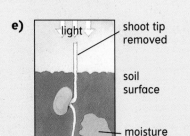
light
shoot tip removed
soil surface
moisture

f)
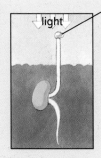
light
blob of vaseline (containing auxin)
soil surface

! Charles Darwin, the scientist who proposed the theory of evolution, was the first scientist to investigate why shoots grow towards the light, in 1880.

5 Plant hormones allow plants to respond to the environment. Humans and other animals also respond to the environment. If dust gets into your eye, you blink. How is this response different from the way a root bends towards water?

Summary

Imagine you are a scientist researching into how plant hormones control plant growth. You have been asked to write a short summary for a TV programme to explain what you have found. You could use the question at the top of page 62 to help you.

Humans and plant hormones

How do humans make use of plant hormones?

Many people prefer to eat seedless grapes because they do not contain pips. Some seedless fruits occur naturally but others are produced using plant hormones. The flowers are sprayed with a plant hormone which causes the fruits to form but not the seeds.

A Grapes growing in Spain.

 B

Grape plants are sprayed with a plant hormone to make seedless fruits.

Fruit ripening is also controlled using plant hormones. Plant hormones are sprayed onto:

- fruit trees to stop the fruit falling off. Bigger fruits are produced.
- fruit trees to speed up ripening. All the fruit ripens together and can be picked in one go.
- unripe fruit to make them ripe. The fruit will reach the supermarkets in a perfect, 'just ripened' condition.

C Bananas are picked unripe in the Caribbean and transported by ship to the UK. They are then ripened using plant hormones before going to the supermarket.

? **1** What do you think would happen if bananas were picked ripe in the Caribbean, which is over 9000 kilometres from the UK?

Large numbers of plants can be produced quickly using rooting powders. These contain plant hormones which makes the roots grow more quickly. Parts of a plant (**cuttings**) are taken, dipped in rooting powder and placed in water. After the roots have grown, the cuttings are planted and develop into new plants.

D The cutting on the left was dipped in rooting powder.

2 Many plant cuttings develop roots without using rooting powder. What is the advantage of using rooting powder on cuttings?

P How would you find out whether some makes of rooting powder are better than others?

! Cut flowers produce a plant hormone which makes the flowers die faster. Adding aspirin to their water stops the production of this plant hormone so the flowers last longer. Sometimes, cut flowers are sold with packets of a chemical which does the same thing. **E**

Plant hormones are also used as weedkillers. The plant hormones change the way plants with broad leaves grow and so they die. Plants with narrow leaves are not affected and so farmers can kill all the weeds in a field of a cereal crop (like wheat) without affecting their crop.

F *This spray, containing plant hormones, will kill the weeds but not the wheat.*

3 What is the advantage of using a weedkiller containing plant hormones over one that kills all plants?

4 Weeds are a problem on playing fields. What do you think is the easiest way of getting rid of the weeds on a playing field, without destroying the grass? Explain your answer.

! Agent Orange was a weedkiller containing plant hormones used in the Vietnam War. It destroyed the jungle so that enemy movements could be seen by the Americans. It also caused many health problems to people who came into contact with it.

5 There is a huge range of exotic fruit in supermarkets. Twenty-five years ago the range was much smaller. Explain why you think this is so.

6 Why do you think some people are against the use of plant hormones in food production?

7 Find out the names of the plant hormones used in weedkillers, in rooting powders and for fruit ripening.

Summary

Make a list of the ways in which humans make use of plant hormones.

Human senses

How do humans detect changes in their surroundings?

Most people think that humans only have five senses – sight, hearing, taste, touch and smell. In fact we have six. We also have a sense of balance.

Many of our organs and tissues contain **receptors** which detect changes in and around our bodies. These changes are called **stimuli** (the singular is **stimulus**).

All the information that the receptors receive is sent to the **brain** or the **spinal cord** along **nerve cells** (**neurones**).

Information also needs to be sorted and directed around your body and this is done by the **nervous system**. The nervous system contains many neurones which are connected together so that they can pass information between each other.

1 How does your body detect changes in your surroundings?

2 Name the two organs found in the nervous system.

The eye contains receptors that are sensitive to light. These receptors are found at the back of the eye in the **retina**. Information from these receptors is passed to the brain along the **optic nerve**.

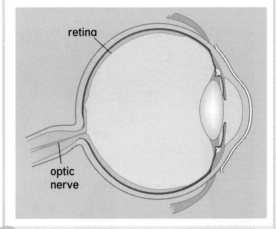

retina

optic nerve

3 How does information get from the eye to the brain?

If you hold your nose or have a cold, you cannot tell the difference between the tastes of some things like tea and coffee. This is because your sense of smell is also involved in tasting things.

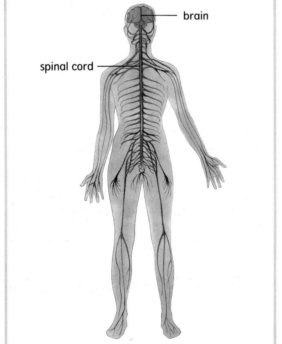

brain

spinal cord

The ear contains receptors which are sensitive to sound. There are also receptors that sense changes in your position to help you keep your balance.

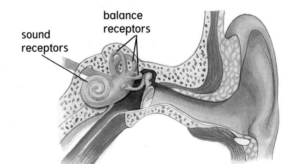

balance receptors

sound receptors

4 What stimuli do the ears detect? C

 A *The nervous system contains nerves and two organs.*

Receptors in the roof of the nose are sensitive to chemicals in the air. The chemicals dissolve in the moist lining of the nose.

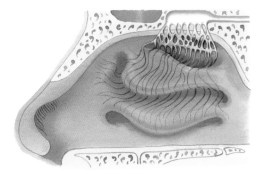

 5 Why do you think people lose their sense of smell when they have a cold? D

Your skin is also a sense organ. It contains receptors called **nerve endings** which detect things like touch, pressure and temperature.

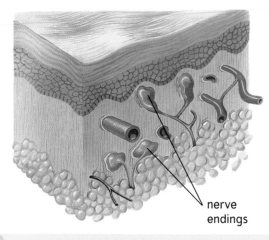

nerve endings

8 There are two sorts of pressure receptors in the skin. Some for heavy pressure and others for light pressure. Which type do you think are closer to the surface of the skin? **F**

P Some parts of your skin are more sensitive than other parts. If two pencils are held together and pressed gently onto the skin, some areas of your skin will feel two points and others only one. How would you find out which parts of the skin are the most sensitive?

Receptors in the tongue, called **taste buds**, sense chemicals in our food and allow us to taste things. You can only taste chemicals which dissolve in the liquid in your mouth.

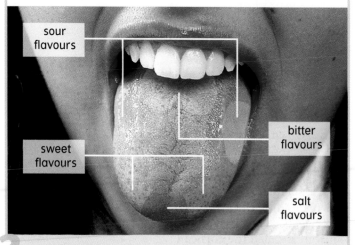

sour flavours

sweet flavours

bitter flavours

salt flavours

6 Where on the tongue do you think receptors would pick up the taste of a chocolate bar? **E**

7 Why can't you taste insoluble things?

Summary

Draw a table like this to show which sense organs are used to detect which stimuli.

Sense	Organ where this sense is detected	Stimulus that is detected

The eye

How do humans see things?

When a photograph is taken, the picture is actually upside down. You can see this by using a pin-hole camera with a screen at the back.

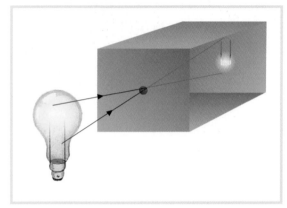

A

B

Inside the eye

The **sclera** is a tough layer surrounding the eye which protects it. The part at the front is called the **cornea**, which is transparent so that light can get into the eye. The cornea is curved which bends light rays helping to make a clear image on the retina.

The **pupil** is a gap in the middle of the **iris** that light goes through. The iris is a muscle which makes the pupil larger or smaller.

The **cornea** and the **lens** both bend light rays to make the image on the retina clear (in focus). The lens is held in place by the **suspensory ligaments**. The **ciliary muscles** change the shape of the lens by contracting and relaxing.

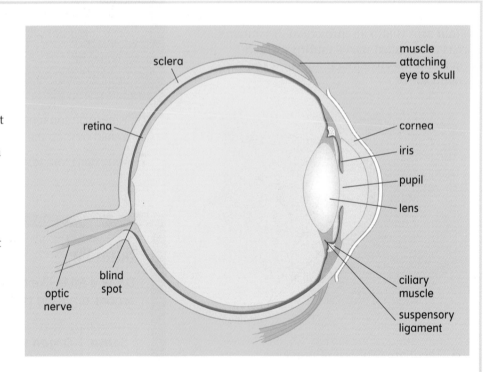

- sclera
- retina
- optic nerve
- blind spot
- muscle attaching eye to skull
- cornea
- iris
- pupil
- lens
- ciliary muscle
- suspensory ligament

The **retina** contains the receptors that are sensitive to light.

The **optic nerve** is actually many neurones bundled together, taking information from all over the retina to the brain. The brain turns this information into what you see, which is the right way up.

? 1 Which two parts of the eye bend light rays to focus the image on the retina?

C

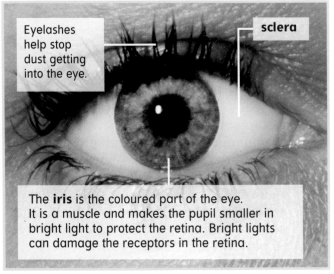

Eyelashes help stop dust getting into the eye.

sclera

The **iris** is the coloured part of the eye. It is a muscle and makes the pupil smaller in bright light to protect the retina. Bright lights can damage the receptors in the retina.

 D

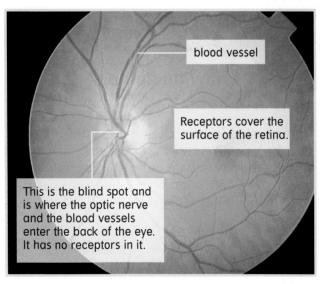

blood vessel

Receptors cover the surface of the retina.

This is the blind spot and is where the optic nerve and the blood vessels enter the back of the eye. It has no receptors in it.

 E   *The author's retina.*

Focusing

The ciliary muscles change the shape of the lens to help your eyes to focus light onto the retina. These muscles run in a ring around the lens. When the ciliary muscles **contract** (get shorter), the lens becomes fatter. This focuses light from near objects onto the retina.

F

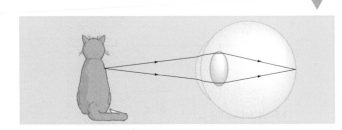

When the ciliary muscles **relax**, the lens is thin. This focuses light from distant objects onto the retina.

G

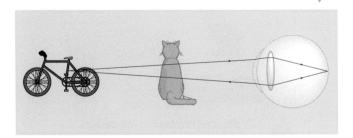

Many people's lenses do not work very well and they wear extra lenses (glasses).

? 2 In a dark room, will the pupil be large or small?

3 Why do you think the blind spot is called that?

4 **a)** What part of your eye contains the colour?
   b) What is the white part of the eye called?

5 How are the eyes protected from dust?

6 Which two parts of your eye are transparent?

7 Why do many people need to wear glasses?

8 **a)** What happens to your eyes when you walk into bright sunshine?
   b) Why do you think it is a good idea that this happens?
   c) Why do you think you should never look directly at the Sun?

9 Explain how your eye focuses light:
   a) when you are reading a book
   b) when you are looking out of the window at the trees.

Summary

Draw a table to show the functions of the parts of the eye. Use all of the words in bold on these pages.

The nervous system

How do humans detect and respond to stimuli?

Your nervous system co-ordinates different parts of your body so that they can work together. The brain and the spinal cord are called the **central nervous system**. They are connected to different parts of the body by neurones.

A nerve cell or neurone.

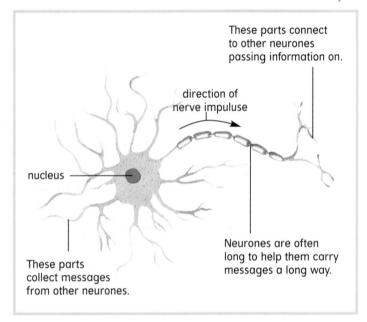

These parts connect to other neurones passing information on.

direction of nerve impuluse

nucleus

These parts collect messages from other neurones.

Neurones are often long to help them carry messages a long way.

1 **a)** What is the function of a neurone?
   b) How is a neurone adapted to this function?

Normally, your brain decides what to do when it receives an impulse. It **processes** the information that it receives and then sends new impulses along **motor neurones**. The parts of the body which respond to these impulses are called **effectors**. For example, muscles are effectors and **contract** to move part of your body when they receive impulses. **Glands** (e.g. salivary glands and glands in the pancreas) can also be effectors and secrete substances when they receive an impulse.

Receptors detect changes (**stimuli**) in and around our bodies and send information to the **brain** as electrical signals called **impulses**. These impulses travel along **sensory neurones**. For example, receptors in the eye send impulses to the brain down a bundle of sensory neurones called the **optic nerve**. Impulses from receptors below the neck travel through the **spinal cord** up to the brain.

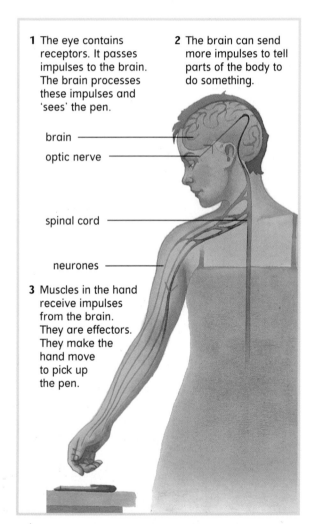

1 The eye contains receptors. It passes impulses to the brain. The brain processes these impulses and 'sees' the pen.

2 The brain can send more impulses to tell parts of the body to do something.

brain

optic nerve

spinal cord

neurones

3 Muscles in the hand receive impulses from the brain. They are effectors. They make the hand move to pick up the pen.

 This is what happens in the nervous system when you pick up a pen.

Reflex actions

Sometimes it is important to respond to a stimulus as fast as possible. For example, removing your hand from a hot object. An automatic response like this is called a **reflex action**. The brain does not do any processing to make this happen, since this would slow the response down. Instead, the impulse passes along a sensory neurone to the central nervous system. A **relay neurone** in the **spinal cord** then transfers the impulses from the sensory neurone to a motor neurone. The impulses then travel along the motor neurone to the part of your body that needs to react. In the case of removing your hand from a hot object, a muscle in the arm is the effector.

Neurones are not joined to each other. There is always a tiny gap called a **synapse** between them. When an impulse reaches the end of a neurone, a chemical is released. The chemical diffuses across the gap and starts an electrical impulse in the next neurone. In this way the impulses are passed from the receptors to the effectors.

5 **a)** What is a reflex action?
b) Why is a reflex action quicker than a normal response?

6 What do muscles do to move a part of your body?

7 **a)** What is a synapse?
b) How do impulses get across a synapse?
c) How many synapses are there in the reflex action in diagram C?

8 A song you like is played on the radio and you turn up the volume. Explain what happens in the nervous system when you do this.

9 Explain what is meant by: **a)** a stimulus **b)** a receptor **c)** an effector **d)** a response.

10 **a)** Why do nerve cells need to connect to each other?
b) Draw and label a diagram to show how two nerve cells connect together.
c) How do impulses get from one nerve cell to another?
d) Why do synapses slow down the speed of impulses along nerve pathways?

11 In what way is the internet similar to the brain?

2 **a)** What is an effector?
b) Name the two types of effector.

3 Look at diagram B which shows what happens when you pick up a pen.
a) What is the stimulus?
b) Which type of nerve cell carries impulses from the eye to brain?
c) Which type of nerve cell carries impulses from the central nervous system to muscles in the hand?

4 What co-ordinates your body's responses to different stimuli?

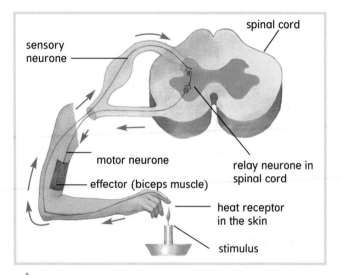

spinal cord

sensory neurone

motor neurone

relay neurone in spinal cord

effector (biceps muscle)

heat receptor in the skin

stimulus

C

Summary

A Use the sequence: stimulus → receptor → co-ordinator → effector → response to explain what happens when:

i) dust gets into your nose and you sneeze
ii) a bee stings you on the leg and you move
iii) you are riding a bicycle and a car pulls out into the road in front of you.

B Briefly explain what a synapse is and how impulses get across a synapse.

B14 Excretion

How are waste products removed from your body?

Many chemical reactions which happen inside your body produce poisonous waste that needs to be removed. Removing these wastes is called **excretion**.

1 a) Why does your body need to remove the waste products from chemical reactions?
  b) What is this process called?

Respiration is a chemical reaction that occurs in the **mitochondria** of all your living cells and releases energy from glucose.

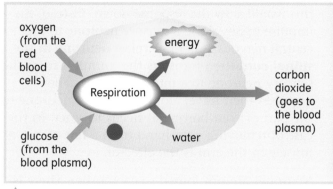

A   *Aerobic respiration.*

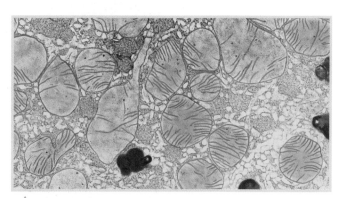

B   *Electron micrograph of mitochondria, ×12 000.*

2 In which part of the cell does respiration take place?

The carbon dioxide is a waste product and needs to be removed. It diffuses out of the cells where it has been made and dissolves in the blood plasma and is then carried to the lungs. It diffuses out of the blood in the lungs and leaves your body when you breathe out.

3 a) What process produces carbon dioxide?
  b) Which organs excrete carbon dioxide?
  c) Why does carbon dioxide diffuse out of the blood in the lungs? (*Hint*: see A10 on page 25.)

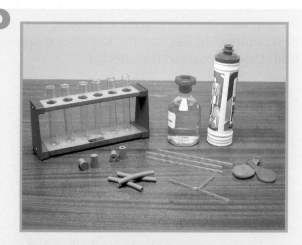

How would you show that there is more carbon dioxide in the air that you breathe out than the air you breathe in?

C

As well as carbon dioxide, your blood contains many other poisonous waste products that need to be removed.

The food that you eat contains proteins. These are broken down (digested) in the digestive system into **amino acids**. Amino acids are very important for your body. They are needed to make proteins for growth and repair of tissues and for making enzymes. The body cannot store excess amino acids, so if you have more amino acids than you need, the liver breaks them down into a chemical called **urea**.

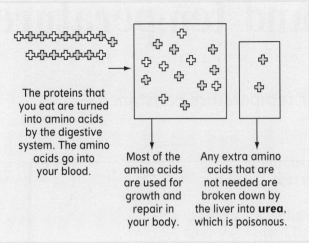

The proteins that you eat are turned into amino acids by the digestive system. The amino acids go into your blood.

Most of the amino acids are used for growth and repair in your body.

Any extra amino acids that are not needed are broken down by the liver into **urea**, which is poisonous.

D

The urea goes into the blood and is removed from the blood by the **kidneys**. The urea is dissolved in water, forming **urine**. The urine is stored in the **bladder** until you go to the toilet and **urinate**. Your kidneys also remove excess water and salts (ions) from the blood.

E

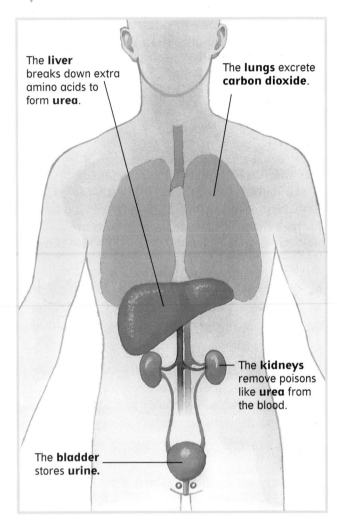

The **liver** breaks down extra amino acids to form **urea**.

The **lungs** excrete **carbon dioxide**.

The **kidneys** remove poisons like **urea** from the blood.

The **bladder** stores **urine**.

4 a) Why are amino acids important for the body?
b) What does the liver do to amino acids that are not needed?

5 What substances are dissolved in urine?

6 Where is urine stored before it is excreted?

7 a) What substance do the kidneys excrete?
b) What substance do the lungs excrete?

8 The percentage of carbon dioxide in two samples of air was measured. Sample A contained 0.04 % and sample B contained 4.1 %. Which sample do you think was 'breathed out' air? Explain your reasoning.

9 The person in the photograph has kidneys that do not work. Her blood supply is flowing through a dialysis machine.
a) What is the dialysis machine doing?
b) Why does the machine need to do this?

F

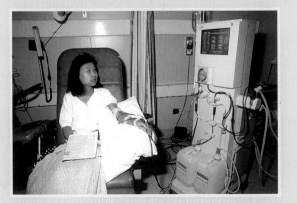

All your blood passes through your kidneys every 5 minutes.

Summary

Describe how waste products such as carbon dioxide and urea are excreted from your body.

B15 Homeostasis and temperature control

How does your body keep your temperature constant?

A thermostat is used in homes to keep a constant temperature. If the house gets colder than a set temperature, it turns the heating on. When the right temperature is reached, it switches the heating off again. This is an example of **feedback control**. Information about the house temperature is fed back to the thermostat. It acts by either switching the heating on or off. There are also feedback control systems working inside your body.

The speed (rate) of all the chemical reactions in your body are controlled by substances called **enzymes**. Human enzymes work best at around 37 °C. This is called the **optimum temperature**. If they are heated to temperatures above 45 °C they are damaged or **denatured**, and no longer work.

Any slight change in conditions can slow down or stop an enzyme working. It is important to keep temperature, pH, water and ion content as steady as possible. Keeping all the conditions inside your body constant is called **homeostasis**.

Part of your brain acts a bit like a thermostat. The **thermoregulatory centre** in the brain has receptors which are sensitive to the temperature of blood flowing through the brain. Temperature receptors in the skin also send impulses to the brain, giving information about skin temperature.

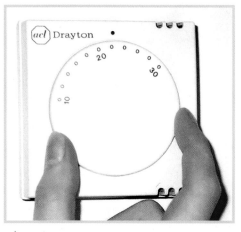

A A thermostat.

? **1** Graph B shows how well an enzyme works at different temperatures.
  a) What is the optimum temperature for the enzyme?
  b) Explain why the enzyme no longer works at 50 °C.

B

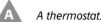

? **2** Why is it important to keep conditions in the body constant?

3 Which organ acts like a thermostat in your body?

If your body temperature goes above 37 °C, your brain detects this and sends impulses down neurones to the skin. Blood capillaries in the skin **dilate** (get wider). This allows more blood to flow to the surface of the skin, so that more heat is lost from your body. At the same time, sweat glands in your skin release more sweat. Sweat evaporating from the skin cools you down.

? **4** Where are changes in body temperature detected?

5 What changes take place in your body when blood temperature rises above 37 °C?

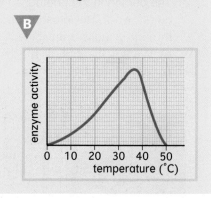

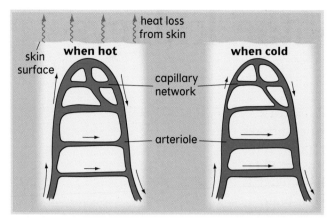

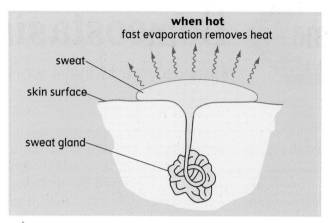

 C   *How blood capillaries in the skin regulate body temperature.*

D   *How sweating cools you down.*

If your body temperature goes below 37 °C, your brain detects this and sends impulses to your muscles. You start to shiver. Shivering warms you up, because **respiration** taking place during muscle contraction releases some energy as heat. At the same time, impulses go from the brain to the skin. Blood capillaries in the skin **constrict** (get narrower) to reduce the flow of blood through the capillaries, so less heat is lost. The way your blood temperature is controlled is an example of feedback control.

 Most people need to get about 2 litres of water into their bodies each day, from food and drink. Visitors to very hot places must drink between 4 and 8 litres each day.

E   *Death Valley in California, the hottest place on Earth.*

6   What changes take place in your body when you get out of a warm swimming pool and go into a cold room?

7   What is homeostasis?

8   Why is it important to drink a lot of liquid when you have been doing vigorous exercise?

9   Explain why you could suffer from hypothermia (cooling of the body below 35 °C) if you went out in damp clothing on a windy, cold day.

10   Why do you think Polar explorers and climbers are in danger of getting frostbite – a condition where skin tissue dies?

Summary

Explain how your body uses feedback control to keep your temperature constant at 37 °C. You could present your answer as a flow chart starting like this:

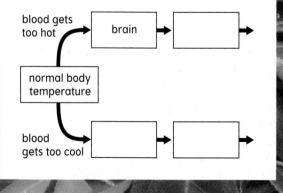

Homeostasis - the kidneys

How do your kidneys work?

You lose water when you breathe. The moisture on the inner surfaces of the lungs evaporates and so you breathe out water vapour. You also lose water when you sweat. If your body has more water than it needs, the extra water is removed by the kidneys and excreted as extra urine. If your body has less water than it needs, your brain makes you feel thirsty.

Ions are atoms or molecules that carry an electrical charge. Some ions are important for the body. You lose ions in your sweat. Any extra ions are removed from the body by the kidneys.

 1 Write down three ways in which your body loses water.

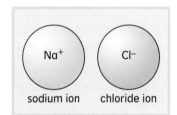

sodium ion   chloride ion

Sodium chloride (common salt) is made of sodium ions and chloride ions. Sodium ions are important for allowing nerve cells to carry impulses. A

B *A vertical section through a human kidney.*

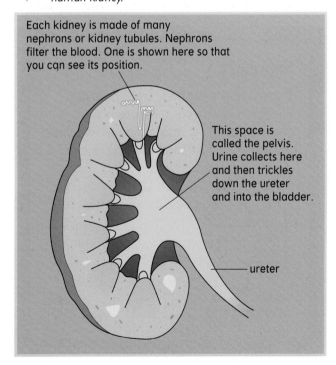

Each kidney is made of many nephrons or kidney tubules. Nephrons filter the blood. One is shown here so that you can see its position.

This space is called the pelvis. Urine collects here and then trickles down the ureter and into the bladder.

ureter

Inside the kidneys

Blood is brought to the kidneys in blood vessels called **renal arteries**. The blood contains dissolved nutrients such as glucose and amino acids as well as ions and waste chemicals like urea. The renal arteries branch many times, ending in a bunch of blood capillaries called a **glomerulus**. As the blood enters the narrow capillaries the pressure increases, causing liquid and dissolved substances to be forced out of the capillaries. Only small molecules such as glucose, urea, ions and water are able to pass through the walls of the capillaries into the **tubule**. Large molecules and blood cells stay in the capillaries. This process is called **filtration**.

All of the glucose, some ions and a lot of the water are needed by your body. They have to be **reabsorbed** back into the blood from the kidney tubules. This happens by **active transport** against a concentration gradient. The liquid left in the tubule is **urine**. It contains urea, excess ions and excess water.

 2 a) What is filtration?
  b) What substances can pass into the kidney tubules?

3 Why do you think red blood cells are not found in the liquid in the kidney tubules?

4 Glucose and ions cannot diffuse from the kidney tubules into the blood. They are reabsorbed by active transport. Why?

5 What substances are dissolved in urine?

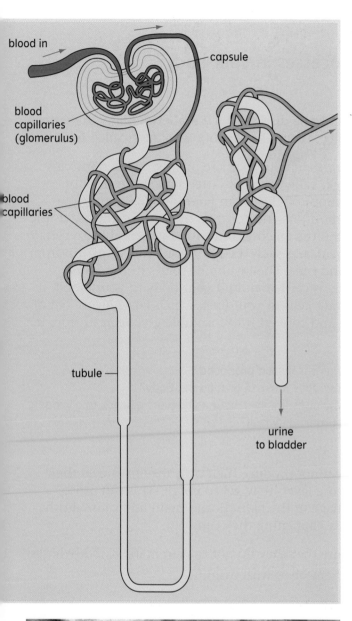

blood in

capsule

blood capillaries (glomerulus)

blood capillaries

tubule

urine to bladder

 The filtering units in the kidneys are called **nephrons**. Nephrons make urine.

 There are about one million nephrons in each of your kidneys.

Control of water content

The amount of water you lose in your urine is controlled by a **hormone** called **ADH**. Hormones are 'chemical messengers' that are carried in the blood and control some of the body's processes. If the water content of the blood is too low, the **pituitary gland** in your brain releases ADH into the blood. This causes the kidneys to reabsorb more water and you produce more concentrated urine. If the water content of the blood is too high, less ADH is released into the blood. Less water is reabsorbed in the kidneys, resulting in more dilute urine. The way your blood water **concentration** is controlled is an example of **feedback control**.

6 **a)** Name the hormone produced by your body to help control the amount of water in the blood.
 b) Which organ produces this hormone?
 c) In which organ does this hormone work?
 d) How do you think the hormone gets from one organ to the other?

7 Describe what you think would happen to the amount and concentration of urine in each of the following situations. Explain your answers.
 a) you drink a lot of lemonade
 b) it is very cold
 c) you are sitting in a hot sauna
 d) you eat a lot of salty crisps

8 **a)** During marathon races, runners drink water and isotonic drinks. (Isotonic drinks contain some of the ions lost from the body in sweat.) Why do you think they do this?
 b) How would running on a hot day affect them?

9 Explain how feedback control keeps the level of water in your body constant. Present your answer as a flow chart.

Summary

Produce a leaflet for runners in the London marathon to explain how the body controls water and ion content. Explain why it is necessary for the runners to drink liquids containing ions (isotonic drinks) during the race. Include these words in your leaflet.

concentration   feedback control
homeostasis   ions   kidneys   urine
water

Hormones

How do hormones control processes in your body?

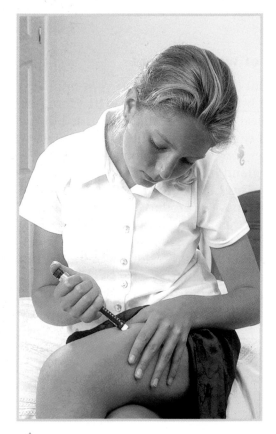

A *This is a daily routine for diabetics.*

This person has a disease called **diabetes**. Many **diabetics** have to inject themselves with a substance called **insulin**.

Carbohydrates in your food are mainly digested into a soluble sugar called glucose. After a meal the amount (concentration) of glucose in your blood goes up. Your **pancreas** monitors and controls the level of glucose in the blood. When the glucose concentration gets above a certain level, the pancreas **secretes** a hormone called **insulin** from special gland cells. The insulin dissolves in the **blood plasma** and is carried around your body in your blood. It affects certain cells in your liver, which take glucose out of the blood, and convert it to insoluble **glycogen** to store it.

? 1
  a) Where is insulin produced?
  b) How does it travel around the body?
  c) Why does the liver have to convert glucose to glycogen in order to store it?

Diabetics cannot produce their own insulin and so their blood glucose levels may get too high. This can cause severe damage to the kidneys and brain and cause death. To stop this happening they can:

- make sure that they do not eat too many carbohydrates
- inject themselves with insulin.

? 2 What organs are damaged if the glucose level in the blood gets too high?

When the glucose levels in the blood of a diabetic get too high, some of the glucose comes out in the urine. Doctors test this with glucose test strips. The ancient Romans used to put saucers of urine out in the Sun. If bees visited the urine, they knew the person was diabetic.

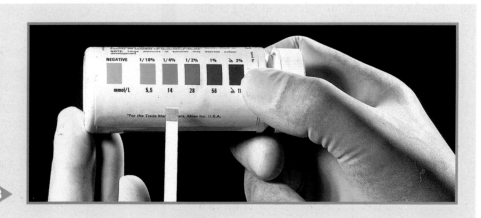

B

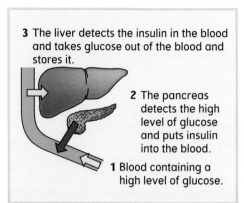

3 The liver detects the insulin in the blood and takes glucose out of the blood and stores it.

2 The pancreas detects the high level of glucose and puts insulin into the blood.

1 Blood containing a high level of glucose.

C

D

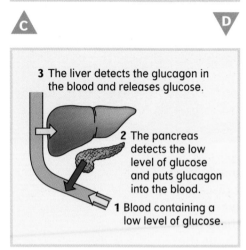

3 The liver detects the glucagon in the blood and releases glucose.

2 The pancreas detects the low level of glucose and puts glucagon into the blood.

1 Blood containing a low level of glucose.

When your blood glucose concentration falls below a certain level, your pancreas secretes another hormone, called **glucagon**. This is also carried in the blood and causes the cells in the liver to convert glycogen back to glucose, which then dissolves back into the blood.

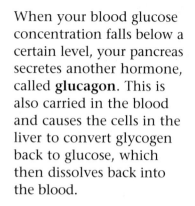

3 a) This is another example of **homeostasis**. What does this word mean?
b) The levels of what substance are being controlled?

Insulin and glucagon are **hormones**. Hormones are 'chemical messengers', making various processes in the body happen.

All hormones are carried in the liquid part of the blood (the **plasma**) and are produced by parts of the body called **glands**. The pancreas contains glands. The organs or cells that are affected by hormones are called **target organs** or **target cells**.

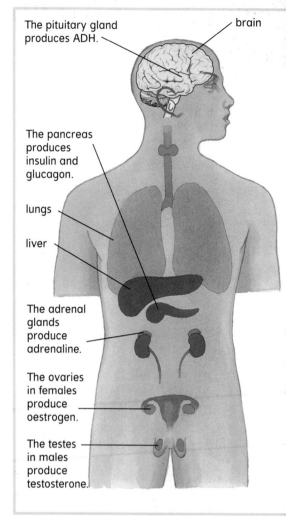

The pituitary gland produces ADH.

brain

The pancreas produces insulin and glucagon.

lungs

liver

The adrenal glands produce adrenaline.

The ovaries in females produce oestrogen.

The testes in males produce testosterone.

E *The human body produces many different hormones.*

4 a) What is a hormone?
b) What parts of the body produce hormones?

5 Write down two ways that diabetics use to control the concentration of glucose in their blood.

6 Neurones and hormones both carry 'messages' around the body. How fast do you think messages are carried by hormones, compared with neurones? Explain your reasoning.

7 a) What happens to the level of glucose in your blood when you exercise?
b) Why does this happen?
c) What does the body do to restore the level of glucose in the blood back to normal?

8 Find out what the other hormones labelled in picture E do.

9 Explain how feedback control works to keep your blood sugar levels constant.

Summary

Produce a leaflet to explain to a diabetic child how hormones control the levels of glucose in the blood. You should also explain how diabetes can be tested for and treated.

Smoking

How does smoking affect the human body?

In 1493, Spanish sailors returning from America, reported that the native people used to 'drink smoke'. This was Europe's first contact with **tobacco**. The leaves of the tobacco plant contain a **drug** called **nicotine**. People use tobacco to get this drug into their bodies in different ways.

Tobacco plants and some tobacco products.

Drugs are substances that affect the chemical reactions happening inside your body. Some drugs, called **medicines**, are useful and are used to treat diseases. Other drugs are not useful and are harmful. Many drugs are **addictive** (including some medicines) and people feel that they have to take them just to survive. A person like this is said to be **dependent** on a drug. Without the drug, a person may start to feel unwell and have **withdrawal symptoms**.

1 a) What is a drug?
b) What is the addictive drug found in tobacco ?
c) What is a medicine?

Nicotine is a poison. It is used in some sprays to kill insects. This product is so poisonous you cannot buy it in the shops.

Nicotine is a poison. In fact, it is used to kill insects. It can cause the heart to stop beating regularly and causes arteries to get narrower.

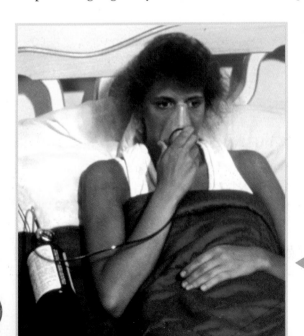

Narrow arteries cannot carry as much blood as they should and so less oxygen gets to parts of the body. When this happens to arteries supplying the heart muscle, the cells do not get enough oxygen and they die. This is called **heart disease**.

Smoking has damaged this woman's lungs so much that she needs to carry oxygen around with her.

2 What are the harmful effects of nicotine?

Tobacco smoke also contains tar. Tar contains chemicals that cause **cancer**. Tar also irritates the lungs and causes more of a sticky liquid called **mucus** to be produced.

The mucus sitting around in the lungs can get infected with bacteria and become very sore, causing **bronchitis**. Smokers have to cough to get the mucus out of their lungs because the tar stops the cilia from working.

 3 What do the cilia in the lungs do?

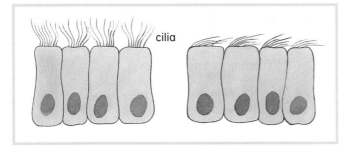

 Normally, mucus is swept out of the lungs by **ciliated epithelial cells** which have hair-like **cilia** on them. However, the tar stops the cilia working.

Coughing, over a long period of time, causes the delicate walls of the lungs to break apart and become swollen. This results in a disease called **emphysema**, in which people are permanently breathless.

Smoke also contains **carbon monoxide**, a poisonous gas which combines irreversibly with haemoglobin in red blood cells. Haemoglobin is a substance that carries oxygen around the body, but if it is combined with carbon monoxide, it cannot combine with oxygen. If a pregnant woman smokes, the growing baby (**fetus**) may not get enough oxygen and may be born too early and smaller than it should be.

6 Many people die each year due to carbon monoxide produced by badly fitted or badly looked after gas central heating boilers. Carbon monoxide is a gas without any smell. Explain why the people die.

7 A lot of people say smoking should be banned from all public places. Others say smokers have a right to smoke where they like. What do you think? Give reasons for your answer.

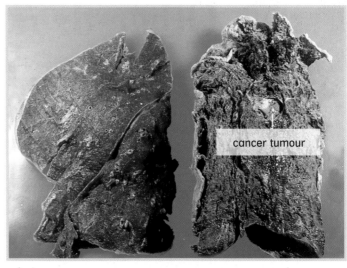

cancer tumour

The lung on the right is from a smoker. The tar makes the lungs go black and can cause cancer. 90% of lung cancers are caused by smoking.

4 Make a list of all the diseases on these two pages and write down how each is caused.

5 Look at graph F.
a) Describe the trend in the graph.
b) Suggest reasons for the trend.

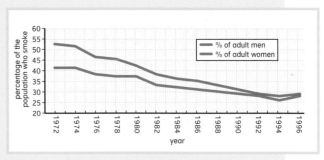

 Percentage of adults in the UK who smoke.

Summary

Produce a leaflet to be given out in a health centre to describe the effects of smoking on the body.

Other drugs

What are the affects of alcohol and solvents?

Drugs that slow down the nervous system are called **depressants**. **Alcohol** (**ethanol**) is an example. In small quantities it makes people feel good but it also slows down the time it takes for people to react to things.

In larger amounts alcohol causes vomiting. In very large amounts it can cause death since it stops the brain sending impulses to the lungs and so breathing stops.

 1 What is a depressant?

2 Why do you think people are advised not to drink and drive?

 Every week in the United Kingdom, 10 people are killed as a direct result of drinking and driving.

A *The effects of alcohol on the body.*

 3 Look at pictures A and B. Someone at a party drinks two pints of beer and one measure of vodka.
   a) How many units will they have drunk?
   b) What effect will this have on the person's body?

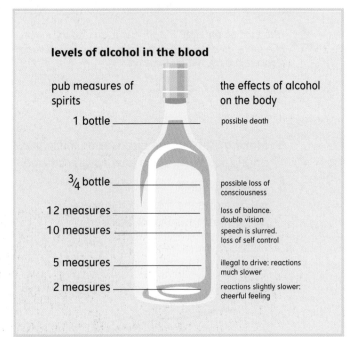

levels of alcohol in the blood

pub measures of spirits	the effects of alcohol on the body
1 bottle	possible death
¾ bottle	possible loss of consciousness
12 measures	loss of balance. double vision
10 measures	speech is slurred. loss of self control
5 measures	illegal to drive; reactions much slower
2 measures	reactions slightly slower; cheerful feeling

The liver is responsible for destroying alcohol in the body. Drinking large amounts over a long time can damage the liver and can also damage the brain.

Like other drugs, alcohol is addictive. People who are dependent on alcohol are called **alcoholics**.

 B

The amount of alcohol in different drinks varies. All these drinks contain the same amount of alcohol – 1 unit.

¼ a pint of strong beer, lager or cider

1 single pub measure of spirits, e.g. vodka or whisky

1 small glass of wine

½ a pint of ordinary beer, lager or cider

Solvent abuse

Solvents are chemicals used to dissolve solids. The solvents used in paints, glues and lighter fluid are dangerous if they are breathed in. However, some people breathe them in for 'kicks' to give them a 'high' feeling. Using solvents in this way is known as **solvent abuse**. It can be addictive, like other forms of drug taking.

4 a) What is a solvent? **b)** What is solvent abuse?

People below the age of 16 are not allowed to buy substances containing these solvents. This law was made to try to reduce the number of people who die each year from breathing in solvent fumes.

5 Look at graph D.
  a) How many 15–19 year olds died from solvent abuse in 1986?
  b) How many 15–19 year olds died from solvent abuse in 1996?
  c) How do the numbers of people dying from solvent abuse in the 1990s differ from the numbers in the 1980s?
  d) Give one reason why there might be a difference between the numbers in the 1980s and 1990s.

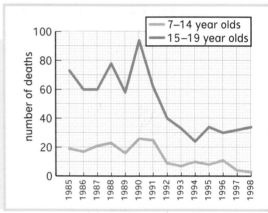

Graph showing the number of deaths from solvent abuse each year. **D**

Solvents found in glues and paints are dangerous depressants which can stop the lungs and heart from working, causing severe brain damage. They also cause lung and liver damage. Sometimes the solvent can kill straight away. Solvents can also make people believe that they can fly and so some abusers throw themselves off high buildings and fall to their deaths.

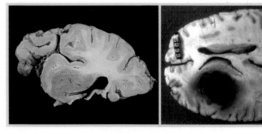

E *The brain on the left is normal. The brain on the right has been badly damaged by solvent abuse.*

6 'Short-term effects' describe what a drug does to someone's body straightaway.

  a) What are the short-term effects of drinking 10 units of alcohol?
  b) What do you think 'long-term effects' means?
  c) What are the long-term effects suffered by an alcoholic?

7 People who abuse solvents often develop poor co-ordination. Why do you think this might be?

8 Some drugs can interfere with the diffusion of chemicals across synapses. What effect do you think alcohol has on the speed of diffusion of chemicals across synapses in the brain?

Summary

You have been asked to appear on a TV program about drugs and health issues. You may be asked questions about the abuse of illegal substances and excess alcohol. Prepare a list to help you remember the main points.

Further questions

1 Marimo duckweed, from Japan, is found in balls. It is often found near the bottom of lakes. During the day, bubbles of gas collect inside the ball and make it float to the surface. The bubbles are released and it sinks again.

a) Name the gas that is found in the bubbles. (1)

b) What process produces this gas? (1)

c) i) Where in a lake would you expect to find balls of Marimo duckweed at night?

ii) Explain your answer. (2)

d) It has been found that increasing the light intensity (shining brighter light) makes more gas collect in the balls of weed. Look at the graph below.

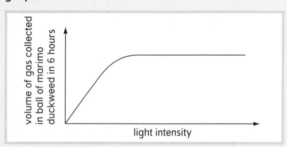

i) Increasing the light intensity does not keep on increasing the volume of collected gas. Explain why not. Use the words 'limiting factor' in your answer.

ii) Name *one* limiting factor in the experiment. (2)

e) The duckweed makes glucose during this process.

i) Name *two* substances that glucose can be changed into by the plant. (2)

ii) What use does the plant make of each substance? (2)

2 a) What is the difference between a stimulant and a depressant? (2)

b) Explain why the following are not true:

i) It is safe to drive after drinking small amounts of alcohol. (1)

ii) Smoking occasionally is not harmful. (2)

3 a) What is homeostasis? (2)

b) Describe the changes that take place in the human body on a very hot day. (2)

c) Why is it important to keep human body temperature constant at 37 °C? (2)

4 Look at this drawing of a root hair cell. Its job is to absorb water.

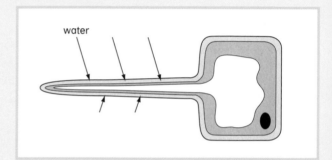

water

a) How is the cell adapted to do its job? (1)

b) By which process does water get into this cell? (1)

c) How do mineral ions get into this cell? (1)

d) Why do plants need mineral ions such as nitrates? (1)

e) Water is passed through other root cells until it reaches cells shaped like this:

These cells take water up to the leaves.

i) What are these cells called?

ii) How are they adapted to their function?

iii) What is the name of the process which transports water up a plant? (3)

5 Copy out this drawing of an animal cell.

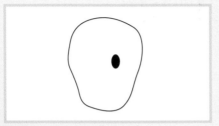

a) Add these labels to your drawing: cytoplasm, nucleus, cell membrane. (1)

b) Most of the chemical reactions in a cell happen in one part. Which part? (1)

c) Name *one* part that you would expect to find in a plant cell but not in an animal cell. (1)

6 a) Rubber plants grow in rainforests where very little light reaches them. Explain why rubber plants have large leaves. (2)

b) Explain why cactus plants have i) leaves reduced to spines ii) green stems and iii) long roots. (3)

c) Plants sometimes wilt in winter when the ground is frozen. Why is this? (1)

7 Look at this picture of dogs on a hot day. Dogs have the same organs that humans do.

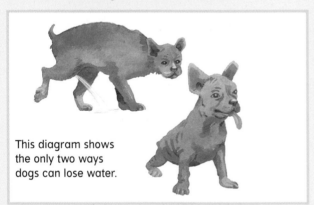

This diagram shows the only two ways dogs can lose water.

a) List three ways in which humans can lose water. (3)

b) Which one of these ways can dogs not lose water by? (1)

c) Name *two* waste products that need to be removed from the body of a human and the body of a dog. (2)

d) Which organs get rid of this waste? (2)

e) What is getting rid of waste like this called? (1)

f) Which organ regulates the ion content of the body? (1)

8 Look at this diagram of the eye.

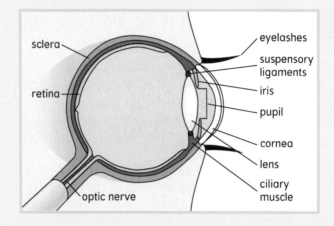

a) List two parts of the eye that must be transparent to let light through. (2)

b) What organ does the optic nerve connect to? (1)

c) What is a reflex action? (2)

d) Describe the reflex action that takes place when a bright light shines into the eye. Use the following terms in your answer: (5)

| stimulus | receptor | co-ordinator |
| effector | response |

e) How does this reflex action help the body? (1)

f) Explain how the eyes focus light when you are looking at distant objects. (2)

9 a) What is a hormone? (1)

b) Describe *two* ways in which the hormonal system is different from the nervous system. (2)

c) i) Which hormone lowers the amount of glucose in the blood?
   ii) Where is this hormone made? (2)

d) After exercise, the level of glucose in the blood falls. How does the body restore the level of glucose to normal? (2)

e) i) Which hormone controls the level of water in the urine?
   ii) Where is this hormone made? (2)

f) Which hormone is found in the tips of growing plants? (1)

 # The Periodic Table

What is the Periodic Table?

There are 92 elements that are found naturally on Earth. 150 years ago not all these elements were known. Scientists were trying to put the elements that they did know about into a logical order.

In 1865, an English scientist called John Newlands arranged the elements in order of their relative atomic masses. The **relative atomic mass** is how much mass an atom of an element has compared with an atom of hydrogen. He found that every eighth element had similar properties.

Later, in 1869, a Russian scientist called Dimitri Mendeleev continued Newlands' work and also put the elements in order of relative atomic mass. But this time he put them into a table. The elements were arranged in rows called **periods**. New rows were started so elements that were alike could line up in columns. These columns are called **groups**. The table was called the **Periodic Table**. Back in 1869 not all the elements were known and Mendeleev left gaps in his table because he felt sure that there were some elements still to be discovered.

A John Newlands.　　**B** Dimitri Mendeleev.

? 1 What pattern did John Newlands find in the elements?

2 Explain the difference between a period and a group on the Periodic Table.

Some elements were switched around to make them fit into the same group as other elements with similar properties. For example, argon has a bigger relative atomic mass than potassium so it would have come after potassium in the table. But it made more sense to switch them round so that potassium was in group 1 (the alkali metals) and argon was in group 0. This meant that some elements were no longer in order of relative atomic mass.

In the modern Periodic Table, the elements are arranged in order of **atomic number**. The atomic number is the number of **protons** in the atom. An atom of argon has 18 protons. This means the atomic number of argon is 18. An atom of potassium has an atomic number of 19. This means that an atom of potassium has 19 protons.

C An atom has a nucleus in the centre, which contains protons and neutrons. Tiny electrons orbit around the nucleus.

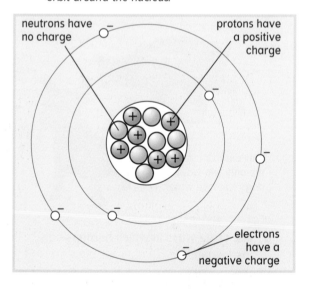

neutrons have no charge

protons have a positive charge

electrons have a negative charge

? 3 Mendeleev did not just put the elements in order of their masses. What two things did he do to make elements fit into groups with similar properties?

4 How do we decide the order of the elements in the Periodic Table today?

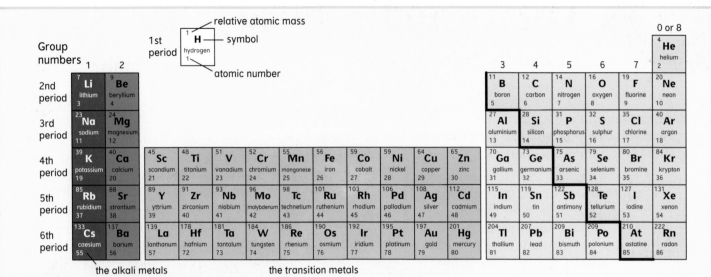

Group numbers	1	2												3	4	5	6	7	0 or 8

relative atomic mass — symbol — atomic number

1st period: H hydrogen 1

He helium 2 (4)

2nd period: Li lithium 3 (7), Be beryllium 4 (9) | B boron 5 (11), C carbon 6 (12), N nitrogen 7 (14), O oxygen 8 (16), F fluorine 9 (19), Ne neon 10 (20)

3rd period: Na sodium 11 (23), Mg magnesium 12 (24) | Al aluminium 13 (27), Si silicon 14 (28), P phosphorus 15 (31), S sulphur 16 (32), Cl chlorine 17 (35), Ar argon 18 (40)

4th period: K potassium 19 (39), Ca calcium 20 (40), Sc scandium 21 (45), Ti titanium 22 (48), V vanadium 23 (51), Cr chromium 24 (52), Mn manganese 25 (55), Fe iron 26 (56), Co cobalt 27 (59), Ni nickel 28 (59), Cu copper 29 (64), Zn zinc 30 (65), Ga gallium 31 (70), Ge germanium 32 (73), As arsenic 33 (75), Se selenium 34 (79), Br bromine 35 (80), Kr krypton 36 (84)

5th period: Rb rubidium 37 (85), Sr strontium 38 (88), Y yttrium 39 (89), Zr zirconium 40 (91), Nb niobium 41 (93), Mo molybdenum 42 (96), Tc technetium 43 (98), Ru ruthenium 44 (101), Rh rhodium 45 (103), Pd palladium 46 (106), Ag silver 47 (108), Cd cadmium 48 (112), In indium 49 (115), Sn tin 50 (119), Sb antimony 51 (122), Te tellurium 52 (128), I iodine 53 (127), Xe xenon 54 (131)

6th period: Cs caesium 55 (133), Ba barium 56 (137), La lanthanum 57 (139), Hf hafnium 72 (178), Ta tantalum 73 (181), W tungsten 74 (184), Re rhenium 75 (186), Os osmium 76 (190), Ir iridium 77 (192), Pt platinum 78 (195), Au gold 79 (197), Hg mercury 80 (201), Tl thallium 81 (204), Pb lead 82 (207), Bi bismuth 83 (209), Po polonium 84 (209), At astatine 85 (210), Rn radon 86 (222)

the alkali metals   the transition metals

Of the 92 elements found naturally on Earth, more than three-quarters are **metals** and the rest are **non-metals**.

We can draw a line on the Periodic Table to divide the metals and non-metals. The metals are on the left-hand side of the line. The non-metals are on the right hand side of the line.

D The modern Periodic Table. The elements are arranged in order of atomic number. Each element has a shorthand **symbol**.

! Some of the elements do not fit neatly into the pattern of metals and non-metals. Elements such as boron, silicon and germanium are similar to metals in some ways, and similar to non-metals in other ways. Elements like these are sometimes called semi-metals.

? **5** Three pairs of elements would be in the wrong order in the Periodic Table if they were put in order of relative atomic mass. Write down one of these pairs.

6 a) Name one element that you would expect to be similar to chlorine.

b) Explain your answer.

7 a) Which group is potassium in?

b) Which group is calcium in?

c) Are these two elements metals or non-metals?

d) Which group is sodium in?

e) Would you expect sodium or calcium to be most similar to potassium? Explain your answer.

E Some of these are metals and some are non-metals. Can you tell which is which?

Summary

A Imagine that you are Mendeleev, and write a short letter to John Newlands to explain how you decided on the order of the elements in the Periodic Table.

B Now imagine that you are a modern scientist, and write a short note to Mendeleev to tell him how our modern Periodic Table is different to the one he produced.

C2 Metals and non-metals

What are the differences between metals and non-metals?

When you think of a metal or a non-metal there will be words you use to describe it. These words are its **properties**.

 1 a) What words could be used to describe a metal like iron?
  b) Carbon is a non-metal used in pencil leads. What words could be used to describe a non-metal like carbon?

Physical properties of non-metals

Most non-metals are:

- dull
- poor conductors of electricity
- poor conductors of heat.

Physical properties of metals

All metals are:

- shiny
- good conductors of heat
- good conductors of electricity.

P Your school is having an open evening, and displays will be set out in the science labs. Design a set of simple experiments to demonstrate the different properties of metals and non-metals. Try out each experiment to make sure it works, and write a short explanation for each one.

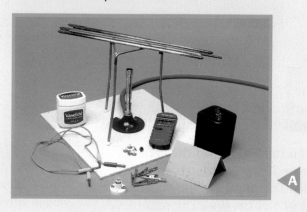

A

All metals have these properties. Diagram B shows how the physical properties of Group 1 metals are different from transition metals.

B

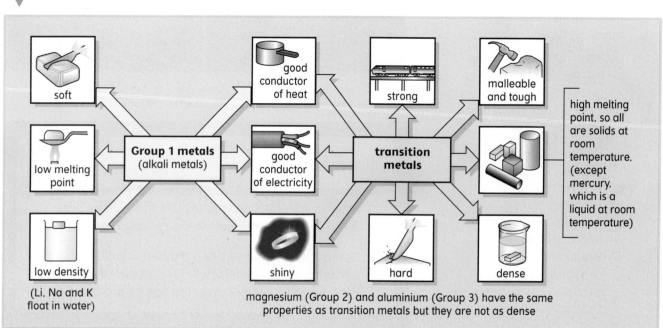

soft

good conductor of heat

strong

malleable and tough

Group 1 metals (alkali metals)

low melting point

good conductor of electricity

transition metals

low density

shiny

hard

dense

high melting point, so all are solids at room temperature, (except mercury, which is a liquid at room temperature)

(Li, Na and K float in water)

magnesium (Group 2) and aluminium (Group 3) have the same properties as transition metals but they are not as dense

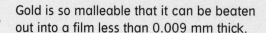

2 a) Write down two physical properties that Group 1 metals have but transition metals do not.

b) Write down two physical properties that transition metals have but Group 1 metals do not.

Gold is so malleable that it can be beaten out into a film less than 0.009 mm thick.

Chemical properties of metals

Group 1 metals:

- are very reactive
- react very quickly with oxygen
- react quickly with water releasing hydrogen
- form hydroxides, which dissolve in water to form alkaline solutions (this is why the Group 1 metals are often called the **alkali metals**)
- react with non-metals to form compounds that are white solids. These white solids dissolve in water to form colourless solutions.

This copper roof has reacted slowly over time with gases from the air and water. The compound formed is green.

Transition metals:

- are much less reactive than Group 1 metals
- react very slowly with oxygen and water
- form coloured compounds (these can be seen in the different coloured glazes in pottery and on old copper roofs).

3 When Group 1 metals are freshly cut, they are shiny inside. But they quickly tarnish and turn dull again. Explain why this happens.

4 a) What will happen if you put a piece of potassium in water?

b) How could you work out that this will happen without actually putting it into water? (*Hint*: think about density.)

Summary

Make a table to compare the physical and chemical properties of Group 1 metals and transition metals. You could start your table like this

Property	Group 1 metals	Transition metals
melting point	low	high
density		

Uses of metals

Why are metals so useful?

A

Metals have lots of uses. You use metals every day of your life. Think about having breakfast. Your cereal spoon is probably made of metal, so are the radiators, the taps in the sink, parts of the microwave, and the fridge. There are also many other things made from metals like grill pans and satellite dishes. All of these metals before you even leave your house!

Transition metals in particular are very useful.

 1 Write down five different things that are made from metals. Explain which property of metals is most important for each object.

Copper

Wires and cables are made of copper with a plastic coating on them. Copper is used to make electrical wiring because it can easily be drawn into wires and is an excellent conductor of electricity.

B

C   *The Statue of Liberty in New York Harbour, USA, is made out of copper. It is hollow inside.*

Iron

Iron is used to make gates because it is **malleable**. It can easily be hammered into shape. It is also very strong. When it is mixed with carbon to make steel it is even stronger. Steel can be used to make cars and the girders that are used in buildings and bridges.

D

E

This aeroplane is made of an alloy of aluminium, copper and magnesium F

Catalysts

Transition metals are useful as **catalysts** in industry. Catalysts speed up chemical reactions. Iron is used as a catalyst in the reaction to make a gas called ammonia. Ammonia is then used to make fertilisers. Platinum is used in catalytic converters that are fitted to car exhausts. It cuts down the amount of pollution in car exhaust fumes.

2 a) What is a catalyst?
  b) Give the names of two metals used as catalysts, and describe the reactions that they speed up.

Alloys

Aluminium is light and can be used to make aeroplanes. But aeroplanes are not made of pure aluminium because it is not strong enough. The wings might bend too much and snap off! Mixing aluminium with other metals like copper and magnesium makes it harder, stronger and stiffer. A mixture of metals is called an **alloy**.

3 a) What is an alloy?
  b) Why are alloys sometimes used instead of pure metals?

4 Copper is a better conductor than aluminium. Why do you think aluminium is used for overhead power lines?

5 Silver conducts electricity better than copper. Why do you think copper is used in electrical wiring rather than silver?

6 Lithium is a very light metal. Why isn't lithium used to make aeroplanes?

Summary

Draw a table to summarise some of the uses of metals, and *why* each metal is used for a particular purpose. You can have more than one use for each metal. Use these column headings: Metal, Use, Reason.

C4 Metals and air

What is made when metals react with air?

Different elements can join together to make a **compound**. When magnesium burns, it joins up with oxygen from the air to make a new compound. When metals join up with oxygen they form **oxides**. The new compound made when magnesium joins up with oxygen is called magnesium oxide.

The **word equation** is:

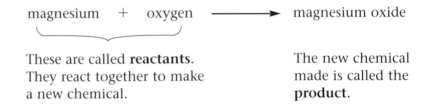

magnesium + oxygen ⟶ magnesium oxide

These are called **reactants**. They react together to make a new chemical.

The new chemical made is called the **product**.

> **?** **1** Write a word equation to show what happens when aluminium reacts with oxygen. Label the reactants and products.

A *Magnesium burning.*

Reactants and products in an equation can be written in a short-hand way. You can re-write the word equation above using the **chemical formula** for each substance. So now you can write a **symbol equation** for burning magnesium:

$$2Mg(s) \quad + \quad O_2(g) \quad \longrightarrow \quad 2MgO(s)$$

2 atoms of magnesium.

Oxygen in the air exists as molecules. Each molecule is 2 oxygen atoms joined together.

There is 1 oxygen atom for each magnesium atom in the compound magnesium oxide.

When writing symbol equations, you may need to put numbers in front of a formula or symbol. This makes sure that you have the same numbers of atoms of each element on each side of the equation. Equations with the correct numbers of atoms on each side are called **balanced equations**. The small letters in the brackets after the formulae show that the elements are solid (s) or a gas (g). Other **state symbols** are (l) for liquid, and (aq) to show that something is in a solution.

Group 1 metals

If you cut lithium, sodium or potassium with a knife (yes, they are soft!) they are shiny inside. But if you look closely, they start turning dull very quickly. This is because the metal is reacting with oxygen to form an oxide. The dull colour is the oxide.

B *Freshly cut sodium.*

The word and symbol equations are:

lithium + oxygen $\longrightarrow$ lithium oxide
$4Li(s) + O_2(g) \longrightarrow 2Li_2O(s)$

sodium + oxygen $\longrightarrow$ sodium oxide
$4Na(s) + O_2(g) \longrightarrow 2Na_2O(s)$

Potassium reacts more quickly than sodium. This means that potassium is more **reactive** than sodium. Sodium reacts more quickly than lithium. This means that sodium is more reactive than lithium.

2 a) Why does sodium change colour after it has been freshly cut?
b) Which would stay shiniest longer after it was cut: a piece of sodium or a piece of potassium? Explain your answer.

Transition metals like zinc, iron and copper need to be heated to make them react with the oxygen in the air. Group 1 metals are more reactive and do not need to be heated. We can write a general equation to show the reaction of metals with oxygen.

metal + oxygen $\longrightarrow$ metal oxide

3 Which metal would you expect to be most reactive: potassium or chromium? Explain your answer. (*Hint*: you may need to look at the Periodic Table on page 87.)

Summary

Draw a concept map to summarise the information on this page. You could start your map like this:

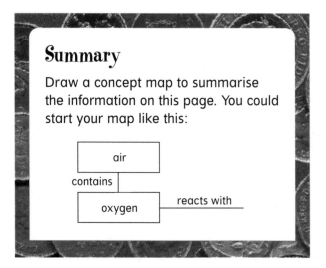

P How would you find out how quickly other metals react with oxygen? C

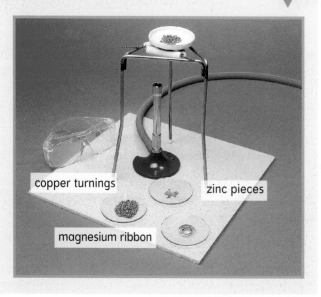

copper turnings   zinc pieces

magnesium ribbon

Metals can be put in a list, in order of **reactivity**. The most reactive metal is at the top of the list. The least reactive metal is at the bottom.

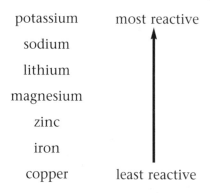

potassium   most reactive

sodium

lithium

magnesium

zinc

iron

copper   least reactive

4 Light bulbs have a metal filament that electricity flows through. The filament gets so hot that it glows. Why are light bulbs filled with an unreactive gas such as argon?

5 Write word equations and balanced symbol equations to show what happens when:
a) calcium burns to form calcium oxide (CaO)
b) potassium reacts to form potassium oxide (K_2O).

6 Which is more reactive: rubidium or sodium? Explain your answer. (*Hint*: you may need to look at the Periodic Table on page 87.)

Metals and water

How quickly do metals react with water?

Some metals react quickly with water. Others react slowly and some, like gold, do not react at all. You have probably seen what happens to a metal when it has been in contact with air and water for a long time. It **corrodes**. When iron corrodes, we call it **rusting**.

 1   What is the difference between corroding and rusting?

When reactive metals like sodium react with water, a **metal hydroxide** is made.

The word equation is:

metal + water $\longrightarrow$ metal hydroxide + hydrogen

e.g. sodium + water $\longrightarrow$ sodium hydroxide + hydrogen

The symbol equation is:

$$2Na(s) + 2H_2O(l) \longrightarrow 2NaOH(aq) + H_2(g)$$

The sodium moves about on the surface of the water very quickly. There is lots of fizzing because a gas is being made. The gas is **hydrogen**.

Potassium reacts in a similar way to sodium but this reaction is more **violent**. Potassium is more reactive than sodium and sodium is more reactive than lithium.

B   *Sodium (left) and potassium (right) reacting with water*

A

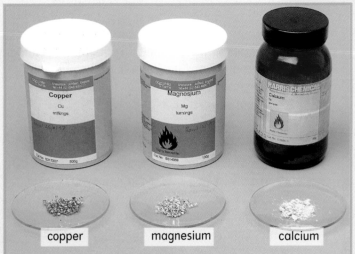

copper   magnesium   calcium

P

2   How can you tell that potassium is more reactive than sodium?

3   What are the products when a metal reacts quickly with water?

   C   How would you find out which metal reacts quickest with water: calcium, magnesium or copper?

Calcium reacts quickly with water, but not violently.

calcium + water $\longrightarrow$ calcium hydroxide + hydrogen
Ca(s) + 2H$_2$O(l) $\longrightarrow$ Ca(OH)$_2$(aq) + H$_2$(g)

Magnesium reacts very slowly with cold water. We can speed up the reaction by using hot water.

magnesium + water $\longrightarrow$ magnesium hydroxide + hydrogen
Mg(s) + 2H$_2$O(l) $\longrightarrow$ Mg(OH)$_2$(aq) + H$_2$(g)

The reaction works best if we heat the magnesium with steam instead. When a metal reacts with steam instead of water, a **metal oxide** is made instead of a metal hydroxide. Hydrogen gas is still made. The magnesium reacts strongly with steam leaving a white powder which is magnesium oxide.

magnesium + steam $\longrightarrow$ magnesium oxide + hydrogen
Mg(s) + H$_2$O(l) $\longrightarrow$ MgO(s) + H$_2$(g)

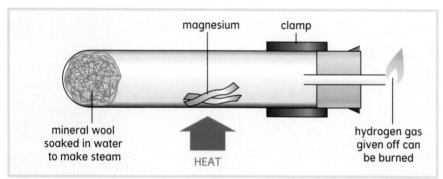

magnesium   clamp

mineral wool
soaked in water
to make steam

HEAT

hydrogen gas
given off can
be burned

Iron also reacts with steam to form iron oxide and hydrogen. Copper, silver and gold do not react with water or steam.

We can write general equations to show what happens when metals react with water.

metal + water $\longrightarrow$ metal hydroxide + hydrogen
metal + steam $\longrightarrow$ metal oxide + hydrogen

Summary

The metals described on these pages can be divided into three groups: metals that react with cold water, metals that only react with steam and metals that do not react with water at all.

List the metals in each group, and write a word and balanced symbol equation for the reaction with water of one of the metals in each group.

4 a) Which is more reactive, calcium or magnesium?
   b) Explain your answer.

We can put the metals we have met so far in order of reactivity, as follows:

potassium   most reactive

sodium

lithium

calcium

magnesium

iron

copper

silver

gold   least reactive

5 a) Write word and balanced symbol equations to show what happens when lithium reacts with water.
   b) Describe what you might see if you added a piece of lithium to water with some universal indicator added.

6 Do you think lithium would react with steam? Explain your answer.

7 Do you think that beryllium would react with water more quickly than magnesium? Explain your answer.

C6 Metals and acids

What happens when metals react with acids?

Metals that are less reactive than calcium react very slowly with water and some of them do not react at all. However, metals react more quickly with dilute acid. This makes it easier to see which metals are the most reactive.

When a metal reacts with an acid a **salt** is made. Hydrogen gas is also made. For example, if you put a small piece of magnesium into dilute hydrochloric acid you can see bubbles of gas. The bubbles are hydrogen gas.

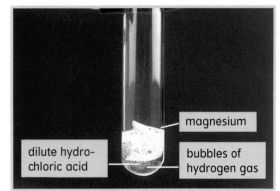

magnesium

dilute hydro-chloric acid

bubbles of hydrogen gas

A

B

The equations are:

magnesium + hydrochloric acid $\longrightarrow$ magnesium chloride + hydrogen

$$Mg(s) \ + \ 2HCl(aq) \ \longrightarrow \ MgCl_2(aq) \ + \ H_2(g)$$

The salt made in this reaction is called magnesium chloride. Another salt you may have heard of is sodium chloride. This is the salt you put on your food and is often called common salt.

1 a) Write a word equation to show what happens when calcium reacts with hydrochloric acid.

b) Write a balanced symbol equation for the reaction. (*Hint*: the formula for calcium chloride is $CaCl_2$.)

The hydrogen gas can be collected easily by using a test tube as shown in diagram B. Hydrogen is lighter than air, so it rises upwards and is trapped in the empty test tube. You can't see or smell hydrogen gas but you can do a test to see if it is there.

If a test tube of hydrogen is held next to a lighted splint, the hydrogen will burn in the air. It burns very quickly and makes a squeaky 'pop'.

You can compare the reactivity of different metals by seeing how quickly hydrogen is made when they react with acid. The faster the hydrogen is made, the more reactive the metal. Some results from the experiment are shown in diagram C.

2 Why is it easy to collect hydrogen in an upside down test tube?

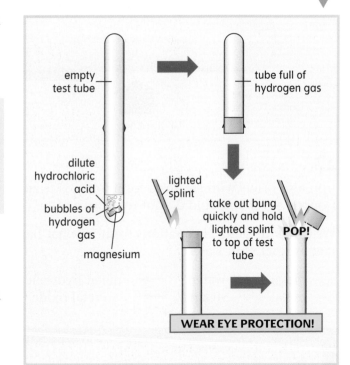

empty test tube

tube full of hydrogen gas

dilute hydrochloric acid

bubbles of hydrogen gas

magnesium

lighted splint

take out bung quickly and hold lighted splint to top of test tube

POP!

WEAR EYE PROTECTION!

Airships and balloons used to be filled with hydrogen because it is lighter than air. Unfortunately, hydrogen is also very flammable and airships were in danger of exploding into flames. Helium is now used instead. It is also lighter than air but is unreactive and does not burn like hydrogen.

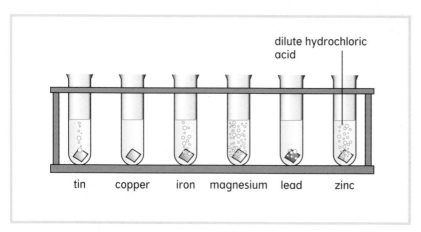

dilute hydrochloric acid

tin   copper   iron   magnesium   lead   zinc

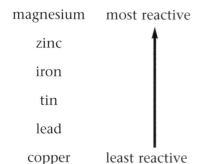
C

The acid in the test tubes containing tin and lead has to be warmed before these two metals will react. Copper does not react with dilute acid, even if it is warmed.

The other metals do react. For example:

zinc + hydrochloric acid $\longrightarrow$ zinc chloride + hydrogen

$Zn(s) + 2HCl(aq) \longrightarrow ZnCl_2(aq) + H_2(g)$

Very reactive metals like potassium explode in dilute acid.

We can write a general equation to show what happens when metals react with acids.

metal + acid $\longrightarrow$ metal salt + hydrogen

From the results we can put the metals in order of reactivity:

magnesium   most reactive

zinc

iron

tin

lead

copper   least reactive

Summary

Look back at topic C5. Draw up a table to summarise the similarities and differences between the ways metals react with water and acid.

3 Look at diagram C. How can you tell which metal is the most reactive?

P How would you investigate which metal reacts the fastest with acid?

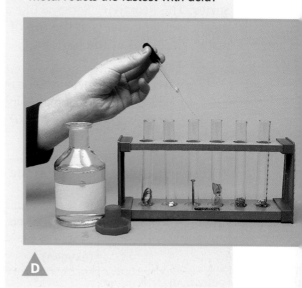
D

4 Photograph D shows an experiment being carried out to find out which metal reacts fastest with acid.
 a) How could you change the experiment shown to make sure the test was fair?
 b) What would you expect to see when you added the acid?
 c) How could you show that hydrogen gas was being produced?

5 a) Copy the test tubes shown in diagram C. Draw in the number of bubbles you would expect to see for each metal if the acid in all the tubes was cold.
 b) Explain why your answer looks different to diagram C.
 c) Describe what you would expect to see if the acid in all the tubes was heated before the experiment.

C7 The Reactivity Series

What is the Reactivity Series and what does it mean?

We have seen that some metals are more reactive than others. If you look back to see how reactive the metals were with oxygen, water and acid you can put all the results together. From these results you can put the metals into a list called the **Reactivity Series**. The Reactivity Series is like a league table for metals. The most reactive metal is at the top of the league table and the least reactive metal is at the bottom.

1 a) What is the Reactivity Series?
  b) How is the order of metals in the reactivity series worked out?

We can put all the results from the last three topics together:

Metal	Symbol	Reaction when heated in air (oxygen)	Reaction with cold water	Reaction with dilute acid
potassium	K		fizzes violently, giving off hydrogen; forms metal hydroxide solutions	very violent reaction (explodes – extremely dangerous)
sodium	Na			
lithium	Li			
calcium	Ca	burn brightly forming an oxide		fizz giving off hydrogen gas; form metal salts
magnesium	Mg		very slow reaction	
aluminium	Al		no reaction except for slow rusting of iron; all react with steam	
zinc	Zn			
iron	Fe			
tin	Sn	oxide layer forms but metal does not burn		react very slowly giving off hydrogen
lead	Pb		no reaction, even with steam	
copper	Cu			no reaction
silver	Ag			
gold	Au	no reaction		
platinum	Pt			

most reactive

metal	symbol
potassium	K
sodium	Na
lithium	Li
calcium	Ca
magnesium	Mg
aluminium	Al
zinc	Zn
iron	Fe
tin	Sn
lead	Pb
copper	Cu
silver	Ag
gold	Au
platinum	Pt

least reactive

A *The Reactivity Series.*

2 Which metals form oxides without burning when heated in air?

3 Which metals react with cold water giving off hydrogen gas?

4 Which metals don't react with water or steam?

B

We can use the Reactivity Series to make predictions about chemical reactions. Look at diagram C.

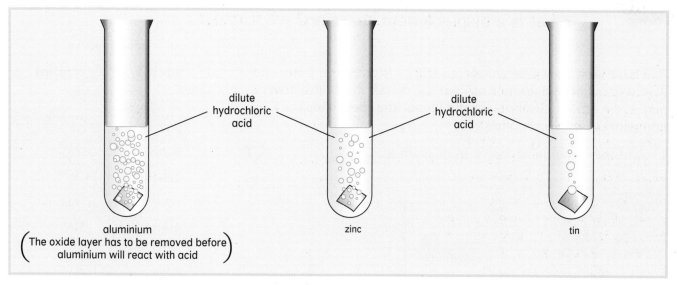

dilute hydrochloric acid

dilute hydrochloric acid

aluminium
(The oxide layer has to be removed before aluminium will react with acid)

zinc

tin

Aluminium is higher in the Reactivity Series than zinc, so it is more reactive. If you put pieces of each metal in acid they will react and give off hydrogen gas. We can show that aluminium is more reactive by drawing more bubbles. Tin is lower than aluminium and zinc in the Reactivity Series. We can predict that there will be fewer bubbles than with aluminium or zinc. We can show this by drawing fewer bubbles on the diagram than there are for zinc.

Summary

Draw three tables to summarise the reactions of metals with oxygen, water and dilute acids. You may need to look back at topics C4, C5 and C6. Your table for the reactions of oxygen could look like the one below. You will need more rows in your other two tables.

Metals	Reaction	Equation
K, Na, Li, Ca, Mg, Al Zn, Fe	burns brightly	metal + oxygen ⟶ metal oxide
Sn, Pb Cu		

5 Draw test tubes to show iron and zinc reacting with dilute acid.

6 a) Which metals don't react with water but do react with steam?
   b) What is made when these metals react with steam?

7 a) Which metals fizz when they react with acid giving off hydrogen gas?
   b) What else is made when these metals react with acid?

8 Copy and complete these word equations:
   a) aluminium + steam ⟶
   b) lead + hydrochloric acid ⟶
   c) silver + steam ⟶
   d) calcium + water ⟶

9 Put these groups of metals in order of reactivity, and explain how you worked out your answer.

**Transition metals   Group 1 metals
Group 3 metals**

You may need to look back at the Periodic Table on page 87.

C8 Displacement reactions

What is a displacement reaction?

You have seen how different metals react with oxygen, water and acid. We used these reactions to put the metals into a Reactivity Series. We can also judge reactivity by putting metals into competition with each other.

Look at the experiment shown in diagram B:

B

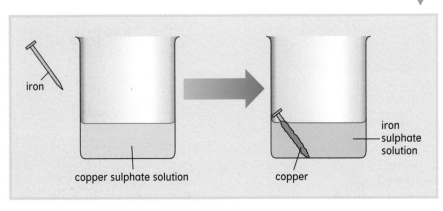

The word and symbol equations are:

iron + copper sulphate ⟶ iron sulphate + copper

$$Fe(s) + CuSO_4(aq) \longrightarrow FeSO_4(aq) + Cu(s)$$

(grey)   (blue)   ⟶   (green)   (red-brown)

Iron is higher in the Reactivity Series and 'kicks out' or **displaces** copper from its solution. You can see the red-brown copper coating the nail. The iron has taken its place in solution and forms iron sulphate solution, which is green. A more reactive metal can displace ('kick out') a less reactive metal from its solution. This type of reaction is called a **displacement reaction**.

P How would you investigate whether other metals carry out displacement reactions?

C

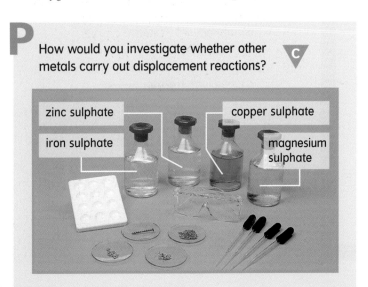

most reactive	
metal	**symbol**
potassium	K
sodium	Na
lithium	Li
calcium	Ca
magnesium	Mg
aluminium	Al
zinc	Zn
iron	Fe
tin	Sn
lead	Pb
copper	Cu
silver	Ag
gold	Au
platinum	Pt
least reactive	

A The Reactivity Series.

? **1** What is a displacement reaction?

2 Why does iron displace copper from solution?

If we put copper into iron sulphate solution, there would be no reaction, because copper is below iron in the Reactivity Series. Copper cannot displace iron. This means it cannot kick iron out of its solution and take its place.

? **3** Why can't copper displace iron from its solution?

Iron versus copper

We can put metals into competition with each other to win oxygen. If we heat iron metal and copper oxide together, the iron and the copper will compete for the oxygen. Copper has the oxygen to start with. Iron is higher in the Reactivity Series so it takes the oxygen from copper.

If you mix a spatula of iron filings and copper oxide in a test tube and heat it strongly, you will see a red glow after a while. This tells you there is a reaction happening.

After a few minutes, if you pour the mixture into an evaporating basin, you can see small pieces of red–brown copper.

The iron has displaced the copper and has won the competition for oxygen. It takes the oxygen from copper because it is higher in the Reactivity Series. It is more reactive.

iron + copper oxide ⟶ iron oxide + copper

If we heat copper with iron oxide there is no reaction. The iron keeps the oxygen because it is more reactive than copper.

copper + iron oxide ⟶ no reaction

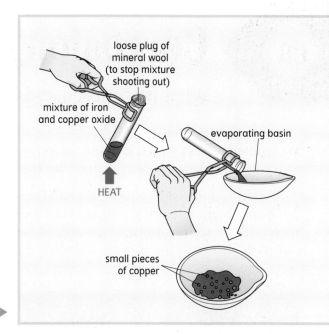

4 a) Which metal wins the competition, iron or copper?

b) Explain why this happens.

5 How could you tell that there was a reaction happening?

Summary

Someone who does not know much about chemistry has asked you why a nail turns reddish brown if it is put into copper sulphate solution. Explain in your own words what happens and why it happens.

6 Look at table A. Predict whether there will be a reaction between these pairs. Write down 'yes' or 'no' for each of your answers.

a) Magnesium and zinc sulphate.

b) Copper and zinc oxide.

c) Aluminium and iron sulphate.

d) Explain each of your answers for a), b) and c).

e) Write word equations for any reactions that work.

7 Write symbol equations for the reactions in question 6 that work. You may need the following formulae: $MgSO_4$, CuO, $Al_2(SO_4)_3$.

Corrosion of metals

What is corrosion and how can we prevent it?

When metals react with water and oxygen from the air they can turn into oxides or hydroxides. This is called **corrosion**.

Corrosion is not useful. If a metal bridge corrodes it becomes weak and might fall down. Iron (or steel) corrodes much faster than other transition metals. Corroded metals have to be replaced. This costs the country millions of pounds each year.

 B

A

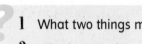

1 What two things make metals corrode?

2 Why is corrosion a problem? Give at least two reasons.

Preventing the corrosion of iron (or steel)

When iron corrodes, it is called **rusting**. Oxygen and water are both needed to make iron rust. If oxygen and water can be kept away from iron or steel then it won't rust.

Coating the metal with paint, oil (or grease), or plastic forms a barrier and stops oxygen and water getting to the iron or steel.

C *Blocks of magnesium can protect a ship's hull from rust. They corrode instead of the steel.*

3 Why are iron railings usually painted?

Iron can also be coated with a more reactive metal like zinc. Zinc is more reactive than iron. Oxygen and water will react with the zinc instead of the iron. The zinc sacrifices itself for the iron. This is called **sacrificial protection**.

Magnesium is sometimes used instead of zinc.

4 **a)** What metals are used for sacrificial protection?
   b) Explain why they can be used.
   c) Why do the blocks on a ship's hull have to be replaced every few months?

Chromium and nickel can be added to steel to make an alloy called **stainless steel**. This does not rust easily. It is useful for small items like knives and forks, but is expensive.

Aluminium is quite a reactive metal, but doesn't corrode very quickly. This is because a thin layer of aluminium oxide forms on the surface. This oxide layer stops oxygen and water getting to the metal underneath.

D These knives and forks are made from stainless steel.

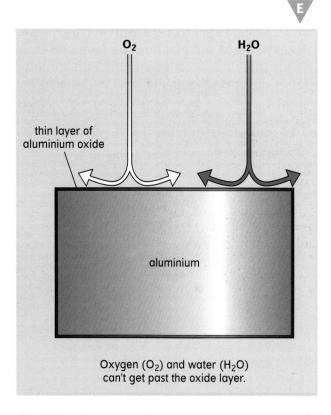

Oxygen (O_2) and water (H_2O) can't get past the oxide layer.

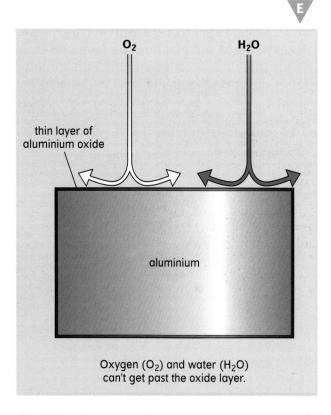

? 5 Write down three ways that rusting can be stopped.

6 **a)** What is stainless steel?
b) What is the advantage of stainless steel over ordinary steel?

7 Why is stainless steel not used to make cars?

8 **a)** Why might you expect a car body made of pure aluminium to corrode faster than a car made from iron?
b) Why doesn't this happen?
c) Why is pure aluminium not used to make cars? (*Hint:* you may need to look back at topic C3.)

Summary

Answer the topic question at the top of page 102 in your own words. Make sure you include all the bold words on these pages in your answer.

Extraction of metals

Where do we find metals?

The Earth's crust is a thin layer of rock covering the whole of the planet. We call the Earth's crust the ground. Metals are found in the Earth's crust.

Metals at the bottom of the Reactivity Series are unreactive. They can be found as the metals themselves, not joined up with other elements as compounds. Metals like gold and platinum are found on their own. We say that these metals are found in their **native** state. Copper is sometimes found in its native state.

A

1 Gold is found in its native state. What does this mean?

2 Why is gold found in its native state?

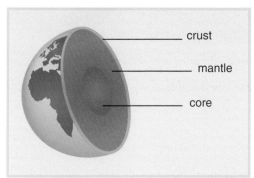

B

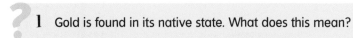

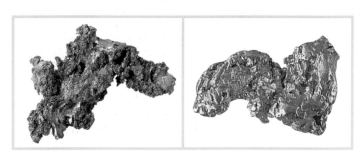

C   Copper.

D   Gold.

Panning for gold, a metal found in its native state.   E

We don't find many metals just lying around on the ground. Most metal elements are joined up with other elements to make compounds. The metal compounds are mixed with rock and this mixture is called an **ore**. An ore contains enough of the metal compound to make it worth extracting. An ore often contains a metal oxide. To **extract** the metal, we have to remove oxygen from the metal oxide.   F

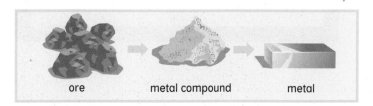

ore   metal compound   metal

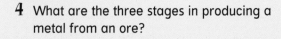

3 What is an ore?

4 What are the three stages in producing a metal from an ore?

Extraction of metals and the Reactivity Series

To extract a metal from its ore, the oxygen must be taken away from the metal oxide. Taking oxygen away from something is called **reduction**.

There is a link between a metal's place in the Reactivity Series and how easy it is to extract from its ore. The more reactive a metal is, the more difficult it is to extract from its ore. Reactive metals like aluminium and sodium 'want' to stay joined up with other elements in their ores. This makes it difficult to extract very reactive metals.

We use electricity in a process called **electrolysis** to extract very reactive metals, like aluminium, from their ores. Less reactive metals, like iron, can be extracted by heating the metal oxide with carbon. Carbon is more reactive than iron, so it 'grabs' the oxygen and displaces the iron (a **displacement reaction**).

e.g.   iron oxide + carbon $\longrightarrow$ iron + carbon dioxide

$$2FeO(s) + C(s) \longrightarrow 2Fe(s) + CO_2(g)$$

Electrolysis can be used for metals lower down in the Reactivity Series, but it is not used because it is a very expensive process.

potassium		
sodium		
lithium		
calcium	Use electrolysis.	
magnesium		
aluminium		
(carbon)		
zinc		
iron	Ores are heated with carbon.	
tin		
lead		
(hydrogen)		
copper		
silver	Found in native state (although copper is often found as an ore).	
gold		
platinum		

hard to extract

getting harder to extract

easy to extract

  Carbon and hydrogen are non-metals but they can be added to the Reactivity Series.

?
5   What is reduction?

6   Why is iron easier to extract from its ore than aluminium? Explain in as much detail as you can.

7   a) Which method would you use to extract tin from its ore?
    b) Which method would you use to extract sodium from its ore?
    c) Explain your choices for a) and b).

8   a) How could you extract iron from its ore using zinc?
    b) Why isn't this method used in industry?

! There is more aluminium in the Earth's crust than any other metal. Unfortunately it is very difficult to get aluminium from its ore.

  This is a bauxite mine. Bauxite is mined from the surface of the Earth.

Summary

Write sentences in your own words to explain the meanings of all the words in bold on these pages.

105

Extracting metals with carbon

How can carbon be used to extract metals from their ores?

Carbon is a non-metal but we can put it in the Reactivity Series. Carbon is less reactive than aluminium but more reactive than zinc. That means it slots in between those two metals as shown in diagram A.

Carbon can **displace** any metal below aluminium in the Reactivity Series. This means we can use carbon to extract metals below aluminium from their ores. For example, iron is less reactive than carbon, so carbon can be used to extract iron from its ore. Carbon 'grabs' the oxygen from the ore and becomes carbon dioxide.

Carbon is found in the form of coal so it is cheap. Remember, the ore usually contains the metal oxide, so all we have to do is heat the metal oxide with carbon to get the metal. The reaction is a **displacement reaction**.

?

1 Where is carbon in the Reactivity Series?

2 **a)** Name a metal that can be extracted by using carbon.
   b) Why is this method less expensive than electrolysis?

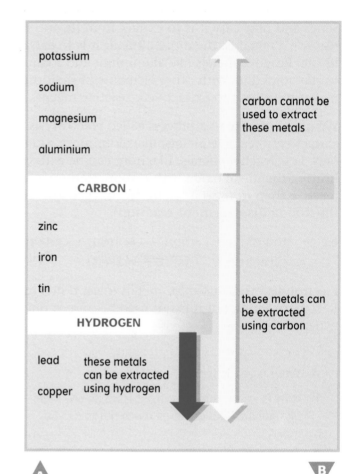

potassium

sodium

magnesium

aluminium

CARBON

zinc

iron

tin

HYDROGEN

lead   these metals
        can be extracted
copper using hydrogen

carbon cannot be used to extract these metals

these metals can be extracted using carbon

A

B

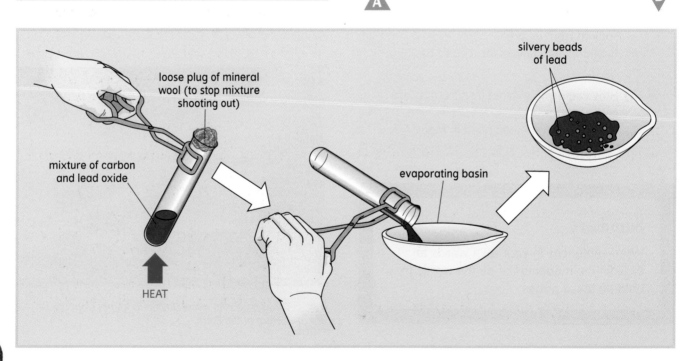

loose plug of mineral wool (to stop mixture shooting out)

mixture of carbon and lead oxide

HEAT

evaporating basin

silvery beads of lead

Hydrogen is also a non-metal and can be put into the Reactivity Series like carbon. It is more reactive than lead and could be used to extract lead from its ore. However, it is much lower down in the reactivity series than carbon so is not as useful. Carbon is easier to use than hydrogen because it is a solid and is also cheaper. Carbon is usually used to extract metals from their ores instead of hydrogen.

Extracting lead from its ore

Lead oxide is a yellow powder. We can get it from an ore called massicot.

Carbon is more reactive than lead. If we heat lead oxide with carbon, the carbon takes oxygen away from lead oxide in a displacement reaction. Carbon has displaced lead from lead oxide. Taking oxygen away from a compound is called **reduction**.

Carbon has **reduced** lead oxide to lead.

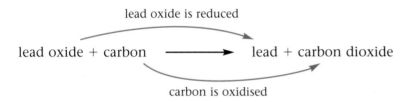

lead oxide is reduced

lead oxide + carbon $\longrightarrow$ lead + carbon dioxide

carbon is oxidised

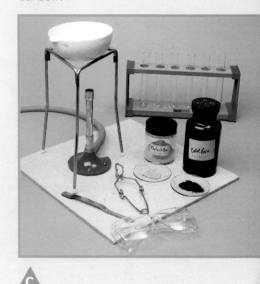

P How can you extract copper from its ore 'malachite' using carbon?

C

When oxygen is added to a chemical we say it has been **oxidised**. Adding oxygen to something is called **oxidation**. Carbon is oxidised when it takes oxygen away from lead oxide.

If one chemical in a reaction is oxidised, another chemical must have been reduced. Oxidation and reduction always happen together. Reactions like this are called **redox** reactions.

?

3 What do the words oxidation and reduction mean?

4 What is a redox reaction?

5 Why can't carbon be used to extract aluminium from its ore? Explain as fully as you can.

6 Write a word equation to show the reaction that happens when lead is extracted from lead oxide using hydrogen.

7 Look at this word equation

zinc oxide + carbon $\longrightarrow$ zinc + carbon dioxide

   a) What has been oxidised?
   b) What has been reduced?
   c) Write a balanced symbol equation for the reaction.
      (The formula for zinc oxide is ZnO).

8 a) Write a balanced symbol equation to show what happens when magnesium reacts with steam. Include state symbols.
   b) In this reaction, which substance is oxidised and which substance is reduced?

Summary

Answer the topic question at the top of page 106 in your own words. Make sure you include all the bold words on these pages in your answer, and include a word equation.

Getting iron from its ore

How do we get iron from its ore?

 From this …

… to this.

Iron is an extremely useful metal and we use a lot of it.
To get iron we need three raw materials:

1. **Iron ore** — mainly haematite, which contains iron oxide

2. **Coke** — a cheap form of carbon made from coal

3. **Limestone** — to get rid of impurities.

The three raw materials are crushed and heated together in a
blast furnace. It is called a blast furnace because hot air is
blasted in at the bottom. It is very hot inside a blast furnace;
the temperature can be up to 1900 °C.

 1 What are the raw materials used for extracting iron
from its ore?

Reactions in the blast furnace

The coke (carbon) burns. It reacts with oxygen from the hot
air blasted in and makes carbon dioxide. This reaction
produces lots of heat and makes the blast furnace even hotter.

carbon + oxygen $\longrightarrow$ carbon dioxide

$$C(s) + O_2(g) \longrightarrow CO_2(g)$$

The carbon dioxide formed reacts with hot coke (carbon) to
make **carbon monoxide** gas.

carbon dioxide + carbon $\longrightarrow$ carbon monoxide

$$CO_2(g) + C(s) \longrightarrow 2CO(g)$$

 A blast furnace.

The carbon monoxide then **reduces** the iron oxide to iron. Carbon monoxide is called a **reducing agent**.

iron oxide + carbon monoxide $\longrightarrow$ iron + carbon dioxide

$$Fe_2O_3(s) + 3CO(g) \longrightarrow 2Fe(l) + 3CO_2(g)$$

The carbon monoxide is itself oxidised when it joins up with oxygen from the iron ore.

Limestone reacts with the acidic impurities in the iron ore to make a liquid waste called **slag**.

2 What substance reduces the iron ore to iron?

3 What is a reducing agent?

As the temperature in the furnace is very high, the iron formed is a liquid and sinks to the bottom of the furnace. The slag is also a liquid, but it is lighter (less dense) than liquid iron and so floats on top of it. The slag and molten iron are run off separately. When the slag has cooled and solidified it is used for making roads and making breeze blocks for buildings.

The blast furnace can run continuously. The molten iron and molten slag are run off through separate pipes at the bottom of the furnace. As the iron oxide, carbon and limestone are used up, more raw materials are added at the top of the furnace.

4 When the iron is formed, it is liquid (molten). Why is this?

5 Give two uses for the slag.

A modern blast furnace can make 3000 tonnes of iron each day using 3000 tonnes of coke and 4000 tonnes of air!

6 The hot air blasted into the furnace does two things. What are they?

7 Write out the equations for the reactions that happen in the blast furnace, and say which substances have been reduced and which have been oxidised in each reaction.

8 The waste gases from the blast furnace are used to heat the air blasted in at the bottom of the furnace.
   a) How does this make the blast furnace more efficient?
   b) Why can't the waste gases be blown into the blast furnace directly?

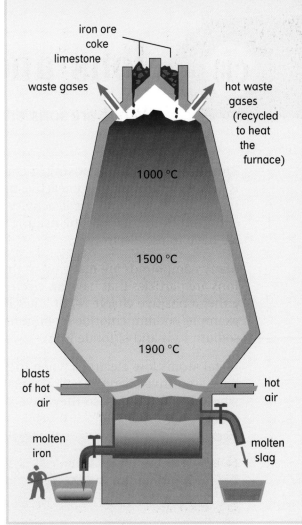

The blast furnace.

Summary

Draw a simplified diagram of a blast furnace, and add labels to summarise the information on these pages. Part of your diagram might look like this:

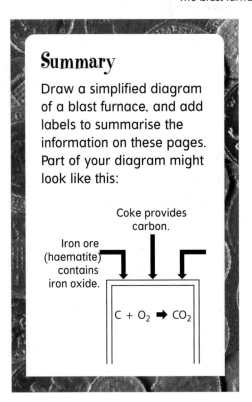

Coke provides carbon.

Iron ore (haematite) contains iron oxide.

$$C + O_2 \rightarrow CO_2$$

109

Ions and electrolytes

What are ions and electrolytes?

Breaking down (**decomposing**) a chemical by using electricity is called **electrolysis**. Very reactive metals like aluminium are higher than carbon in the Reactivity Series. They can't be extracted from their ores by heating with carbon. Instead, we have to use electrolysis.

Many compounds are made up of tiny particles called **ions**. Ions are particles that have an electric charge. They can have either a positive charge (+) or a negative charge (–). For example, sodium chloride (common salt) is made up of sodium ions and chloride ions.

Metal atoms lose electrons when they form ions, so metal ions have a positive charge (+). Non-metal atoms gain electrons when they form ions, so they have a negative charge (–).

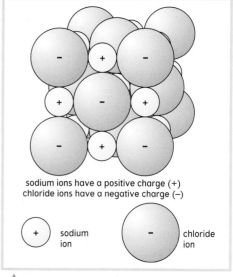

sodium ions have a positive charge (+)
chloride ions have a negative charge (–)

+   sodium ion   −   chloride ion

A   *Sodium chloride.*

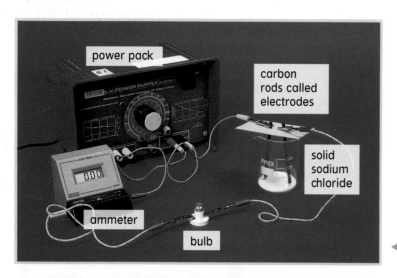

B

1   Why do sodium ions have a positive charge?

2   Why do chloride ions have a negative charge?

Look at the circuit shown in picture B and diagram C. The bulb is not lit. The solid does not conduct electricity.

C

This can be shown as a circuit diagram.

4V

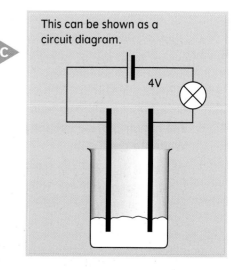

D

WARNING: CHLORINE GAS

If we add water and stir the sodium chloride so that it dissolves and makes a solution, the bulb now lights! The solution conducts electricity.

We can carry out a similar experiment on solid lead bromide. Look at diagram E. The bulb is not lit. Solid lead bromide does not conduct electricity.

Now look at diagram F. The lead bromide has been heated so that it melts. It is now a liquid. The bulb now lights. Molten lead bromide conducts electricity.

If the solid compound is made of ions it won't conduct electricity when it is solid. However, if it is made into a liquid by dissolving it in water or melting it, then it can conduct electricity. Liquids that conduct electricity are called **electrolytes**.

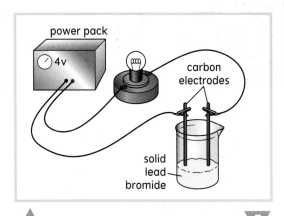

E

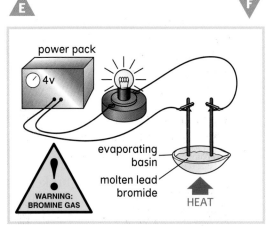

F

3 What is an electrolyte?

4 A solid made of ions does not conduct electricity. What two things can we do to make it conduct?

5 How can you tell if a substance is conducting electricity?

Electrolytes and electricity

Electricity is a flow of charged particles. In a wire, the charged particles are electrons. Ions are charged particles, so they can conduct electricity when they are free to move. Ions in a solid cannot move around because they are tightly packed together, but if the solid is dissolved to make a solution the ions break away from each other and can move around in the water. The ions can also move about if the solid is melted.

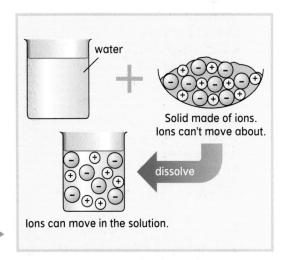

Solid made of ions. Ions can't move about.

dissolve

Ions can move in the solution.

G

6 Why can't a solid compound made of ions conduct electricity?

7 Why can a compound made of ions conduct electricity after it has been melted?

8 a) Copper sulphate is a solid made of ions. Will it conduct electricity?
b) What could you do to the solid copper sulphate to make it conduct?
c) Why will it now conduct electricity?

9 a) Is aluminium oxide made from ions? Explain how you worked out your answer.
b) If the answer to part a) was 'yes', which ion is positive and which is negative?
c) Suggest the names of two metals that can be extracted using electrolysis, but cannot be extracted using carbon.

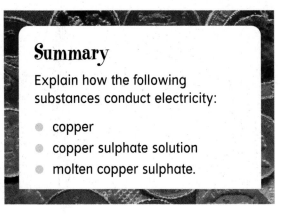

Summary

Explain how the following substances conduct electricity:

- copper
- copper sulphate solution
- molten copper sulphate.

Electrolysis of copper chloride

How does electrolysis actually work?

To understand how we extract reactive metals from their ores, we need to know what happens to the ions in **electrolysis**. Electrolysis is when a compound is split up by electricity.

The electrolysis of copper chloride solution helps us to understand what is going on. Copper chloride is dissolved in water to make a solution and then a circuit is set up.

Look at diagram A. The carbon electrodes have special names. The one connected to the positive (+) terminal on the power pack or battery is called the **anode**. The anode has a positive charge. The electrode connected to the negative (−) terminal is called the **cathode**. The cathode has a negative charge.

Copper metal is formed at the cathode (negative electrode). Chlorine gas is formed at the anode (positive electrode). The copper chloride has been broken down into its elements, copper and chlorine, by electrolysis.

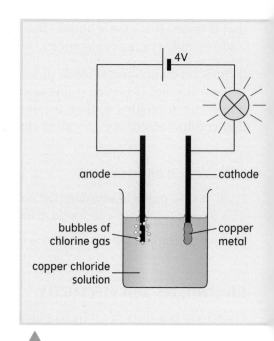

A

anode — cathode

bubbles of chlorine gas

copper metal

copper chloride solution

B

Remember that some compounds like copper chloride are made up of ions. When the compound was formed in the first place, copper atoms and chlorine atoms reacted with each other. When they did this they became **ions** with an electric charge.

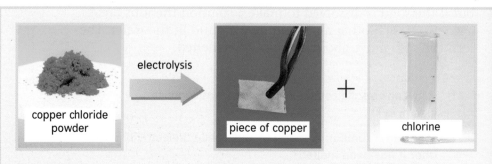

copper chloride powder

electrolysis

piece of copper

+

chlorine

When we split up these ions using electrolysis, they turn back into **atoms**.

?

1 **a)** Do copper ions have a positive or a negative charge?
   b) Which electrode will copper ions be attracted to? Explain your answer.

2 What is the difference between an ion and an atom?

P

Malachite is an ore containing copper compounds. How can you use electrolysis to get copper from malachite?

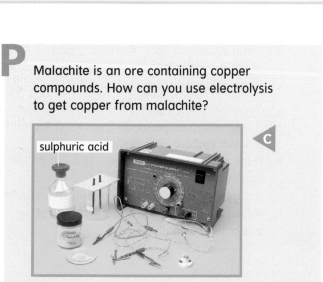

sulphuric acid

C

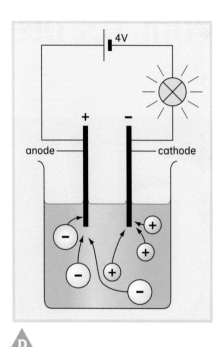

D

Copper ions have a positive charge, and they are attracted to the negative electrode (cathode). At the cathode, the positive copper ions gain electrons and are converted into copper atoms. Copper forms as a solid on the electrode.

Chloride ions have a negative charge, and they are attracted to the positive electrode (anode). At the anode, the chloride ions lose electrons and turn back into chlorine atoms. Molecules of chlorine gas form, and the anode gives off bubbles of chlorine gas.

We say that copper ions are **reduced**, because they have gained electrons. The chloride ions have been **oxidised**, because they have lost electrons. The words oxidation and reduction do not just apply to reactions that involve oxygen.

E

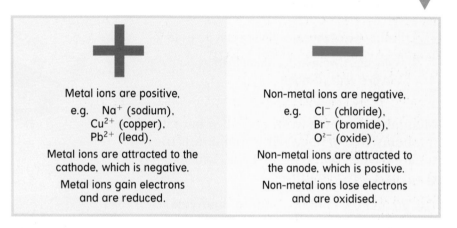

+	**–**
Metal ions are positive, e.g. Na^+ (sodium), Cu^{2+} (copper), Pb^{2+} (lead).	Non-metal ions are negative, e.g. Cl^- (chloride), Br^- (bromide), O^{2-} (oxide).
Metal ions are attracted to the cathode, which is negative.	Non-metal ions are attracted to the anode, which is positive.
Metal ions gain electrons and are reduced.	Non-metal ions lose electrons and are oxidised.

You can remember what happens in oxidation and reduction by remembering the word OILRIG.

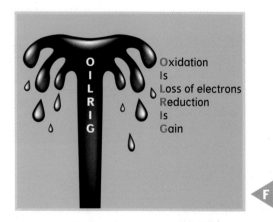

Oxidation
Is
Loss of electrons
Reduction
Is
Gain

F

Summary

Describe what happens at the anode and the cathode when a solution of copper chloride is electrolysed. Use all the bold words on these pages in your summary.

?

3 If we carried out electrolysis on lead bromide:
  a) what would happen at the cathode
  b) what would happen at the anode
  c) which ions would be reduced
  d) which ions would be oxidised?

4 If a solution of sodium chloride is electrolysed, hydrogen is given off at the cathode.
  a) What might you expect to be formed at the cathode? Explain your answer.
  b) Why is hydrogen given off instead? (*Hint*: look at the reactivity series on page 105, and think which elements water is made from.)

Getting aluminium from its ore

How do we get aluminium from its ore?

Aluminium is an extremely useful metal. It is used to make overhead power cables, drink cans, saucepans, aeroplanes, kitchen foil and many other things.

Aluminium is more reactive than carbon. This means that we can't extract it from its ore by heating it with carbon. We have to use **electrolysis**.

?
1 Name two things aluminium can be used for.
2 Why can't we extract aluminium by heating the ore with carbon?

A

Aluminium is found in an ore called **bauxite** (pronounced *'borx –ite'*). It is found near the surface of the ground in Australia, Jamaica, Brazil and other countries.

The ore mainly contains aluminium oxide, mixed with impurities like bits of rock and other compounds. The ore must be purified, which means the impurities are taken out of the ore leaving just the aluminium oxide behind.

Then the aluminium can be extracted from the aluminium oxide.

?
3 What is the main compound in bauxite?

Digging out bauxite. **B**

bauxite (impure aluminium oxide)	**purify** →	pure aluminium oxide	**electrolysis** →	aluminium

C

?
4 Why does bauxite have to be purified?

There is more aluminium in the Earth than any other metal, but it was first extracted only in 1827. It was so rare that the Tsar of Russia gave his baby son an aluminium rattle to play with because aluminium was more expensive than gold!

Electrolysis of aluminium oxide

Once we have pure aluminium oxide it has to be melted before electrolysis is carried out. The melting point of aluminium oxide is 2050 °C! This makes it difficult to melt. However, it can be dissolved in a molten chemical called **cryolite** at a much lower temperature, about 850 °C. This saves a lot of energy, but a lot of electricity is still needed to carry out the electrolysis.

In the school laboratory, electrolysis is carried out in a beaker. In industry it is carried out in large containers called **cells**. The one shown in diagram D is about half the size of a classroom.

The oxygen gas reacts with the carbon anodes to make carbon dioxide. The anodes have to be replaced quite often.

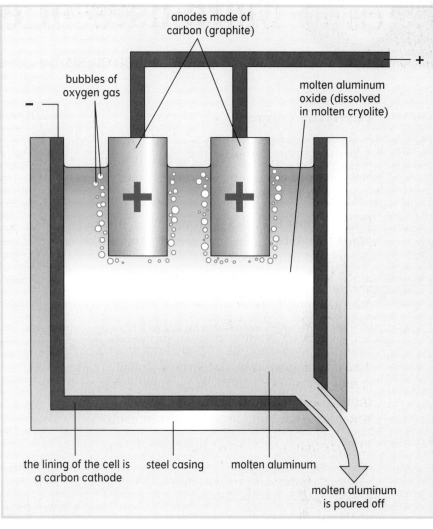

anodes made of carbon (graphite)

bubbles of oxygen gas

molten aluminum oxide (dissolved in molten cryolite)

the lining of the cell is a carbon cathode

steel casing

molten aluminum

molten aluminum is poured off

 D

Summary

Draw a simplified diagram of a cell used to produce aluminium, and add labels to summarise the information on these pages. (*Hint*: you can use diagram D as a starting point, but you will need to add more information.)

5 In the electrolysis of aluminium oxide:
   a) which ions are attracted to the cathode
   b) do these ions lose or gain electrons
   c) are they oxidised or reduced
   d) what is formed at the cathode?

6 Explain what happens at the anode during aluminium extraction, in as much detail as you can.

7 Why do the carbon anodes need to be replaced?

8 Why is cryolite needed to produce aluminium?

9 a) Why do you think it is expensive to extract aluminium from its ore?
   b) Why is it cheaper to make aluminium products from recycled drinks cans?

More uses of electrolysis

What else can electrolysis be used for?

Purifying copper

Copper is used for many things. One reason why it is used for electrical wiring is that it is an excellent conductor of electricity. However, it must be very pure to do its job well.

When copper is extracted from its ore, it is not pure enough to be used for electrical wiring. It can be purified using electrolysis.

Diagram B shows how electrolysis can be used to purify copper. It can be done this way in a school laboratory.

In industry, electrolysis is carried out in large cells (like the extraction of aluminium) and there are many cells running at the same time. Diagram B shows the electrolysis before and after. In the laboratory, you can see the results in about 15 minutes.

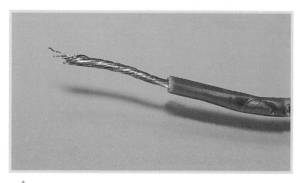

A

 When purifying copper, the sludge that is left over is not wasted. It contains precious metals like silver and gold.

B

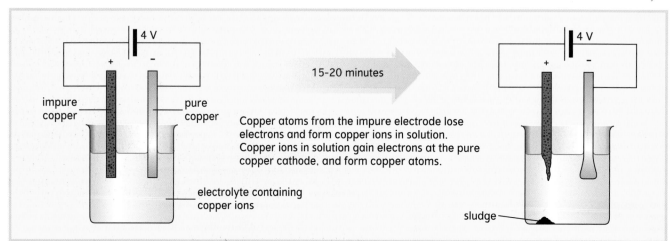

4 V

impure copper

pure copper

15-20 minutes

Copper atoms from the impure electrode lose electrons and form copper ions in solution. Copper ions in solution gain electrons at the pure copper cathode, and form copper atoms.

electrolyte containing copper ions

4 V

sludge

The anode (positive electrode) is made out of the impure copper that you are trying to purify. The cathode is made out of pure copper. The electrolyte contains copper ions.

The anode (impure copper) gets smaller and smaller. The cathode (pure copper) gets bigger and bigger. The impurities fall off into the solution forming sludge at the bottom of the beaker.

1 Why does copper need to be purified if it is to be used for electrical wiring?

2 Are the copper atoms at the anode being reduced or oxidised?

3 Why must the electrolyte contain copper ions?

Electroplating

Look at diagram D. If you swap the cathode for a metal object like a key, then the key becomes coated with copper.

You can coat lots of metal objects with a different metal using electrolysis. This is called **electroplating**.

If you have a bike, the handlebars might be covered with chromium (chrome). This is a very shiny metal which does not rust. Underneath, the handlebars are actually made of steel. The steel has a layer of chromium to protect it from rusting. It is put onto the steel by electroplating.

Many metal objects are electroplated with different metals to protect them from rusting or to make them look nice. For example, most silver cups and trophies are really only steel with a thin layer of silver on them.

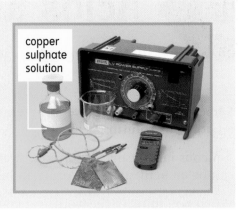

P How would you investigate what affects the speed of electrolysis?

C

copper sulphate solution

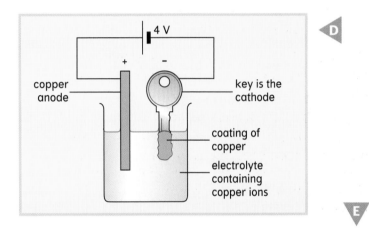

D

4 V

copper anode

key is the cathode

coating of copper

electrolyte containing copper ions

?

4 Why are metal objects often electroplated?

5 Why do you think sports trophies are not usually made from solid silver?

6 You cannot electroplate a plastic spoon. Explain why electroplating will not work on plastic spoons.

7 a) How would you adapt the apparatus shown in diagram D to plate the key with zinc?
b) Explain, in detail, what would happen at the anode and cathode.

E

F The Oscar trophies awarded to film stars are electroplated.

Summary

You are writing encyclopaedia entries on 'Purifying copper' and 'Electroplating'. Write a short paragraph for each to summarise what you have learnt.

Acids and alkalis

What are acids and alkalis?

Some compounds dissolve in water. When they do, an **aqueous solution** is made.

Aqueous just means 'dissolved in water'. The solution can be an **acid**, an **alkali** or it can be **neutral**.

When you think of the word acid you might think of something dangerous like battery acid. But not all acids are dangerous. Look at the food and drink in picture A. They all have a sharp, sour taste because they all contain **weak acids**.

You may have used hydrochloric acid (HCl) in school. When it dissolves in water it forms hydrogen ions (H^+). The **hydrogen ions** make the solution **acidic**. Hydrochloric acid is a **strong acid**. You must *never* drink it!

A *All these foods and drinks contain acids.*

1 Write down one property of an acid.

2 What ions are present in acids?

B *All of these contain alkalis.*

Picture B shows some substances that contain alkalis. Some of them are **weak alkalis**, like soap and toothpaste. They are safe to use. But some are **strong alkalis** and so are dangerous, like oven cleaner.

A strong alkali you may have used in school is sodium hydroxide (NaOH). When it dissolves it forms hydroxide ions (OH^-). The hydroxide ions make the solution alkaline.

Neutral solutions

Acids and alkalis are chemical opposites, a bit like up and down or black and white.

Some solutions are neither acidic nor alkaline. They are **neutral**.

It's a bit like a football match. Somebody might watch the game as a *neutral supporter*. They don't support either team.

Pure water is neutral. It is not an acid or an alkali.

3 Name a material that contains a weak alkali.

4 Name a strong alkali.

5 What ions are present in alkalis?

Indicators

Indicators tell us if a chemical is an acid, an alkali or is neutral. **Litmus** is an indicator. It can be in a liquid form or on paper.

Acids turn litmus indicator **red**.

Alkalis turn litmus indicator **blue**.

Neutral solutions don't change the colour of litmus indicator.

Litmus indicator does not tell us how strong an acid or alkali is.

Other chemicals also act as indicators, and turn different colours in acids and alkalis. Universal indicator is a mixture of different indicators, chosen so that the mixture turns different colours depending on how strong the acid or alkali is. The different colours are put onto a scale and given a number called a **pH number**. This is the pH scale.

C *Litmus indicator comes in different forms.*

You can see that the lower the pH number, the stronger the acid. The higher the pH number, the stronger the alkali.

A neutral solution is pH 7.

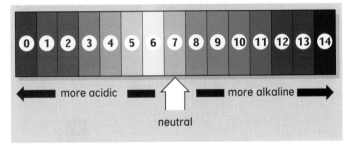

D *The pH scale.*

! The pH number is actually a way of measuring the concentration of hydrogen ions in a solution. The lower the number, the more hydrogen ions there are.

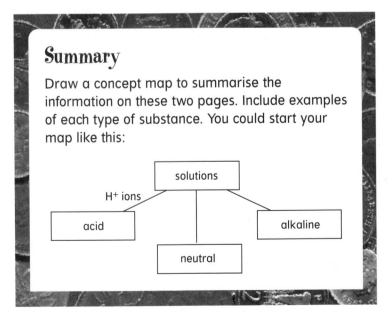

Summary

Draw a concept map to summarise the information on these two pages. Include examples of each type of substance. You could start your map like this:

?

6 Why is universal indicator usually more useful than litmus?

7 Match the pH numbers with the solutions.

pH: 3, 6, 7, 9, 14

solutions: fizzy orange, oven cleaner, indigestion tablets, distilled water, milk

8 Sugar is a compound that is not made of ions. Will it form an acidic, an alkaline or a neutral solution when it is dissolved in water? Explain your answer.

C18 Neutralisation

What happens when an acid and an alkali react together?

Acids and alkalis are chemical opposites. If we mix them together in the right amount, they react together and cancel each other out. A **salt** and water are made.

The salt is dissolved in the water and forms a **neutral solution**, which is pH 7. An indicator such as universal indicator can show that this has happened.

The word equation is:

acid + alkali ⟶ salt + water

When an acid and an alkali react together to make a salt and water, the reaction is called **neutralisation**. The hydrogen ions in the acid combine with the hydroxide ions in the alkali to form water. We can write a symbol equation to show this:

$$H^+(aq) + OH^-(aq) \longrightarrow H_2O(l)$$

You may have had indigestion or heartburn. The burning feeling you get is caused by too much acid in your stomach. You can neutralise the acid by taking an antacid tablet. This contains a weak alkali which reacts with the acid.

A bee's sting is acidic. It can be neutralised with an alkali. Bicarbonate of soda (a weak alkali) can be used to ease the pain.

A wasp's sting is alkali. Vinegar can be used to relieve the pain of a wasp sting because the vinegar is an acid and it neutralises the alkali in the wasp's sting.

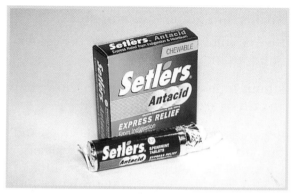

A These tablets neutralise excess acid in your stomach.

 B

bee sting neutralised by   wasp sting neutralised by

 1 a) What kinds of ion are present in a wasp's sting? Explain your answer.

b) What kinds of ion are present in vinegar?

c) Write an equation to show what happens when these two kinds of ion react.

Salts

We know that a salt is made in neutralisation. Most salts contain metals. Look at this word equation:

hydrochloric acid	+	sodium hydroxide	→	sodium chloride	+ water
HCl(aq)	+	NaOH(aq)	→	NaCl(aq)	+ H_2O(aq)
an acid	+	an alkali	→	a salt	+ water

Notice that the metal part of the salt formed is sodium and that it came from the alkali. The salt is called sodium chloride and is the common salt that is put on your food.

The salt made depends on the *metal* in the alkali. For example, if we used potassium hydroxide instead of sodium hydroxide:

hydrochloric acid + potassium hydroxide → potassium chloride + water

$HCl(aq)$ + $KOH(aq)$ → $KCl(aq)$ + $H_2O(aq)$

This time the salt is called potassium chloride.

The salt made also depends on which acid is used. Different acids make different salts. Table E shows which type of salt is made from different acids.

Acid	Type of salt made	Example
hydrochloric acid – HCl	chlorides	sodium chloride – $NaCl$
sulphuric acid – H_2SO_4	sulphates	magnesium sulphate – $MgSO_4$
nitric acid – HNO_3	nitrates	potassium nitrate – KNO_3

?

2 What two things does the type of salt made depend on?

3 What type of salt is made if sulphuric acid is used?

4 You have 25 cm³ of acid in a beaker. The pH is 1.
   a) Describe how the pH of the acid would change as you slowly added 30 cm³ of alkali.
   b) Explain why these changes happen.

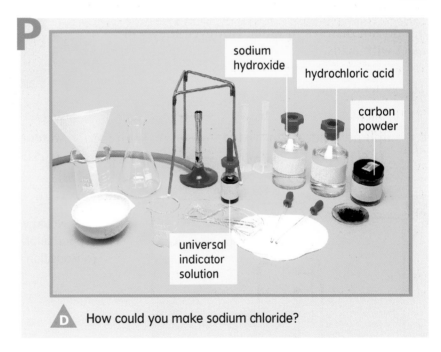

sodium hydroxide

hydrochloric acid

carbon powder

universal indicator solution

D How could you make sodium chloride?

Summary

Make a poster to tell people how to treat bee and wasp stings. Include information about how the treatments work, and why they must not use stronger acids or alkalis.

?

5 a) Write a word equation to show what happens when sulphuric acid reacts with magnesium hydroxide.
   b) Write a balanced symbol equation for the reaction (the formula for magnesium hydroxide is $Mg(OH)_2$).

6 In a reaction such as the one at the bottom of page 120, the sodium and chloride ions are sometimes called 'spectator ions'. Why do you think they are called this? (*Hint*: think about what happens to the ions in a compound when the compound is dissolved in water.)

Transition metal salts

How can we make transition metal salts?

We have seen how salts are made by neutralisation. Salts are made by reacting an acid with an alkali. Alkalis are part of a larger group of compounds called **bases**. Bases that dissolve in water are called alkalis and form **alkaline solutions**. Most bases do not dissolve in water, but they still react with acids.

 1 How are alkalis different from other bases?

Transition metal salts can be made by reacting transition metal oxides or hydroxides with acids.

Transition metal oxides and hydroxides are bases but do not dissolve in water. However, they will react with acids.

The general equation is:

$$\text{acid} + \text{base} \longrightarrow \text{salt} + \text{water}$$
$$\text{e.g. sulphuric acid} + \text{zinc oxide} \longrightarrow \text{zinc sulphate} + \text{water}$$
$$H_2SO_4 + ZnO \longrightarrow ZnSO_4 + H_2O$$

A Transition metal salts can be very useful. For example, copper sulphate can be used in a spray to protect these grapevines from insects.

dilute sulphuric acid

copper oxide

B How would you make copper sulphate (a transition metal salt)?

Non-metal salts

Ammonia (NH_3) is a compound made from two non-metals, nitrogen and hydrogen. Ammonia is a gas and dissolves in water to form ammonia solution. Ammonia combines with the water to form hydroxide ions and ammonium ions. The hydroxide ion mean that ammonia solution is an alkali.

$$\text{ammonia} + \text{water} \longrightarrow \text{ammonium} + \text{hydroxide}$$
$$\text{ions} \quad\quad \text{ions}$$

$$NH_3(g) + H_2O(l) \longrightarrow NH_4^+(aq) + OH^-(aq)$$

Ammonia solution can be neutralised by reacting it with an acid to make an **ammonium salt**. For example:

ammonia solution + sulphuric acid → ammonium sulphate

It is easier to see what is happening if we write out a symbol equation that includes the ions formed when ammonia combines with water:

$$2NH_4^+(aq) + 2OH^-(aq) + H_2SO_4(aq) \rightarrow (NH_4)_2SO_4(aq) + 2H_2O(l)$$

Another ammonium salt used in fertilisers is ammonium nitrate. It can be made by neutralising ammonia solution with nitric acid.

ammonia + nitric acid → ammonium nitrate
$NH_3(aq)$ + $HNO_3(aq)$ $NH_4HO_3(aq)$

2 Why does ammonia solution act like an alkali?

3 Write out a balanced symbol equation for making ammonium nitrate, showing all the ions involved.

P How would you make a salt used in fertilisers?

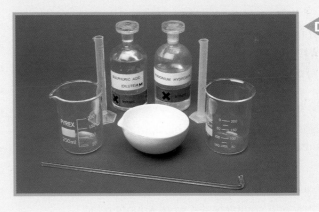

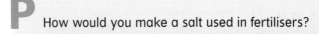

C

D

Summary

Write sentences in your own words to explain the meanings of all the words in bold on these pages.

4 Give two uses for transition metal salts.

5 Which compounds would you need to make the following salts?
  a) zinc sulphate
  b) copper nitrate
  c) copper sulphate

6 a) Write a word equation to show how ammonium chloride can be formed.
  b) Write a balanced symbol equation for the reaction.

Further questions

1 Copy and complete these sentences using words from the box. You may use each word once, more than once, or not at all.

Metals like copper and aluminium are good conductors of _____. This means that copper can be used to make _____ and aluminium can be used to make overhead _____ _____. Iron is used to make _____ and cars because it is very _____. (5)

> bridges   power cables   electricity
> energy   flexible   nails
> strong   weak   wires

2 The diagram shows part of the Periodic Table.

sodium	magnesium		aluminium	silicon	phosphorous	sulphur	chlorine	argon
11	12		13	14	15	16	17	18

a) From the elements in the table, write down the name of
  i) a Group 1 metal
  ii) a Group 2 metal
  iii) a non-metal. (3)

b) What is the name of the block of metals that is in the centre of the Periodic Table? (1)

3 This question is about acids and alkalis.

a) Copy and complete the word equation for neutralisation.
  acid + alkali ⟶ _____ + _____ (2)

b) Name the salt that would be formed by reacting dilute hydrochloric acid with sodium hydroxide. (1)

c) Which ions are present in all acids? (1)

d) Which ions are present in all alkalis? (1)

e) Write a balanced symbol equation to show what happens to these ions in a neutralisation reaction. (3)

4 Group 1 metals and transition metals have similar properties, but there are also some differences. The table shows some properties of Group 1 metals and transition metals. Two rows have been completed for you. Write down the letters of the other boxes that should have ticks in them. (5)

Property	Group 1 metal	Transition metal
shiny	✓	✓
hard	✗	✓
soft	a	b
good conductor of electricity	c	d
good conductor of heat	e	f
low density	g	h
high density	i	j

5 Copy and complete these word equations:

a) magnesium + oxygen ⟶ (1)

b) sodium + water ⟶ (1)

c) magnesium + steam ⟶ (1)

d) zinc + hydrochloric acid ⟶ (1)

6 Zinc chloride solution is electrolysed. Zinc metal and chlorine gas are formed.

a) Sketch and label the apparatus that could be used to carry out the electrolysis. (5)

b) Do zinc ions have a positive or negative charge? (1)

c) Describe what happens at the negative electrode, in as much detail as you can. (4)

d) Is the zinc oxidised or reduced? (1)

7 Three metals, X, Y and Z, were found on another planet. The table shows their reactions with water and dilute acid.

Metal	Reaction with water	Reaction with acid
X	no reaction	slow reaction
Y	fast reaction	violent reaction
Z	no reation	no reaction

a) Arrange the three metals in order of reactivity starting with the most reactive. (1)

b) Another test was tried on metal X, as shown in the diagram below.

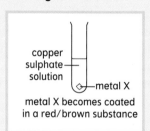

Explain, as fully as you can, the results of this test. (2)

8 Look at the diagram below.

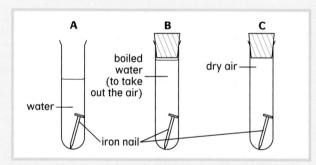

a) Explain, as fully as you can, why the nails in tubes B and C do not rust. (2)

b) Write down *three* ways that rusting can be prevented. (3)

c) The picture below shows the hull of a ship. The zinc blocks protect the hull from rusting. Use the Reactivity Series to help you explain why the zinc blocks corrode away instead of the iron hull. (2)

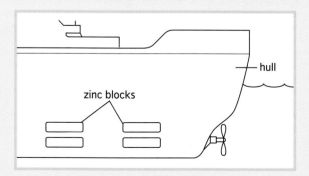

9 Some metals are found in a native state. However, most metals are found as metal compounds mixed up with rock. This mixture is called an ore.

a) Explain what native means. (1)

b) Name a metal that is found in a native state. (1)

c) Name a metal that is extracted from an ore. (1)

d) Why are some metals found as ores and others found in a native state? (2)

10 Look at the Reactivity Series below.

potassium
sodium
lithium
calcium
magnesium
aluminium
(carbon)
zinc
iron
tin
lead
(hydrogen)
copper
silver
gold
platinum

a) i) Write down the name of a metal that could be extracted by heating its ore with carbon. (1)

ii) Explain your answer. (1)

b) i) Write down the name of a metal that cannot be extracted by heating its ore with carbon. (1)

ii) Explain your answer (1)

iii) How could you extract this metal from its ore? (1)

11 A student was trying to extract the metals from lead oxide and aluminium oxide. She heated each oxide with carbon in a fume cupboard. She was able to extract lead from lead oxide but not aluminium from aluminium oxide.

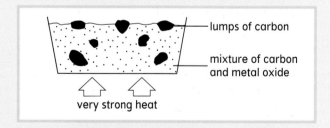

a) Explain the results of these experiments as fully as you can. (2)

b) i) Copy and complete the word equation for the reaction between lead oxide and carbon.

lead oxide + carbon $\longrightarrow$ _____ + _____

ii) What is reduced in this reaction?

iii) What is oxidised in this reaction? (4)

The planet Earth, our home

What is the Earth made from?

A

?
1 Name the three major layers of the Earth.

2 **a)** What is the mean thickness of the Earth's crust?
 b) What is the mean thickness of the mantle?
 c) What is the mean radius of the core?
 d) What is the mean radius of the Earth?
 e) Why is the radius of the Earth a mean?

3 What makes the outer part of the Earth move?

4 Which two metals are found in the Earth's core?

! No one has ever managed to drill down into the mantle. Attempts have been made and the deepest hole ever made was 12 km deep in Russia, but the mantle was not reached.

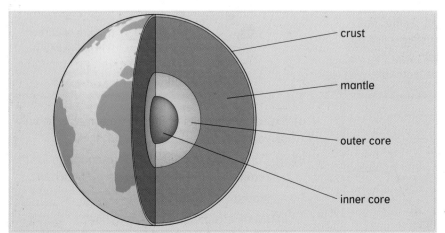

crust

mantle

outer core

inner core

B

Scientists think that the Earth was formed 4.6 billion years ago from a ball of gas and dust. Our planet is still changing now. While you are reading this volcanoes are erupting, mountains are being made, earthquakes are shaking the ground, and the surface you are standing on is moving!

The Earth

The Earth is made up of three major layers called the **crust**, **mantle** and **core**. The temperature increases towards the centre of the Earth. Scientists believe that the temperature may be over 4000 °C at the centre of the Earth.

● **Crust:** This is a layer of solid rock. It is very thin compared to the other layers. It has a mean (average) thickness of 35 km. It is not flat. It has low parts under the oceans and high mountains. The parts of the crust under the sea are called **oceanic** crust, while the other parts are called **continental crust**.

● **Mantle:** This layer is mainly solid rock, but near the crust some of the rock is molten. It has a mean thickness of 2865 km. This molten rock is very viscous (thick) which means it flows very slowly. The Earth's crust moves due to this movement of molten rock in the upper part of the mantle.

● **Core:** The core has a radius of 3470 km and is made from the metals iron and nickel. The inner part of the core is solid, while the outer part is a viscous liquid.

Density

The density of a material tells you what the mass of 1 cm³ of it would be. Lead is a dense material. A 1 cm³ block of lead has a large mass and feels heavy. Polystyrene is not very dense at all. A 1 cm³ block of polystyrene has a small mass and it feels light.

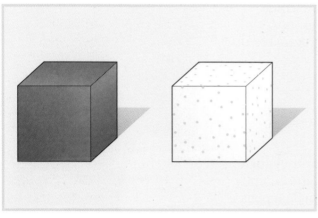

C ▲ *1 cm³ of lead has a mass of 11.35 grams.*

D ▲ *1 cm³ of polystyrene has a mass of 0.01 grams.*

P How could you work out the density of different rocks?

E ▲

5 The density of iron is 7.8 g/cm³. Explain in your own words what this means.

6 a) Which has the bigger mass, 1 cm³ of lead or 1 cm³ of polystyrene?.

b) Which is denser, lead or polystyrene?

The mean density of the Earth has been calculated as 5.5 g/cm³. However, the mean density of the rocks in the Earth's crust is 2.7 g/cm³. This means that the density of the mantle and core together is greater than that of the crust. The core is the densest part of the Earth. A 1 cm³ piece of the core would have a bigger mass than a 1 cm³ piece of the crust. This means that the mantle and core must be made of different materials to the crust.

7 How do scientists know that the different layers of the Earth have different densities?

8 a) Which is the least dense layer of the Earth?

b) Which is the most dense layer of the Earth?

9 What is the density of a 10 cm³ block of lead?

10 Calculate the mass of the Earth using your answer to 2 d). (Assume the Earth is a sphere and the average density of the Earth = 5.5 g/cm³.)

The volume of a sphere of radius r is 4πr³/3.

Summary

Sketch a 2D diagram of the inside of the Earth.

● Label your diagram and write on the key features of each layer.

● Add to your diagram a note about the most and least dense layers.

● Explain clearly underneath what density is.

Igneous rocks

What are igneous rocks and how are they formed?

There are many different types of rock which make up the crust. You may have heard of rocks like granite, sandstone, limestone and marble. Rocks like these are classified into three groups depending on how they were made. The three groups are **igneous** rocks, **sedimentary** rocks and **metamorphic** rocks.

1 Write down the names of four rocks.

2 Write down the names of the three groups of rock.

Rocks under the surface of the Earth can get so hot that they melt to form a liquid rock called **magma**. The hot magma can rise up in the Earth's crust or out onto the Earth's surface. If this happens the magma cools down and turns into solid rock. Rocks made from magma like this are called **igneous** rocks.

3 **a)** What is magma?

b) Why is magma formed underground?

c) What does magma form when it cools down?

A

Magma is less dense than the rocks around it, so it forces its way upwards. If it reaches the surface a **volcano** is formed.

When volcanoes erupt red hot magma pours out. Magma that flows down the side of a volcano is called **lava**. When the eruption is over the lava cools down and solidifies as a layer of igneous rock. Each new eruption adds another layer of rock to the volcano and so it gets bigger.

B C

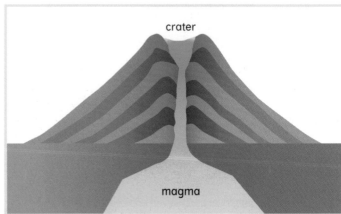

A volcano may not erupt for many years. It is said to be **dormant** (or **inactive**). Some dormant volcanoes suddenly erupt again without warning.

4 What happens when a volcano erupts?

5 What is lava?

Extrusive rocks are formed from magma which comes out of volcanoes (lava) onto the Earth's surface. As lava cools down, it forms crystals. Lava on the Earth's surface cools down very quickly and the rock which is made has small crystals. Rock formed like this is called extrusive igneous rock. Basalt is an extrusive igneous rock.

Intrusive rocks are made from magma which cools down inside the crust. This magma cools more slowly and the rock which is made has large crystals. Rock formed like this is called intrusive igneous rock. Granite is an intrusive igneous rock.

D *Basalt has small crystals.*

E *Granite has big crystals.*

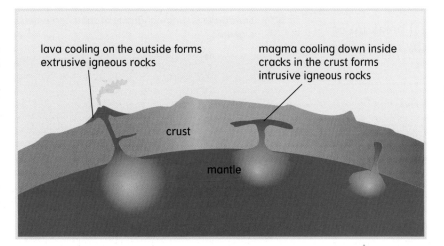

lava cooling on the outside forms extrusive igneous rocks

magma cooling down inside cracks in the crust forms intrusive igneous rocks

crust

mantle

F

? 6 Write down the name of one extrusive igneous rock.

7 Write down the name of one intrusive igneous rock.

Igneous rocks are made up of interlocking crystals. Crystals are solids with a regular shape and flat surfaces which reflect light. The crystals in intrusive igneous rocks are big enough to be seen with the naked eye. However, the crystals in extrusive igneous rocks need to be magnified for us to see them. We can use a microscope to do this.

P How could you investigate the sizes of crystals that form at different temperatures?

G

Summary

Imagine you are a geologist writing a book about rocks for Year 7 pupils. Write a paragraph to explain to these pupils what igneous rocks are and the differences between extrusive and intrusive igneous rocks.

? 8 Why does granite have bigger crystals than basalt?

9 Look at diagram C. How many times do you think the volcano has erupted? Write a sentence to explain your answer.

Sedimentary rocks

What are sedimentary rocks and how are they formed?

Although rocks seem very hard, they are being broken into smaller and smaller pieces all the time. Rocks are broken up into smaller pieces by **weathering** and **erosion**. These smaller pieces can form new rocks called **sedimentary** rocks.

Weathering: Weathering is the gradual break up of rocks into smaller pieces, for example by rain, changes in temperature and plant roots.

↓

Transport and erosion: Weathered pieces of rock are carried away by wind and water. This is called **erosion**. The rock pieces can be worn down more as they are transported.

↓

Deposition: The water or wind carrying the tiny pieces of rock slows down. The pieces of rock are deposited. This means they fall to the ground or sink to the bottom of the river or the sea. The settled pieces of rock are called **sediment**.

↓

Compression and cementation: Over millions of years the deposited sediment is **compressed** (squashed) and water is pushed out by the weight of more material that settles on top of it. Minerals that were dissolved in the water **cement** (stick) the grains together forming new sedimentary rock.

 Sandstone is made of grains of sand cemented together.

C *Conglomerate is made of small pebbles cemented together.*

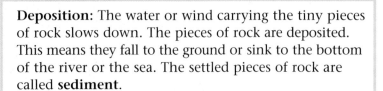

1 Rocks are broken up into smaller pieces by weathering and erosion. What is the difference between weathering and erosion?

2 How are rock particles transported?

3 What happens to rock particles when they are deposited?

4 What happens to the sediment when it is compressed and cemented?

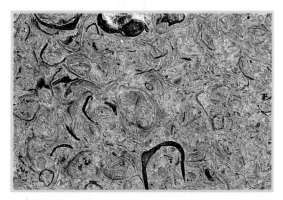

 Limestone is made from fragments of shells from sea creatures.

Ripple marks

If you go down to the beach when the tide has just gone out, the sand often looks bumpy. This is due to the movement of water over the sand. These ripple marks may be buried by sediment and the marks are visible in some sedimentary rocks.

 Ripple marks in rock.

 Layers of rock can be folded upwards.

Folds

Sedimentary rock layers can be found in folds. These folds show that there are large forces acting in the Earth's crust caused by movement of rocks. These forces can bend the sedimentary rock layers into folds.

Younger layers of sedimentary rock usually lie on top of older layers. However, the forces can sometimes be so strong that the layers can be turned upside down.

Faults

A sudden movement in the crust can break rock. This can cause a **fault**. It is easy to see a fault in sedimentary rock as the layers do not line up anymore.

Faults in sedimentary rock. **G**

P

How would you show the effects of movements in the Earth's crust?

H

7 Describe how the forces acting on layers of sedimentary rocks differ when forming faults and folds.

5 a) What is a fault?
  b) How can you tell there is a fault in picture G?

6 What is a fold?

Summary

A Write a paragraph to explain how sedimentary rocks are formed.

B Draw a labelled diagram of a sedimentary rock face that contains both a fold and a fault.

D4 Evidence from rocks

What can rocks tell us about the way they were formed?

 A *Layers of sedimentary rocks.*

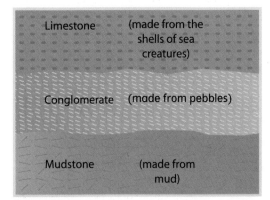

Limestone (made from the shells of sea creatures)

Conglomerate (made from pebbles)

Mudstone (made from mud)

 B   **C**

Sedimentary rocks are usually formed in layers. This is because sediments are not deposited all the time. Each time sediment is deposited, a new layer is formed.

The deeper down a layer of sedimentary rock is, then the older it is. Any layers of rock which are on top of it must have been made from sediment which was deposited later so these rocks must be younger.

? Look at diagram B and answer these questions.

1 How many layers of sedimentary rock are there here?

2 Which is the oldest layer of rock? Explain your answer.

3 Which is the youngest layer of rock? Explain your answer.

Fossils

When animals and plants die their bodies may fall into sediment at the bottom of lakes and rivers. The soft parts of their bodies rot or **decay** away quickly. However, if there are any harder parts such as a shell or a skeleton then this may take much longer to decay, leaving a mould in the sediment. More sediment can fill this mould, hardening over time to form an imprint **fossil**.

Most fossils are imprints of the remains of the plant or animal. Some fossils are the actual **preserved** remains of the creature, but these are rare because the conditions have to be exactly right for this to happen.

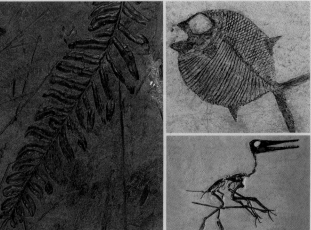

! The oldest human fossil was found in Kenya, a country in Africa. It is between 2 and 3 million years old.

? 4 What are fossils?

5 Why are fossils not found in igneous rocks?

P How could you make your own fossil of a shell? **D**

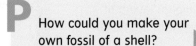

 132

A layer of sedimentary rock may contain fossils of plants and animals that lived at the time that the rock was made. This means that if two rock samples from different places have the same kinds of fossils, they are likely to be about the same age.

Scientists know how old different kinds of fossils are. If they find a type of fossil in a layer of sedimentary rock it will tell them how old the rock is.

Not all fossils can be used to date rocks, however. Some creatures have existed for a long period in the Earth's history. Only the fossils of creatures that existed for relatively short times can be used to date rocks.

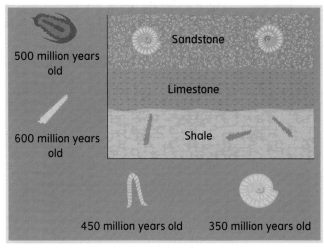

500 million years old

600 million years old

Sandstone

Limestone

Shale

450 million years old   350 million years old

E

6 Look at the fossils and layers of rock in diagram E.

   a) How old is the layer of shale?
   b) How old is the layer of sandstone?

7 Some creatures called *Brachiopods* have existed from around 600 million years ago to the present day. Explain why a fossil of a *Brachiopod* would not be useful for dating a rock.

8 Look at diagram F. It shows the layers of rock at two places, X and Y.

   a) How old is the layer of sandstone?
   b) How old is the layer of conglomerate? How do you know this?
   c) How do scientists know that no sediment was deposited at place X between 450 and 500 millions years ago?

Look a diagram F. The layer of mudstone at place Y is above the limestone, so it must have been made after the limestone. The mudstone is below the conglomerate, so it must have been made before the conglomerate. The sediment which made the mudstone must have been deposited between 450 and 500 million years ago.

Scientists say that these sedimentary rocks were made by **discontinuous deposition**. This means that sediment was not being deposited all the time. At place X, sediment was deposited 500 million years ago to make the sandstone. Then there was no sediment deposited for the next 50 million years. More sediment was then deposited 450 million years ago to make the mudstone.

Sometimes deeper layers of rock can be younger than layers nearer the surface. This can happen if Earth movements cause forces so big that folding turns the layers of rock upside down.

F

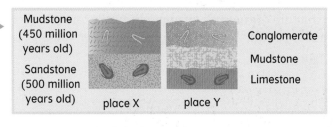

Mudstone (450 million years old)

Sandstone (500 million years old)

place X

Conglomerate

Mudstone

Limestone

place Y

9 What is discontinuous deposition?

10 Different sediment layers have different thicknesses. What things might affect the thickness of sediment layers?

Summary

Imagine you have found a fossil. Describe how the fossil was formed and how it might be used to date the rock it is in.

Metamorphic rocks

What are metamorphic rocks and how are they formed?

Ever since the Earth was formed the crust has continued to move. Sometimes when the crust buckles and folds, igneous and sedimentary rocks which were on the surface can get buried deep underground. When this happens the rocks can be changed into new kinds of rocks called **metamorphic** rocks.

If rocks are pushed underground they are compressed (squashed) by huge pressures and heated. The temperatures are not hot enough to melt the rock back into magma but the pressure and heat can change the structure of the rock.

Rocks contain chemicals called **minerals**. Minerals are chemicals (elements or compounds) that were formed naturally on or in the Earth. Often these minerals are randomly arranged with no real pattern. Huge pressures and high temperatures can force these minerals to line up in layers. When this happens the structure of the rock changes and it becomes a new kind of rock called a metamorphic rock.

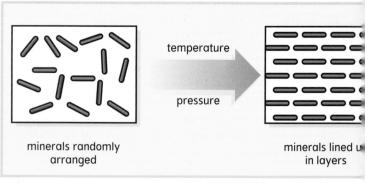

temperature

pressure

minerals randomly arranged

minerals lined up in layers

A

?

1 How are igneous and sedimentary rocks turned into metamorphic rock?

2 Why do many metamorphic rocks have layers?

3 Why is it rare to find fossils in metamorphic rocks?

4 Metamorphic rocks are often formed by the action of heat. If the heat was great enough to melt the rocks, what would be formed instead of metamorphic rocks?

B

Original rock	Limestone	Sandstone	Mudstone
Metamorphic rock	Marble	Quartzite	Slate

Many mountains are made from metamorphic rock. The mountains were made by movements in the crust which pushed layers of rock upwards.

The rock which was pushed and squeezed upwards was put under huge pressure. This pressure compressed the rock and changed it into metamorphic rock. Map C shows mountain ranges which are made from metamorphic rock.

5 Why are many mountains made of metamorphic rock?

6 Which mountains in Britain are made of metamorphic rock?

7 Copy and complete table D. Put each of the following rocks in the correct column.

sandstone   basalt   limestone
granite   marble   mudstone
slate   conglomerate

D

Igneous	Sedimentary	Metamorphic

8 Find out what the metamorphic rocks slate and marble are commonly used for.

9 Describe how you can work out whether a rock is igneous, sedimentary or metamorphic by looking at it.

10 Decide whether each of the following rocks is igneous, sedimentary or metamorphic.

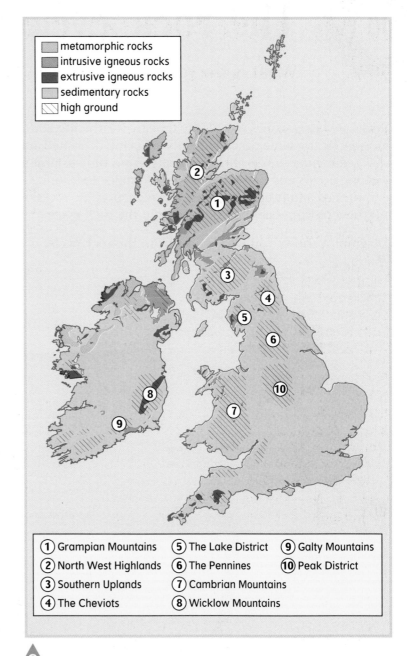

metamorphic rocks
intrusive igneous rocks
extrusive igneous rocks
sedimentary rocks
high ground

① Grampian Mountains   ⑤ The Lake District   ⑨ Galty Mountains
② North West Highlands   ⑥ The Pennines   ⑩ Peak District
③ Southern Uplands   ⑦ Cambrian Mountains
④ The Cheviots   ⑧ Wicklow Mountains

C

E

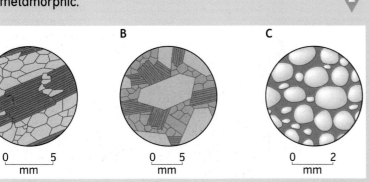

A   B   C

0   5   0   5   0   2
   mm   mm   mm

Summary

Write a paragraph to describe how metamorphic rocks are formed and their appearance.

The rock cycle

What is the rock cycle?

Rocks are being worn away all the time by weathering and erosion. At the same time sediments are being deposited and new sedimentary rocks are being made. From time to time melting occurs and new igneous rocks form, or rocks are compressed and heated, forming new metamorphic rocks. All these processes are linked together in the **rock cycle**

Diagram A shows you what happens in the rock cycle.

A

? **3** How are new mountains made?

Extrusive igneous rocks

Magma can be forced out onto the Earth's surface through volcanoes to form lava. It cools very quickly and turns into extrusive igneous rock with small crystals.

Movements inside the Earth can push rock from inside the crust up to the surface to make new mountains. These mountains replace those worn away by weathering and erosion.

Intrusive igneous rocks

Some of the magma cools down inside the Earth's crust. It cools slowly and turns into intrusive igneous rock with big crystals.

Metamorphic rocks can be pushed deep into the mantle where they melt back into magma.

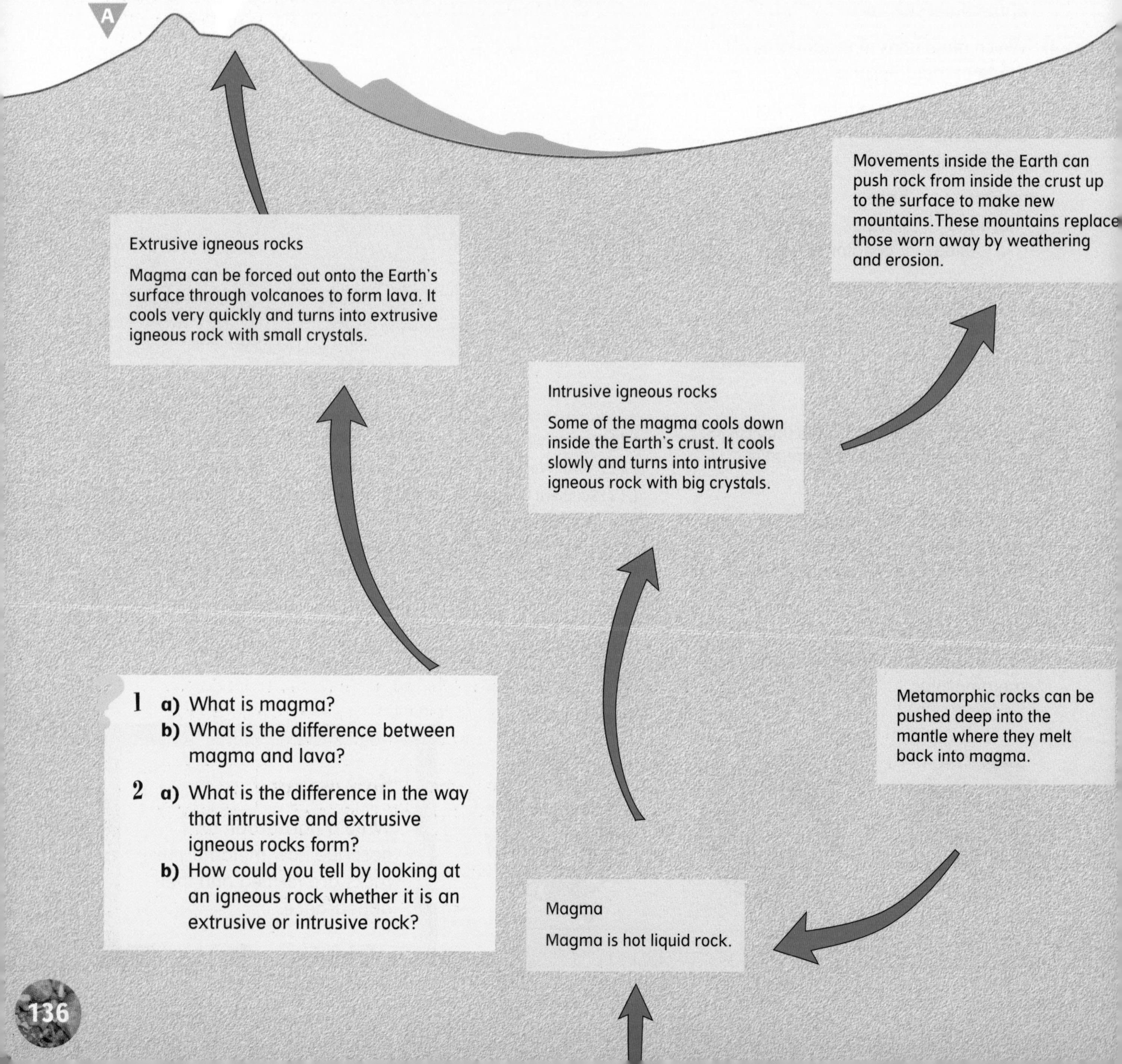

1 **a)** What is magma?
  b) What is the difference between magma and lava?

2 **a)** What is the difference in the way that intrusive and extrusive igneous rocks form?
  b) How could you tell by looking at an igneous rock whether it is an extrusive or intrusive rock?

Magma

Magma is hot liquid rock.

The rock at the surface of the Earth gets worn away into tiny fragments by weathering and erosion.

B

4 Explain how fossils of sea creatures can be found at the top of mountains.

The tiny fragments of rock are carried away from the mountains by gravity, wind, running water or ice.

Sedimentary rocks

Tiny fragments of rock sink to the bottom of rivers or the sea and are deposited as sediment. The sediment gets buried under more and more material. The sediment at the bottom is compressed and cemented back into solid rock called sedimentary rock.

Igneous and sedimentary rocks can be buried. The huge pressures and very high temperatures underground can change them into metamorphic rocks.

5 What does weathering do to rock?

6 How are fragments of rock carried away from mountains?

7 How is sediment turned into sedimentary rock?

8 What can huge pressures and very high temperatures do to igneous and sedimentary rock?

9 What happens to metamorphic rock when it is pushed deep into the crust?

10 Explain how a particle of rock in magma can become a particle of sedimentary rock.

Summary

Complete a table like the one below about igneous, sedimentary and metamorphic rocks. Your table should say what each group of rock is formed from, how it is formed, and give two examples of each type of rock.

Rock group	What the rocks are formed from	How the rocks are formed	Two examples

D7 Tectonic plates

What are tectonic plates?

1 What are tectonic plates?

2 Which tectonic plate is the UK on?

3 Write down the names of two plates that are:
a) moving away from each other
b) moving towards each other.

4 How far do tectonic plates move, on average, in a year?

The lithosphere

The outer part of the Earth is called the **lithosphere**. The lithosphere is the crust and the outer part of the mantle. It is cracked into a number of big pieces called **tectonic plates**. These plates are moving very slowly all the time, at a speed of a few centimetres each year. The map shows the Earth's major plates and the direction in which they are moving.

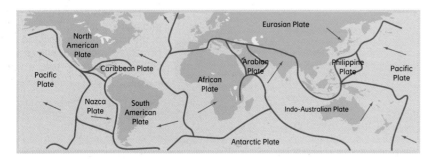

A

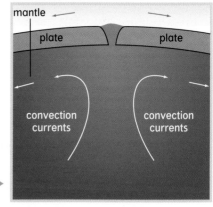

B

Convection currents

The slow movement of tectonic plates is caused by very powerful **convection currents** in the mantle. These currents are caused by heat released from the natural breakdown (decay) of radioactive atoms inside the Earth. As the rock in one part of the mantle heats up it becomes less dense than the surrounding rock and rises. It then spreads sideways until it becomes cooler and denser, then it sinks again. As it moves sideways, it carries the tectonic plates with it as shown in Diagram B.

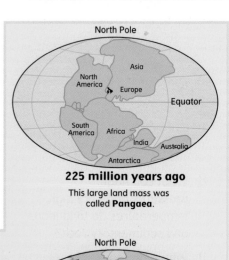

225 million years ago

This large land mass was called **Pangaea**.

The moving continents

Scientists have evidence showing that, at one stage in the past, nearly all the continents were joined together. As the plates of lithosphere moved, the continents were pulled apart. Since then, the plates have continued to move, taking the continents with them. This is why the Earth looks like it does today. Diagram C shows how the continents have moved.

5 Describe fully what causes tectonic plates to move.

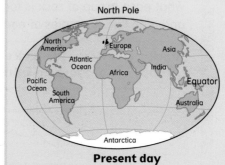

Present day

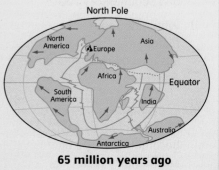

65 million years ago

C

138

Earthquakes and volcanoes

Map D shows the major earthquake zones in the world. It also shows where there are active volcanoes. If you compare this to map A you can see that earthquakes and volcanoes occur at the boundaries between tectonic plates.

Predicting earthquakes

Many people live in areas at risk from earthquakes. If scientists could predict when and where earthquakes are going to happen, many lives could be saved by moving people away to safety. There are some warning signs before major earthquakes, including:

- pre-shocks – these are small earthquakes before a major earthquake
- water levels – the water levels in wells fall
- animal behaviour – some animals act strangely before an earthquake.

However, scientists cannot predict when major earthquakes are going to happen. They can predict where they are likely to happen so many buildings in danger zones are built with special foundations to help them to withstand earthquakes.

Predicting volcanic eruptions

It is much easier to predict volcanic eruptions than earthquakes. There are many warning signs before an eruption that can be detected, including:

- temperature – the temperature of the volcano increases due to moving magma underground
- land levels – the ground level around the volcano rises due to the build up of magma
- sulphur dioxide gas – volcanoes give out more sulphur dioxide gas (SO_2) before an eruption.

These signs all show that a volcano is likely to erupt, but it is difficult to say exactly when it will happen. However, predictions have been made before eruptions and people moved, saving many lives.

10 What can governments do to keep people safe who live near volcanoes or in earthquake zones?

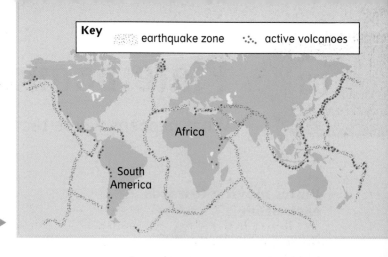

Africa

South America

D

Collapsed building after an earthquake. E

F Lava flowing into a town.

6 Why is it important to be able to predict earthquakes and volcanic eruptions?

7 Which is easier to predict, an earthquake or a volcanic eruption?

8 What signs are there that an earthquake is likely?

9 What signs are there that a volcanic eruption is likely?

Summary

Imagine that you are a journalist living in an earthquake zone near a volcano. Write a short newspaper article explaining why earthquakes and volcanoes occur where you live and what scientists can do to predict earthquakes and eruptions.

D8 Plate boundaries

What happens where tectonic plates meet?

Plates moving towards each other

Some tectonic plates move towards each other. Usually, this is when an **oceanic plate** collides with a **continental plate**.

The thinner, denser oceanic plate is driven down (**subducted**) beneath the thicker continental plate. This forms an ocean trench. The subducted oceanic plate partially melts and magma rises up to the surface, causing volcanoes.

The continental plate is compressed, causing folding and metamorphism of rocks. This produces **fold mountains**. An example of a plate boundary like this is along the western side of South America where the Nazca oceanic plate is colliding with the continental South American plate. The Andes mountains are being formed at this boundary.

Many earthquakes are also caused by the plates colliding.

Plates moving past each other

Some tectonic plates move past each other. Friction stops the plates sliding smoothly, and so the plates move from time to time in sudden jerks, resulting in earthquakes. This is happening along the San Andreas Fault in California in North America, causing earthquakes from time to time.

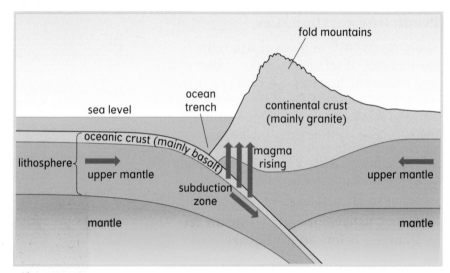

A *An oceanic plate colliding with a continental plate (this is how the Andes mountains in South America are being formed).*

B *This is a fold mountain.*

1 When an oceanic plate collides with a continental plate:
   a) why does the oceanic plate move down beneath the continental plate
   b) why are there volcanoes
   c) why are there earthquakes
   d) why are fold mountains formed
   e) why is an ocean trench formed?

2 Give an example of where an oceanic plate is colliding with a continental plate.

Photograph D was taken after an earthquake in Turkey in 1999 caused by plates moving past each other. The railway line has bent as two plates have moved a few metres past each other.

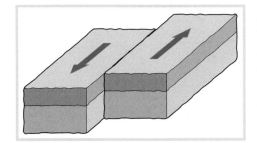

Two plates sliding past each other.

Plates moving away from each other

Some plates move away from each other. The movement of two oceanic plates like this is also called **sea floor spreading**. Magma rises up between the two plates, pushing them apart. New oceanic plate, mainly basalt, builds up as a ridge along the edges of the plates. There are many volcanoes at the boundary, as well as earthquakes.

In the middle of the Atlantic Ocean there is the mid-Atlantic ridge where the Eurasian and North American plates are moving apart. In places, this ridge rises above sea level and forms islands, such as Iceland. In fact, Iceland is getting about 2.5 cm wider each year as the plates move apart.

Two oceanic plates moving away from other.

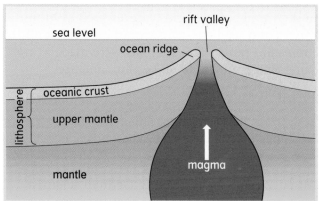

Iron-rich minerals are found in the magma that forms the basalt on the ocean floor. The minerals align themselves with the Earth's magnetic field as they crystallise into basalt. The rocks contain different magnetic alignments as they get further away from the Mid-Atlantic Ridge. This is because the Earth's magnetic field reverses its direction every few hundred thousand years.

The pattern of the magnetic alignments is the same on each side of the ridge. This supports the idea of 'sea floor spreading' with new basalt being formed at the ridge and being pushed away as more basalt forms. Dating the rocks confirms that the rocks nearer the ridge are newer than those further away.

3 Explain how earthquakes occur when plates slide past each other.

4 When an oceanic plate moves away from another oceanic plate:
a) what moves up between the plates
b) what type of rock is formed?

5 Explain how the magnetic alignment of iron-rich minerals in ocean floor rocks supports the idea of sea floor spreading.

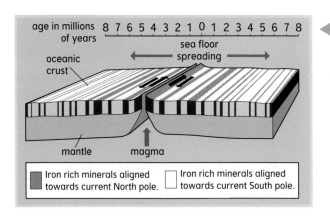

Summary

Draw a table to compare what happens at the different types of plate boundary. Include in your table an example of a location for each type.

Alfred Wegener

How did scientists find out about plate tectonics?

Have you ever noticed that when fruit like tomatoes and apples get older their skins start to go wrinkly? As the fruit gets older it dries up and the inside shrivels and gets smaller. This makes the skin too big so it wrinkles up.

At one time scientists thought that all the features of the Earth's crust were made in a similar way. They thought that as the Earth cooled down it shrank. If the Earth shrank, the crust would wrinkle and crumple up to form features such as mountain ranges and sea beds. This would mean that all the mountain ranges and sea beds were made at the same time and would all be the same age.

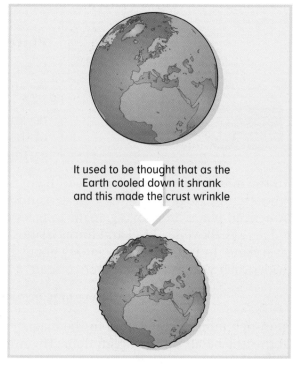

It used to be thought that as the Earth cooled down it shrank and this made the crust wrinkle

A

1 How did scientists think that mountain ranges had been made before they knew about tectonic plates?

Alfred Wegener was a young German scientist who first suggested the idea that the continents were moving around (**continental drift**). He thought that all the continents were once joined together as one big land mass which he called **Pangaea**. He thought that this big land mass then split up to make the different continents which have been moving ever since.

2 Who first suggested that continents were moving around?

3 What was Pangaea?

4 What did Wegener think happened to Pangaea?

In 1912, Wegener wrote his first book called The *Origin of the Continents and Oceans*. Wegener pointed out that many of the continents had shapes which seemed to fit together. He argued that at one time they must have all fitted together like a jigsaw. Scientists would not believe his idea as they could not understand how big continents could move around. Wegener died in 1930 without his ideas being accepted.

B Pangaea.

C Alfred Wegener (1880–1930).

5 What was the name of Wegener's book?

6 Why did other scientists not believe Wegener's ideas?

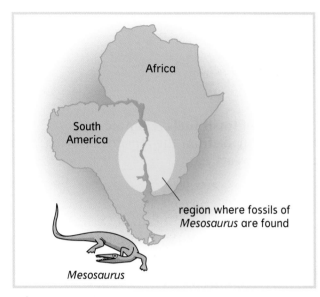

 Position of the continents millions of years ago and the region where fossils of Mesosaurus *have been found.*

In 1928 a South African scientist called Alex du Toit supported Wegener's idea. He looked at the west coast of Africa and the east coast of South America. He noticed three things.

● The shapes of the two coasts seem to fit together like a jigsaw.
● Both coastlines have the same patterns of rock layers.
● Both coasts contain fossils of the same kinds of plants and animals, some of which were only found in those parts of the world. For example, fossils of the small reptile *Mesosaurus* have only been found in the shaded parts of South America and Africa, and nowhere else on Earth. The skeleton of the reptile shows that it could not have swum across the Atlantic Ocean, suggesting that South America and Africa were once joined together.

? 7 Explain how rock patterns support Wegener's ideas of continental drift.

8 Explain how fossils of creatures such as *Mesosaurus* support Wegener's ideas of continental drift.

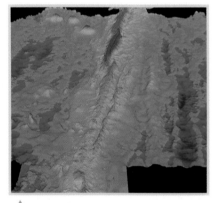

E *Part of the Mid-Atlantic Ridge.*

9 Explain how the age of rocks in the ocean floor support Wegener's ideas of continental drift, and do not fit in with the shrinking Earth idea.

In the 1950s and 1960s more evidence was found that supported Wegener's ideas. The Atlantic floor was surveyed in detail and the underwater ridge found. There were many volcanoes along the ridge.

Soon afterwards it was discovered that the rock in the ocean floor is younger than the rock in the continents. It was found that the rock closest to the ridge is youngest. Symmetrical patterns in the magnetic alignment of the iron-rich minerals in the rock on the ocean floor either side of the ridge were also found.

This evidence all fitted in with the idea of the continents moving apart, as Wegener had suggested. Scientists also discovered a way in which this movement of the crust (continental drift) could take place by way of very powerful convection currents in the mantle. Wegener's ideas were finally accepted in the 1960s, more than 50 years after he had first suggested them, and long after his death.

Summary

Imagine you are a modern geologist. Write a letter to Alfred Wegener to describe all the evidence, both from his day and newer evidence, that supports his theory about moving continents.

Fossil fuels

Where do fossil fuels come from?

A swamp millions of years ago. **A**

Coal, oil and natural gas are all **fossil fuels**. They are called fossil fuels because they were made from the remains of living things which died millions of years ago.

? **1** Write down the names of three fossil fuels.

Coal is made from the remains of plants. Many millions of years ago parts of the Earth were covered by huge forests and swamps. When the trees died they sank to the bottom of the swamps. As time went by, the layers of trees became deeper and deeper as they were covered by more trees which had grown and then died. Later many swamps were covered by rivers which carried **sediment**. The sediment was **deposited** on top of the layers of dead trees.

Over the millions of years which followed more and more sediment was deposited on top of the trees. As there was so little oxygen under all the sediment bacteria couldn't grow and feed on the dead trees. This meant that the trees did not rot away. Instead they were crushed and compressed and eventually turned into coal. Coal is actually a sedimentary rock.

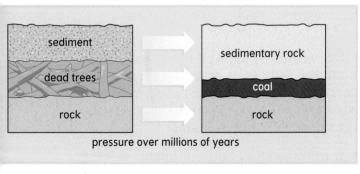

B *Coal formation.*

? **2** Describe how coal was formed.

3 Explain why the plant remains that formed coal did not decay in the usual way.

Oil and **natural gas** were made in a similar way to coal although they were made from the remains of tiny plants and animals in the sea. When they died they sank to the bottom of the sea where they were covered by sediment too. As there was no oxygen under the sediment their remains did not decay in the normal way.

Oil and gas formation.

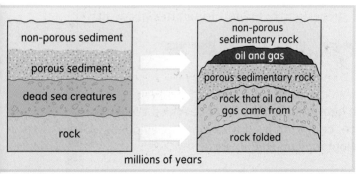

Over millions of years the sediment turned into sedimentary rock. The remains of the sea organisms broke down to release oil and natural gas due to the pressure of the material above and heat from the Earth below. The oil and gas rises up through porous rocks until it is trapped under non-porous rock. Porous rocks have gaps between rock particles which oil and gas can soak into. Non-porous rocks do not.

? **4** Describe how oil and natural gas were formed.

Coal, oil and natural gas are all used as fuels, in particular at power stations to generate electricity. Oil has many other very important uses.

Oil extracted from the ground is known as **crude oil**. It is not very useful in this form. It is a mixture of many different substances called **hydrocarbons**. Hydrocarbons are substances that only contain hydrogen and carbon atoms. The different hydrocarbons have to be separated before we can use them. The crude oil is sent to an **oil refinery** where the separation takes place. Some of the different uses of the separated hydrocarbons are shown in picture D.

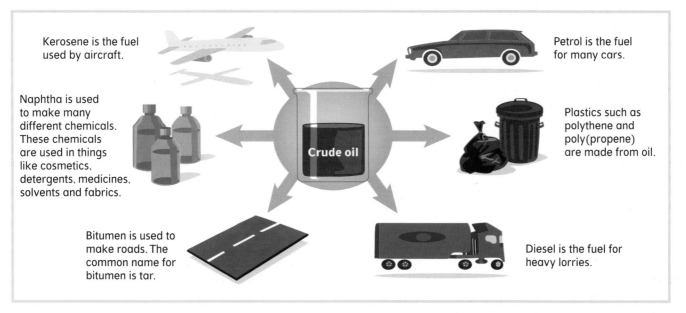

Kerosene is the fuel used by aircraft.

Petrol is the fuel for many cars.

Naphtha is used to make many different chemicals. These chemicals are used in things like cosmetics, detergents, medicines, solvents and fabrics.

Plastics such as polythene and poly(propene) are made from oil.

Crude oil

Bitumen is used to make roads. The common name for bitumen is tar.

Diesel is the fuel for heavy lorries.

If we continue to use oil at the current rate then we could run out by the year 2030.

Summary

Draw two flow diagrams: one to show how coal is formed and one to show how oil and natural gas are formed.

Fractional distillation

How do we separate the different chemicals in oil?

Crude oil is a dark brown liquid. It is a mixture of many different hydrocarbon chemicals which have to be separated from each other before they can be used. The separation of the chemicals in crude oil is done by heating.

In mixtures, the different elements or compounds are not joined together. Each substance in the mixture has its own properties. This makes it possible to separate the substances in a mixture by physical methods, including distillation.

Every liquid has a **boiling point**. The boiling point is the temperature at which a liquid evaporates as fast as it can. The boiling point of water is 100 °C. If a gas cools back down below its boiling point it will **condense** and turn back into a liquid.

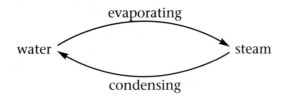

water → steam   (evaporating)
water ← steam   (condensing)

A When the steam (water vapour) from the kettle reaches the cold air it condenses and forms a cloud of water droplets. It also forms condensation on the cold window.

1 Look at picture A.
   a) What happens to water when it boils?
   b) What is between the kettle spout and the cloud?
   c) Why does a cloud form?

2 What is a vapour?

fractionating columns

The different substances in crude oil have different boiling points. **Fractional distillation** can be used to separate liquids with different boiling points. The fractional distillation of crude oil takes place in a **fractionating column** at an oil refinery.

The boiling points of the hydrocarbons depend on the size of their molecules. The larger a molecule is, the higher its boiling point because more energy is needed to separate the molecules from one another.

● The crude oil is heated so that most of it turns into gas. It is then put into a fractionating column which is hotter at the bottom and cooler at the top.

B An oil refinery.

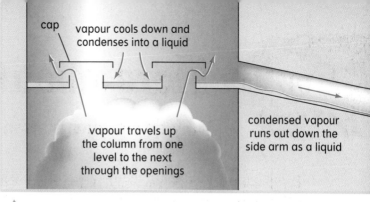

cap vapour cools down and condenses into a liquid

vapour travels up the column from one level to the next through the openings

condensed vapour runs out down the side arm as a liquid

 C

A fractionating column. **D**

- As the hot vapours rise up the tower, they cool down and turn back into liquids (condense). The different substances in the crude oil have different boiling points and so condense at different temperatures. Those with high boiling points turn back into liquids near the bottom of the tower, and those with lower boiling points do not become liquids until they are near the top of the tower.

- The liquids are trapped on trays as they condense and so cannot run back down the column. These trays are designed to allow the gases to rise up, but not to let the liquids fall back down.

The process separates the crude oil into **fractions**. Each fraction is still a mixture of hydrocarbons, but all the hydrocarbons in a fraction have molecules of a similar size.

Diagram D shows a fractionating column. The hydrocarbons with higher boiling points collect in the residue at the bottom. They are taken off and distilled again at low pressure to separate them into more fractions.

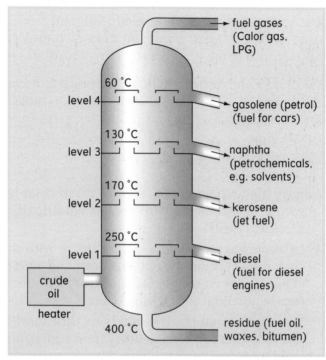

fuel gases (Calor gas, LPG)

60 °C level 4 — gasolene (petrol) (fuel for cars)

130 °C level 3 — naphtha (petrochemicals, e.g. solvents)

170 °C level 2 — kerosene (jet fuel)

250 °C level 1 — diesel (fuel for diesel engines)

crude oil heater

400 °C — residue (fuel oil, waxes, bitumen)

?

3 What is the relationship between the size of a molecule and its boiling point?

4 What happens to the temperature of the fractionating column as you move up?

5 In what state are the hydrocarbons in crude oil put into the fractionating column?

6 Do hydrocarbons with high or low boiling points reach the top of the fractionating column?

7 Explain why hydrocarbons condense in the fractionating column.

8 Does fractional distillation separate all the different hydrocarbons in crude oil?

9 What does the word 'fraction' refer to in fractional distillation?

?

10 Explain how vapours can rise up the tower but not fall back down to the bottom as they condense.

P How would you separate ethanol and water by fractional distillation?

E

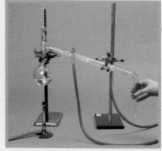

Summary

Explain in no more than 100 words how and why crude oil is separated into fractions.

More about oil

Why do the chemicals in oil have different properties and uses?

Crude oil is a mixture of many different molecules called hydrocarbons. These hydrocarbons are separated into fractions at an oil refinery. Petrol, naphtha and diesel are some of the fractions produced.

The hydrocarbons in crude oil are different sizes. They vary from having just one carbon atom in each molecule to over a hundred. Diagram A shows some hydrocarbon molecules.

The longer the carbon chain, the stronger the forces between the molecules. This means that hydrocarbon molecules with longer chains have different properties to those with shorter chains.

Longer molecules:

- have higher boiling points – this means that hydrocarbons with longer carbon chains are less **volatile** (they turn into gases less easily)
- are more **viscous** liquids – hydrocarbons with short carbon chains are very runny, but hydrocarbons with long carbon chains are viscous (viscous liquids are a bit like syrup or treacle and do not flow very easily)
- are less **flammable** – hydrocarbons with short carbon chains are very flammable (they burn easily), and so are good fuels, but hydrocarbons with long carbon chains are not very flammable and are less useful as fuels.

A small hydrocarbon has a few carbon atoms in a chain, e.g. C_3H_8.

A larger hydrocarbon has more carbon atoms in a chain, e.g. $C_{14}H_{30}$.

This is a way of drawing molecules.

The — represents a chemical bond.

 A Hydrocarbon molecules.

1 Name three fractions of crude oil.

 B

Fraction of crude oil	Boiling point range (°C)	Number of carbon atoms in the chain	Viscosity (thickness)	Flammability
fuel gases	up to 25	1–4	gases	easy to light
gasoline (petrol)	40–100	5–7	runny	
naphtha	100–150	8–11		
kerosene	150–250	11–14		
diesel	220–340	15–19		
mineral (lubricating) oil	over 350	20–30		
fuel oil	over 400	30–40		
wax	over 400	40–50		
bitumen	over 400	over 50	thick	difficult to light

2 What do the following words mean?
a) viscous **b)** flammable **c)** volatile

3 What happens to each of the following properties as the carbon chain in a hydrocarbon molecule gets longer?
a) flammability **b)** viscosity **c)** boiling point **d)** volatility

4 Explain why the boiling points of hydrocarbons change as the carbon chains get longer.

Cracking

Fractions that contain short-chain hydrocarbons, such as gasoline (petrol), are more useful and so are in more demand than some fractions containing long-chain hydrocarbons. However, long-chain hydrocarbons can be broken down into smaller, more useful molecules.

First of all the large hydrocarbon molecules are heated. This changes them from a liquid into a gas (vapour). The vapour is then passed over a hot **catalyst**. A catalyst is a substance that speeds up a reaction without being used up itself. In this reaction the catalyst speeds up the breakdown of large hydrocarbon molecules into smaller ones.

This breakdown of large hydrocarbons into smaller, more useful ones is called **cracking**. This is an example of a **thermal decomposition** reaction (a reaction in which a substance is broken down into simpler substances by heating).

Cracking produces a mixture of shorter hydrocarbons called **alkanes** and **alkenes** (see page 150). The alkanes are used as fuels while the alkenes are used to make plastics.

C *An example of cracking.*

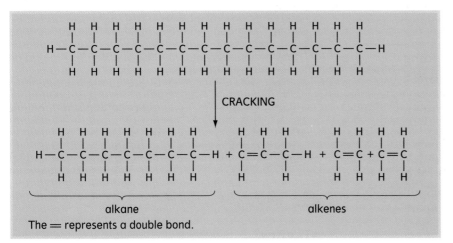

The = represents a double bond.

5 Why are longer hydrocarbons cracked?

6 What happens in cracking?

7 Cracking is a thermal decomposition reaction. What does 'thermal decomposition' mean?

8 What is a catalyst?

9 What are the products of cracking used for?

10 Explain why petrol is a better fuel than mineral (lubricating) oil.

11 Write a balanced equation for the cracking of the hydrocarbon $C_{16}H_{34}$ to form octane (C_8H_{18}) and ethene (C_2H_4).

Summary

A The numbers on the line below represent the numbers of carbon atoms in a hydrocarbon chain. Copy the line and add:
a) labels to show the names of the fractions
b) arrows to show how boiling points, viscosity and flammability change.

| 1 | 5 | 10 | 15 | 20 | 25 | 30 | 35 | 40 | 45 | 50 | 50+ |

B Write a word equation to summarise cracking. You should include reaction conditions and uses for the products. Explain why some hydrocarbons are cracked.

D13 Alkanes and alkenes

What are the differences between alkanes and alkenes?

Covalent bonds

Atoms contain negatively charged electrons that move around a positive nucleus. Molecules are made from atoms which are joined together by sharing electrons between them. This sharing of electrons is called **covalent bonding**. A shared pair of electrons between two atoms is called a **single covalent bond**. The atoms in hydrocarbon molecules are joined together by covalent bonds.

Covalent bonds in a hydrocarbon molecule. A

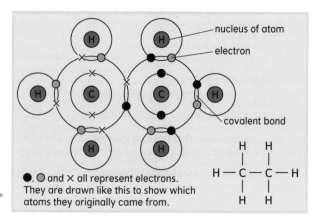

●, ○ and × all represent electrons. They are drawn like this to show which atoms they originally came from.

Alkanes

If all the carbon atoms in a hydrocarbon are joined by single covalent bonds we say that the molecule is **saturated**. Saturated hydrocarbons are called **alkanes**.

The names of all alkanes have the ending **–ane**. The first part of the name indicates how many carbon atoms an alkane contains. For example, *meth-* means one carbon, *eth-* means two, *prop-* means three and *but-* means four.

Alkanes burn very well, giving out a lot of heat. Many fuels such as petrol, diesel and kerosene contain alkanes. However, apart from burning, alkanes are very unreactive.

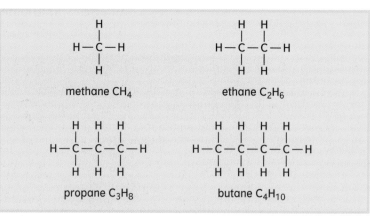

methane CH_4
ethane C_2H_6
propane C_3H_8
butane C_4H_{10}

B *Some alkane molecules.*

C *Natural gas is methane, an alkane.*

 D *Some alkene molecules.*

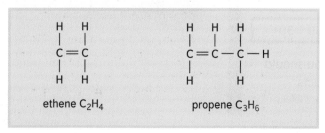

ethene C_2H_4
propene C_3H_6

Alkenes

There are two shared electrons in a single covalent bond. Two carbon atoms can share four electrons forming a **double covalent bond**. Hydrocarbons that contain one or more double covalent bonds are said to be **unsaturated**.

Alkenes are unsaturated hydrocarbons which contain one carbon=carbon double bond. The names of all alkenes have the ending **–ene**. They have the same beginning as alkanes, for example ethene is an alkene with two carbon atoms.

Like alkanes, alkenes burn well. However, alkenes are very reactive because of their double bond, which is involved in many reactions. Alkenes are not normally used as fuels because they are used to make many other substances, such as plastics.

Testing for unsaturated hydrocarbons

A simple test for unsaturated hydrocarbons uses bromine water. Bromine water is a yellow-orange colour. When it reacts with unsaturated hydrocarbons, the bromine water loses its colour.

If bromine water is added to a saturated hydrocarbon, it does not react and the yellow-orange colour remains.

 The bromine reacts with the double bond in the alkene.

 Ethene reacts with bromine.

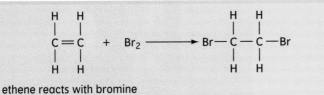

ethene reacts with bromine

P Fats and oils, such as butter, margarine and cooking oils, contain saturated and unsaturated molecules (although fats and oils are not alkanes or alkenes). Some fats and oils are more unsaturated than others, i.e. they contain more carbon–carbon double bonds. Unsaturated fats and oils are thought to be healthier than saturated ones.

How would you design an experiment to compare how unsaturated some fats and oils are?

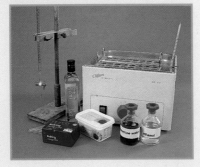

G

? 7 Describe how to test a molecule to see if it is unsaturated or not.

8 a) What would you see if you added a few drops of bromine water to cyclohexane and cyclohexene?
 b) Which part of the alkene molecule reacts with bromine?

9 Draw an equation to show the reaction between propene and bromine.

10 Hexane is an alkane with six carbon atoms. How many hydrogen atoms will it contain?

11 Pentene is an alkene with five carbon atoms. How many hydrogen atoms will it contain?

12 There are two alkanes with the formula C_4H_{10}, one of which is butane. Draw the structure of the other alkane with this formula. (*Hint*: the carbon atoms do not have to be joined in a straight line.)

Summary

Draw a table to summarise the key differences between alkanes and alkenes. You should include how many C=C bonds there are, whether they are saturated or unsaturated, what they are used for and their reactions with bromine water.

Polymers

What are polymers and what are they used for?

Polymers are large molecules made when lots of small molecules called **monomers** join together. The process in which monomers react together to form polymers is called **polymerisation**. Plastics are polymers.

Alkenes are produced by the cracking of long hydrocarbon molecules and are used as monomers. For example, when ethene is heated at very high pressures, the ethene molecules react with each other to form the polymer poly(ethene). This polymer is better known as polythene and is used to make plastic bags and plastic bottles.

Plastic shopping bags are made from polythene. **A**

B *Formation of poly(ethene).*

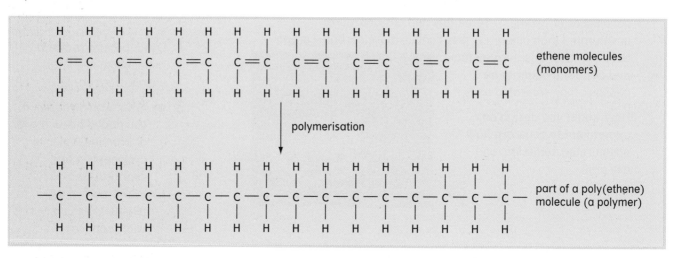

ethene molecules (monomers)

polymerisation

part of a poly(ethene) molecule (a polymer)

An equation can be written for the polymerisation of ethene, as shown in diagram C. The number of molecules that join together is very large. It is often several thousand but the exact number varies. We can write the formula as you can see in the diagram, where n means a large number.

$$n \begin{bmatrix} H & H \\ | & | \\ C = C \\ | & | \\ H & H \end{bmatrix} \longrightarrow \begin{pmatrix} H & H \\ | & | \\ C - C \\ | & | \\ H & H \end{pmatrix}_n$$

C

?
1 What is a polymer?
2 What are monomers?
3 What happens in polymerisation?
4 Name the alkene from which polythene is formed.
5 Give two uses for polythene.

Alkenes can react with each other to form polymers because of their C=C double bonds. The molecules add on to each other. This sort of polymerisation is called **addition polymerisation**. The table below shows some other polymers formed from alkenes.

Monomer	Polymer	Uses
CH_3 H | | C = C | | H H propene	CH_3 H | | (C — C) | | H H n poly(propene)	plastic crates, bins and ropes
C_6H_5 H | | C = C | | H H phenylethene (also called styrene)	C_6H_5 H | | (C — C) | | H H n poly(phenylethene) (also called polystyrene)	packaging

Disposal of plastics

D E

Plastics are very useful materials, but getting rid of them is a problem. There are three ways to dispose of plastics:

- **Burial:** Most plastics are *not* **biodegradable**. This means that micro-organisms cannot break them down so they will not rot away if they are buried in landfill sites (photograph E). However, some new plastics are being developed that are biodegradable.
- **Burning:** When plastics are burned some dangerous substances can be formed.
- **Recycling:** Plastics are not recycled as much as they could be because the different types of plastics need to be separated.

It is very important that more care and thought is given to the disposal of plastics.

Summary

A Write definitions for the following terms: polymer, monomer, addition polymerisation.

B Imagine that you are in charge of waste disposal for your local council. Write a brief report for the council leaders to persuade them to fund a plastic recycling scheme.

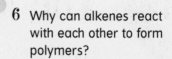

6 Why can alkenes react with each other to form polymers?

7 What type of polymerisation takes place when alkenes react with each other?

8 Write out an equation for the formation of poly(propene) from propene.

9 Give two uses for poly(propene).

10 What is the problem with:
   a) disposing of plastics by burial
   b) recycling plastics?

11 Why is it not advisable to burn plastics?

12 Write an equation for the formation of poly(chloroethene), also called PVC, from chloroethene. Chloroethene is shown below. These are not hydrocarbons. F

H Cl
\| \|
C = C
\| \|
H H

The formation of the atmosphere

How has the Earth's atmosphere changed?

The first billion years

The atmosphere formed during the first billion years after the Earth was made. At this time the surface was covered in volcanoes. When they erupted they gave out gases. These gases formed the atmosphere.

It is thought that the atmosphere formed was made mainly of carbon dioxide (CO_2) and water vapour (H_2O), with small amounts of ammonia (NH_3) and an alkane called methane (CH_4). There was little or no oxygen (O_2) in this early atmosphere. It was similar to the atmospheres on Mars and Venus today.

As the Earth cooled down, the water vapour condensed to form the Earth's oceans and seas

A

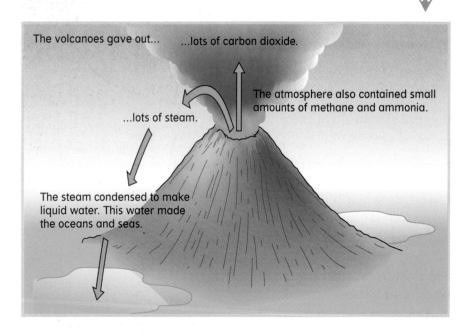

The volcanoes gave out... ...lots of carbon dioxide.

The atmosphere also contained small amounts of methane and ammonia.

...lots of steam.

The steam condensed to make liquid water. This water made the oceans and seas.

?

1 Where did the gases that formed the Earth's early atmosphere come from?

2 **a)** What were the main two gases in this early atmosphere?
   b) What other gases are thought to have made up the early atmosphere?

3 How were the oceans and seas formed?

Early life

The first living things to appear on Earth were simple bacteria. As there was no oxygen in the atmosphere, these bacteria could not have used aerobic respiration to get energy. Living things which can live without oxygen are called **anaerobes**.

The formation of oxygen

About 3 billion years ago, the first organisms that could photosynthesise developed on the Earth. These were single-celled algae. They used carbon dioxide and water, along with energy from the Sun, to make food by photosynthesis. Oxygen is released by this process.

carbon dioxide + water (+ light energy) ⟶ glucose + oxygen

As more plants developed and colonised the Earth, oxygen built up in the atmosphere. This oxygen was a poison to most of the anaerobes. Nowadays there are far fewer habitats where anaerobes can exist.

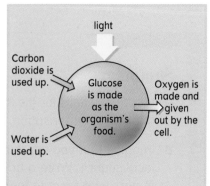

light

Carbon dioxide is used up.

Glucose is made as the organism's food.

Oxygen is made and given out by the cell.

Water is used up.

B *An algal cell.*

The loss of methane and ammonia

As oxygen levels built up, the methane and ammonia from the early atmosphere reacted with the oxygen.

$$\text{ammonia} + \text{oxygen} \longrightarrow \text{nitrogen} + \text{water}$$
$$4NH_3 + 3O_2 \longrightarrow 2N_2 + 6H_2O$$

$$\text{methane} + \text{oxygen} \longrightarrow \text{carbon dioxide} + \text{water}$$
$$CH_4 + 2O_2 \longrightarrow CO_2 + 2H_2O$$

The formation of nitrogen

Although some of the nitrogen in the atmosphere today was formed by the reaction of ammonia with oxygen, most was produced in a different way. It was formed by the action of **denitrifying bacteria** which convert nitrogen-containing compounds into nitrogen gas.

The formation of ozone

High-energy ultraviolet radiation from the Sun is harmful. As oxygen (O_2) built up in the atmosphere, some of it reacted to produce **ozone** (O_3). This ozone formed a layer in the atmosphere that filtered out this harmful radiation. The development of the ozone layer allowed new, more complex living creatures to develop.

What happened to the carbon from the carbon dioxide?

As plants reduced the amount of carbon dioxide in the atmosphere by photosynthesis, the carbon atoms became part of the structure of the plants. Much of this carbon is now locked up in fossil fuels formed from these plants.

Some carbon has also been locked up in compounds called carbonates in sedimentary rocks.

The atmosphere today

The composition of the atmosphere has remained roughly constant for the last 200 million years or so. Pie chart D shows the composition of air today.

4 What process formed the oxygen in the atmosphere?

5 How was the methane removed from the atmosphere?

6 a) Give the main way in which nitrogen was formed.
   b) Give another way in which nitrogen was formed.

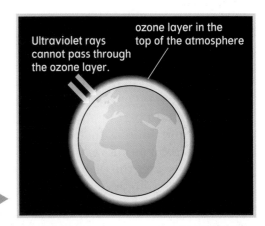

Ultraviolet rays cannot pass through the ozone layer.

ozone layer in the top of the atmosphere

C

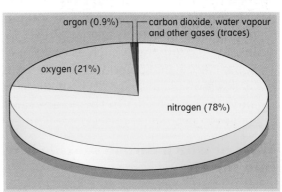

argon (0.9%)

carbon dioxide, water vapour and other gases (traces)

oxygen (21%)

nitrogen (78%)

D Composition of the atmosphere.

7 a) What effect does the ozone layer have on light from the Sun?
   b) What did the development of the ozone layer allow to happen?

8 In some places the ozone layer is thinner than it should be. These are known as 'holes' in the ozone layer. Why is this a problem?

Summary

A List the four main gases in the original atmosphere and describe how they were removed from the atmosphere.

B List the two main gases in today's atmosphere and describe how they were formed.

155

The carbon cycle

What is happening to the amount of carbon dioxide in the air?

For most of the last 200 million years or so, the amount of carbon dioxide in the air has remained roughly the same, at around 0.03%. There are several processes which remove carbon dioxide from the air and several others that return it to the air. All these processes together make up the **carbon cycle**.

Ways in which carbon dioxide is removed from the air

- Plants use carbon dioxide in photosynthesis to make glucose. The carbon atoms become part of the plant and part of any animals that eat those plants (and animals that eat those animals, etc.). These carbon atoms may become locked up in fossil fuels after the plants and animals die.

- Some carbon dioxide dissolves in the oceans.

- Carbon dioxide reacts with substances dissolved in seawater to produce soluble compounds such as calcium hydrogencarbonate and sodium hydrogencarbonate. It may also react to produce insoluble compounds such as calcium carbonate. Some carbonate compounds in the water are used by sea animals to make their shells. These shells and other carbonates in the oceans can become sediment and go on to become sedimentary rock.

Ways in which carbon dioxide is released into the air

- Plants and animals respire, releasing carbon dioxide back into the air.

- When plants and animals die they usually decay, releasing carbon dioxide into the air (unless they go on to form fossil fuels).

- The burning of fossil fuels releases carbon dioxide into the air.

- Earth movements can take sedimentary rocks deep into the Earth where the heat causes the carbonate compounds in the rocks to decompose. This produces carbon dioxide which can then be released back into the atmosphere through volcanoes.

3 Why is some carbon dioxide released into the air from volcanoes?

A Seashells are made of calcium carbonate.

1 Until recently, for how long had levels of carbon dioxide in the atmosphere remained constant?

2 a) How do plants remove carbon dioxide from the air?

b) Give two ways in which the oceans remove carbon dioxide from the air.

c) Give two ways in which plants and animals release carbon dioxide back into the air.

Carbon dioxide, produced by sedimentary rocks being pushed deep underground, can cause problems. During the night of 26th August 1986, every animal and the 1800 people who lived within 25 km of Lake Nyos, in Cameroon, died. They were killed by Carbon dioxide suddenly escaping from the lake. The carbon dioxide gets trapped at the bottom of the lake. A slight movement in the Earth's crust near the lake triggered the release of massive amounts of carbon dioxide. This gas suffocated the animals and people.

Increasing carbon dioxide levels

In the last few years the natural balance that has kept carbon dioxide levels constant has been disturbed. Large-scale burning of fossil fuels means that more carbon dioxide is being released into the atmosphere than is being removed. Carbon dioxide levels are now rising.

Carbon dioxide is a **greenhouse gas**, which means that it allows the Sun's heat to reach the Earth, but stops the Earth's heat from escaping into space. Many scientists think that the increasing levels of carbon dioxide in the atmosphere will cause the Earth to get warmer (**global warming**). They predict that this warming will cause climate change and sea levels to rise, flooding many low-lying countries. There is some evidence that the Earth is getting warmer and that the climate is changing. However, scientists cannot be certain whether this is due to natural variations in the climate or to increasing carbon dioxide levels.

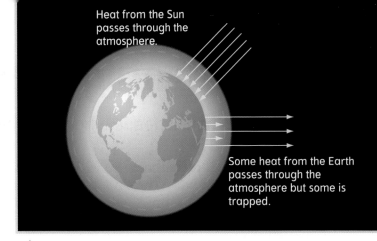

B *The greenhouse effect.*

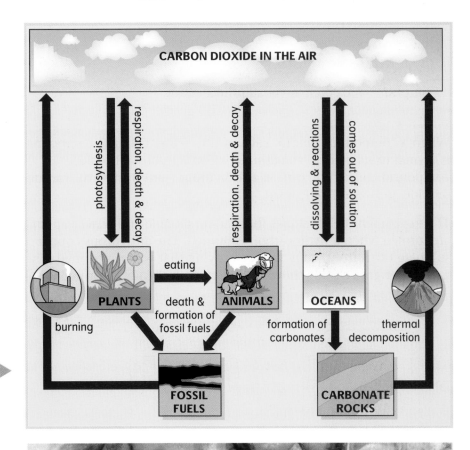

The carbon cycle. **C**

Summary

A Make a table to summarise the ways in which carbon dioxide is removed from and released into the atmosphere.

B Describe how carbon atoms in carbon dioxide in the atmosphere cycles through:
   a) fossil fuels and back into the atmosphere
   b) the oceans and carbonate rocks and back into the atmosphere.

?

4 What is a 'greenhouse gas'?

5 What has happened to carbon dioxide levels in the last few years?

6 What effects could increasing carbon dioxide levels have on the Earth?

7 What evidence would convince you that increasing levels of carbon dioxide are causing global warming?

Burning fuels

What happens when we burn fuels?

When an element burns it joins up with oxygen and forms an **oxide**. For example, when carbon burns it forms carbon dioxide, when sulphur burns it forms sulphur dioxide and when hydrogen burns it forms hydrogen oxide (better known as water). The water is formed as vapour due to the heat.

carbon + oxygen ⟶ carbon dioxide

hydrogen + oxygen ⟶ hydrogen oxide
(hydrogen oxide is better known as water!)

sulphur + oxygen ⟶ sulphur dioxide

A

When a compound is burnt, each of the elements in the compound is turned to its oxide. For example, when a hydrocarbon (a compound containing carbon and hydrogen only) is burnt, carbon dioxide and water are formed.

The experiment below shows that carbon dioxide and water vapour are formed when a hydrocarbon is burned. The anhydrous copper sulphate turns from white to blue proving that water is formed. The lime water goes cloudy showing that carbon dioxide is formed.

B

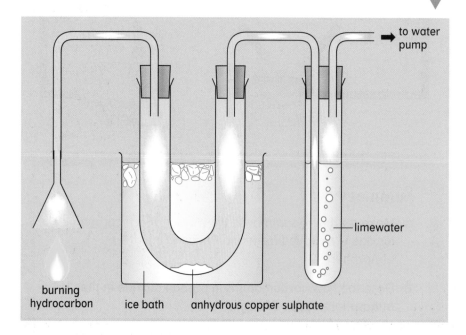

to water pump

limewater

burning hydrocarbon

ice bath

anhydrous copper sulphate

! On average, each person in the UK uses 1.4 tonnes of oil, 1.2 tonnes of natural gas and 1.0 tonnes of coal per year.

? 1 What is formed when each of the following substances is burned?
a) magnesium
b) nitrogen
c) propane (C_3H_6)
d) ammonia (NH_3)

2 Write a word equation to show what happens when a hydrocarbon burns.

P If a candle is placed inside a glass jar, it burns for a short time and then goes out. How could you investigate what affects how long the candle burns?

D

Burning fossil fuels

Oil and natural gas are hydrocarbons, so carbon dioxide and water vapour are formed when they are burned. Coal is mainly carbon and so forms carbon dioxide when it is burned. The problems caused by the release of carbon dioxide were covered on page 157.

Some fossil fuels also contain sulphur, so sulphur dioxide can also be formed when fossil fuels are burned.

Acid rain

Sulphur dioxide reacts in the atmosphere to form **acid rain**. When the rain falls it makes soil more acidic. Many plants cannot live or grow in very acidic soil. Eventually trees can be killed and even large forests destroyed. Acid rain can also make water too acidic for animals to live in. Fish can no longer survive in many lakes and rivers around the world.

There are a number of ways to reduce the amount of sulphur dioxide released by burning fossil fuels:

- We can burn fuels containing less sulphur. Fossil fuels from different parts of the world contain different amounts of sulphur.
- There are ways in which some of the sulphur can be removed from fossil fuels before they are burned.
- The gases formed when fossil fuels are burned in power stations can be sprayed with powdered bases (substances that react with acids) such as limestone or slaked lime. These bases react with the sulphur dioxide, reducing the amount released into the atmosphere.
- As an alternative to these methods, we could burn less fossil fuels. However, we would have to become more energy efficient so that we need less energy or find alternative ways to provide energy.

3 Explain why each of the following are formed when fossil fuels are burned:
   a) carbon dioxide
   b) water vapour
   c) sulphur dioxide.

4 **a)** Which gas causes acid rain?
   b) How can acid rain affect plants?
   c) How can acid rain affect animals living in lakes?

5 Briefly describe four ways in which the amount of sulphur dioxide released into the atmosphere can be reduced.

6 All our electricity used to come from power stations burning fossil fuels. Find out other ways in which we now generate electricity.

Summary

A Write a paragraph to explain why carbon dioxide, water vapour and sulphur dioxide are formed when fossil fuels are burned.

B Imagine that you are the managing director of a coal-fired power station. You need to reduce the emissions of sulphur dioxide from your power station. Write a brief report, describing your options.

Limestone and acid rain

How can limestone help the environment?

Acid rain can cause many problems for the environment. It can make soil too acidic for plants to grow. Some rivers and lakes around the world are too acidic for fish to live in. Scientists now use limestone to treat acidic conditions so that living things can survive there again.

A

B

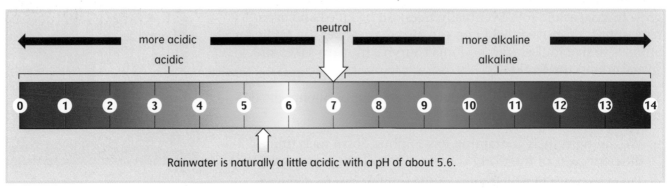

more acidic

neutral

more alkaline

acidic

alkaline

0 1 2 3 4 5 6 7 8 9 10 11 12 13 14

Rainwater is naturally a little acidic with a pH of about 5.6.

The pH scale measures how acidic or alkaline something is. The pH scale usually goes from 0 to 14.

 1 Look at diagram B.
  a) What pH is neutral?
  b) Which is more acidic, pH 2 or pH 5?
  c) Which is more alkaline, pH 8 or pH 13?
  d) What pH is rainwater naturally?

If you **neutralise** an acidic solution you turn it from being acidic to neutral. You can neutralise an acid by adding a **base**. Bases that dissolve in water are called **alkalis**. An alkali can also neutralise an acid.

2 What is a base?

3 What is an alkali?

4 How can you neutralise an acid?

Limestone is mainly **calcium carbonate**, which is a base. Powdered limestone can be added to acidic rivers and lakes to neutralise the water. This means that fish and other animals can live there again. Powdered limestone can also be used to reduce soil acidity.

The most acidic rain ever recorded had a pH of 1.87. It damaged the paint on cars when it rained.

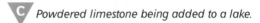

C *Powdered limestone being added to a lake.*

5 Give some uses for powdered limestone as a base.

Farmers and gardeners often use a base called **slaked lime** to neutralise acidic soil so that they can grow crops or flowers. Slaked lime is made from limestone in two stages.

Stage 1

First of all the limestone is heated in a big oven called a kiln. When it is heated the calcium carbonate in the limestone changes into **quicklime** and carbon dioxide. The chemical name for quicklime is **calcium oxide**.

This kind of reaction is called **thermal decomposition**. A decomposition reaction is one in which a substance is broken down into simpler substances. Thermal means heat, so this decomposition is caused by heating.

Stage 2

Water is then added to quicklime. The quicklime reacts with water to make **slaked lime**. The chemical name for slaked lime is **calcium hydroxide**. Calcium hydroxide is a strong alkali.

D

E

Stage 1

$$\text{limestone (calcium carbonate)} \xrightarrow{\text{heated in a kiln}} \text{quicklime (calcium oxide)} + \text{carbon dioxide}$$

$$CaCO_3 \longrightarrow CaO + CO_2$$

Stage 2

$$\text{quicklime (calcium oxide)} + \text{water} \longrightarrow \text{slaked lime (calcium hydroxide)}$$

$$CaO + H_2O \longrightarrow Ca(OH)_2$$

6 How is quicklime made?

7 What is a thermal decomposition reaction?

8 How is slaked lime made?

9 What is slaked lime used for?

10 Give the chemical names and formulae of:
   a) limestone   **b)** quicklime   **c)** slaked lime.

11 Why might it be better and safer to reduce the acidity of lakes and rivers with powdered limestone rather than powdered slaked lime?

Summary

Draw a flow diagram to summarise the conversion of limestone into slaked lime. Include all the details about each step.

Home sweet home

How do we make use of Earth materials for building?

Not only is the planet Earth our home, but it also provides us with all the materials we need to build our houses.

Roof slates come from a quarry.

Mortar is used to stick stone or bricks together. Mortar is made from sand and cement.

Blocks of limestone or sandstone can be used instead of bricks.

Concrete path is made from cement, sand and crushed rock.

Roof tiles are made from clay.

Plastic guttering is made from oil.

Bricks are made from clay.

Drivers Sold 359991

Window glass is made from sand, with some limestone and sodium carbonate.

1 What are the following things made from?
  a) glass
  b) mortar
  c) concrete
  d) bricks and tiles
  e) plastics.

Limestone is a sedimentary rock which was made from the remains of sea creatures. The sediment was fragments of shells which settled at the bottom of the sea. Sea shells are mainly made of calcium carbonate, which is why limestone is mostly calcium carbonate.

Limestone is a very important material for the building trade. It is used to make cement, concrete and glass. It is also cut into blocks and used instead of bricks to build the walls of houses. Small pieces of limestone (chippings) are also used in road making.

B *Limestone is dug out of a quarry.*

2 Give five uses for limestone as a building material.

3 How are rocks dug out of the ground for use as building materials?

Rocks like limestone are dug out of the ground in quarries. Explosives are usually used to blast the rock apart.

Cement is made by heating powdered limestone and powdered clay in a **rotary kiln**. A kiln is a very big oven and it rotates to mix the limestone and clay. The heat makes the limestone and clay react with each other to make cement.

4 Cement is made in a rotary kiln.

  a) What is a kiln?

  b) Why is a rotary kiln used?

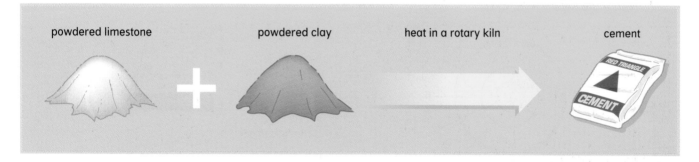

powdered limestone　　　　powdered clay　　　　heat in a rotary kiln　　　　cement

Concrete is made by mixing the cement with water, sand and crushed rock. A chemical reaction takes place and the mixture sets into a hard material a bit like stone.

Glass is made by heating pure sand with limestone and soda (soda is another name for sodium carbonate). At first the mixture melts. When it cools down it makes a transparent solid. If something is transparent it means you can see through it.

5 Look at diagram C. Draw similar diagrams for making concrete and making glass.

D

6 a) Name three kinds of rock which are used in the building trade.
　b) Are these three rocks igneous, sedimentary or metamorphic rocks?

P How would you investigate what the best recipe for concrete is?

Summary

Make a concept map to summarise all the uses of limestone shown on these two pages. Your map should include details of how any substances made from limestone are produced.

E

1 **a)** The diagram shows the four layers of the Earth. Name the layers A, B, C, D. (2)

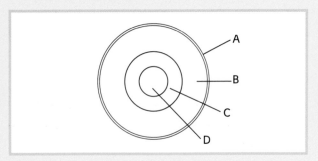

b) What are layers C and D thought to be made of? (2)

c) The Earth has been compared to a hard-boiled egg with a cracked shell. Explain in what ways this is a good model of the Earth and in what ways it is not. (5)

2 Look at the diagram of the rock cycle below.

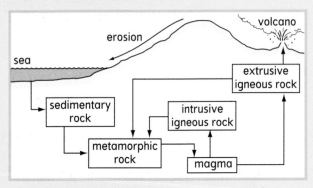

a) Describe how igneous rocks are formed. (2)

b) What would be the difference in appearance between extrusive and intrusive igneous rocks? (1)

c) Describe how sedimentary rocks are formed from sediment. (2)

d) Describe how metamorphic rocks are formed. (2)

3 This diagram shows rocks in a cliff face.

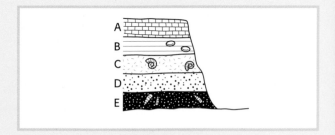

a) i) Which rock is likely to be the oldest?
 ii) Explain your answer. (2)

b) Are rocks B, C and E igneous, sedimentary or metamorphic rocks? (1)

4 Look at the simplified diagram of a fractionating column used to separate the hydrocarbons in crude oil.

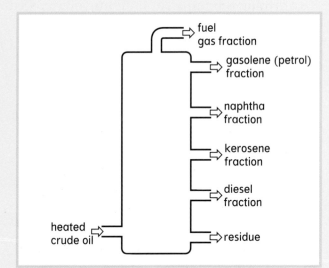

a) What is a hydrocarbon? (2)

b) What physical property allows the separation of hydrocarbons by fractional distillation? (1)

c) Explain how fractional distillation separates the hydrocarbons in crude oil. (3)

d) Which fraction shown on the diagram will be

 i) most volatile

 ii) most viscous

 iii) most flammable? (3)

5 The map shows Africa and South America.

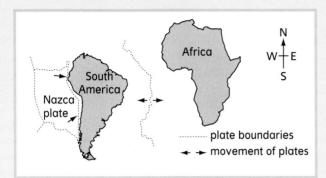

a) Explain how the Andes mountains are forming along the west coast of South America. (3)

b) Give *three* reasons why scientists think that Africa and South America were once joined. (3)

c) Why is there an underwater ridge in the middle of the Atlantic ocean? (3)

d) What makes tectonic plates move? (3)

6 The alkane $C_{10}H_{22}$ is found in the naphtha fraction of crude oil. It can be cracked into a shorter alkane and an alkene called ethene. A molecule of ethene is shown below.

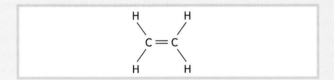

a) Why are some alkanes cracked? (1)

b) Alkanes are saturated hydrocarbons but alkenes are unsaturated hydrocarbons.

　i) What is the difference between a saturated and an unsaturated molecule? (2)

　ii) Describe a test to distinguish alkanes and alkenes. Give the result of the test for both types of compound. (3)

c) Ethene can be made into the polymer poly(ethene).

　i) What is a polymer? (2)

　ii) Write an equation for the formation of poly(ethene) from ethene. (2)

　iii) Give *two* uses of poly(ethene). (2)

7 These pie charts show the composition of the atmosphere at different times in the history of the Earth.

a) What are the gases labelled A, B and C? (3)

b) Where did the gases in the early atmosphere come from? (2)

c) How were the oceans formed? (2)

d) The atmosphere today contains a lot of oxygen. Where did this oxygen come from? (2)

e) The atmosphere today contains a lot of nitrogen. Where did this nitrogen mainly come from? (2)

f)　i) Give *two* ways in which carbon dioxide is removed from the atmosphere. (2)

　ii) Give *two* ways in which carbon dioxide is put into the atmosphere. (2)

　iii) Why are carbon dioxide levels increasing? (1)

8 Limestone has many important uses.

a) Give *two* uses of limestone as a building material. (2)

b) Describe how cement is made from limestone. (3)

c) What is quicklime and how is it made from limestone? (2)

d) What is slaked lime and how is it made from quicklime? (2)

e) Give *two* other uses of limestone. (2)

Types of energy

What different forms of energy are there?

Energy is needed for everything; without it, the Earth would be frozen, dark and silent. Stars would not shine and nothing would move. Life would not exist.

A There would be no life without heat and light energy from the Sun.

Energy in action

There are many types of energy. Objects such as a bowl of hot soup have **heat energy**. Heat energy is sometimes called **thermal energy**. Objects that glow or shine give out **light energy**. Objects that give out light energy often give out heat as well.

? **1** Picture B shows two items that give out both heat and light energy. Name two other things that give out heat and light energy.

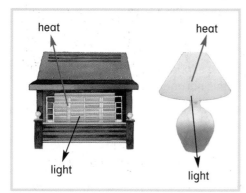

B

Anything making a noise gives out **sound energy**. Sometimes you can feel the vibrations caused by very loud sounds.

? **2** Name something that does not use electricity but does produce sound energy.

All moving objects have energy called **kinetic energy**. A fast car and a moving snail have kinetic energy. Faster objects have more kinetic energy.

Everything is made out of particles and these particles have kinetic energy. The temperature of an object is determined by the kinetic energy of its particles – as the object gets hotter the particles move faster.

? **3** **a)** Explain what would happen to the water molecules in a cup of water as its temperature decreases from 20 °C to −20 °C.
b) What might eventually happen to the molecules if the temperature continued to decrease?

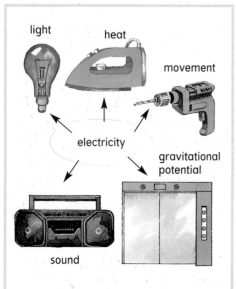

C

Electrical energy is used by anything that plugs into the mains or uses electrical cells (batteries). Electrical energy can be changed into many other types of energy. Our lives would be very different with no electricity.

Energy is measured in **joules** (J).

? **4** Name two things that use electrical energy and produce kinetic energy.

Stored energy

Some types of energy are stored. Anything that can fall down has **gravitational potential energy**. Another type of stored energy is **elastic potential energy**, which is found in objects that are stretched or squashed, such as a stretched elastic band.

Chemical energy is a type of stored energy found in food and fuels. For example a lump of coal and a plate of chips both contain chemical energy.

5 A person sleeping upstairs in a house has gravitational potential energy. Explain why this energy is called potential energy.

6 A blown-up balloon has stored energy. What form of stored energy does it have and how could you release this energy?

P Machines can give out several different forms of energy. What different forms of energy does each piece of equipment give out?

D

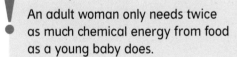

E As the baby bounces, energy changes between gravitational potential energy at the top and elastic potential energy when the spring is stretched.

! An adult woman only needs twice as much chemical energy from food as a young baby does.

7 What type of energy do both petrol and chocolate have?

8 Look at photograph F. For each form of energy, write down three places in the kitchen where it is being used or stored:

a) gravitational potential energy   b) chemical energy
c) thermal energy   d) electrical energy.

F

Summary

Write down each form of energy given in the text. Beside each form, write down an example of where it might be found.

9 Describe the forms of energy a spacecraft would have during a journey from the Earth to the Moon.

Conduction

How is heat transferred through solids?

Hot drinks from fast food restaurants are often served in polystyrene cups to keep them warm. Polystyrene contains lots of little air pockets. Heat does not travel well through the trapped air so the cup loses heat slowly.

 1 How do polystyrene cups keep drinks warm?

When hot objects lose heat, they cool down. Anything hotter than its surroundings loses heat until it reaches the same temperature as the surroundings. Heat energy always flows from a hot place to a cooler place. Opening a door on a cold day does not let the cold in; it lets the heat out!

When heat flows from place to place we say it **transfers**.

 2 Copy diagrams B and C. Add arrows to each diagram to show which way the heat flows.

A

 B C

Heat energy stops flowing when the objects reach the same temperature. The hotter objects stop cooling down and the colder objects stop heating up. A cup of coffee cools down until it reaches room temperature. It will never become colder than room temperature unless it is put into an even colder place like a fridge.

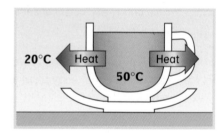

 3 Look at picture D. Sketch a graph to show what will happen to the temperature of the coffee in the cup. Include values on your graph where you can.

D Heat flows from hotter places to cooler places.

Everything is made of particles. In solids, the particles are close together in fixed positions. The particles cannot move past each other, but they can vibrate. As solids become hotter, their particles vibrate more. These vibrations pass their heat energy on to nearby particles. This method of heat transfer is called **conduction**, and mainly takes place in solids.

 4 An iron bar was left with one end in a fire. Use ideas about particles to explain how thermal energy flows along the iron bar.

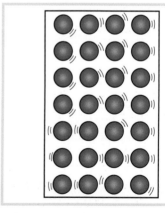

E In solids, the particles are close together and cannot change places.

Solids that transfer heat well are called **heat conductors**. Metals are good heat conductors. Non-metals and gases are poor heat conductors, and are also called **heat insulators**. Heat insulators transfer heat very slowly.

Metals conduct heat well because they have free **electrons** that move within the metal. When a metal is heated, both the larger particles (**metal ions**) and the electrons gain kinetic energy. The ions vibrate more vigorously and transfer energy to neighbouring ions. The electrons diffuse through the metal, carrying the energy with them. As they collide with ions and other electrons the thermal energy is transferred through the metal.

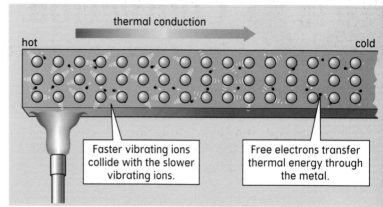

thermal conduction

hot   cold

Faster vibrating ions collide with the slower vibrating ions.

Free electrons transfer thermal energy through the metal.

 Heat (or thermal conduction) in metals.

? **5** What do we mean by 'heat insulators'?

6 Explain why the bottom of a saucepan is made from metal and the handle is usually made from plastic or wood.

 Houses can lose heat through windows and window frames. Window frames can be made of many different materials.

● Which material is best at preventing heat losses through a window frame?

● How would you find out?

● How would you make sure your experiment is a fair test?

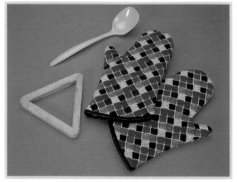

 Non-metals are good insulators.

! Special silica tiles are such good insulators that they can protect astronauts inside space capsules returning to earth from temperatures on the outside of the capsule of over 1500 °C.

? **7** Think about particles in gases and explain why gases are poor conductors of heat.

8 Imagine standing barefoot in a bathroom with one foot on a rug and the other on the tiled floor. The rug and the tiled floor will both be at the same temperature but the tiled floor will feel colder. Why is this?

Summary

A Explain how heat is transferred through solids, particularly metals.

B Write a summary to explain the differences between good heat conductors and poor heat conductors. Give an example of each.

Convection

How is heat is transferred through gases and liquids?

Smoke detectors save lives by warning people that their house is on fire. Smoke detectors are always fitted on ceilings because the hot smoke rises and can be detected quickly.

? **1** Why should you crouch down in a smoke filled room?

! Breathing in smoke kills more people in house fires than the flames do.

Liquids and gases are called **fluids**. They can flow because they do not have fixed shapes like solids. When the tiny particles in fluids flow, they carry heat energy with them. This is called **convection**. The heat travels quickly with the particles as they move.

? **2** What do we mean by convection?

3 Explain why convection does not occur in solids.

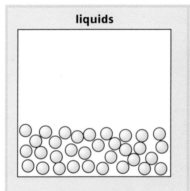 

B In liquids, the particles are close together but can swap places.

C In gases, the particles are far apart and can swap places.

When cold water is heated the particles move faster, causing the water to expand. As it expands the hot water becomes less **dense** and rises through the cold water around it. The resulting movement of water is called a **convection current**.

? **4** Explain why cold water sinks when it is surrounded by warm water.

Convection can warm things up. You can use convection to transfer heat quickly. The heating element of a kettle is at the bottom. As the water at the base of the kettle heats up, it rises. It is replaced by the cooler water above it, which sinks.

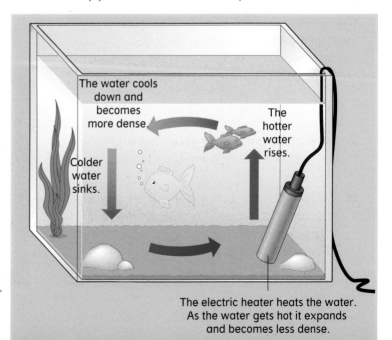

Convection currents in a fish tank. **D**

The water cools down and becomes more dense.

Colder water sinks.

The hotter water rises.

The electric heater heats the water. As the water gets hot it expands and becomes less dense.

How would you find out where the coolest air surrounding a hot object is?

E

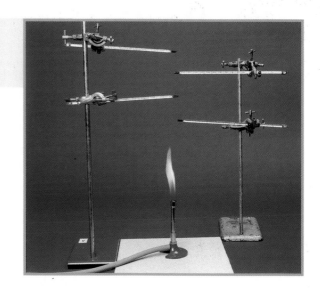

Convection can cool things down. The cooling element for a fridge is in the icebox, which is at the top of the fridge. The cooling element transfers heat out of the fridge.

The air is colder near the icebox, and sinks to cool the lower part of the fridge. The warmer air rises from the bottom of the fridge. This way, the circulating air cools down quickly.

5 Why is a fridge icebox at the top of a fridge?

Nuclear reactors change water to steam. Convection helps to heat the water more effectively.

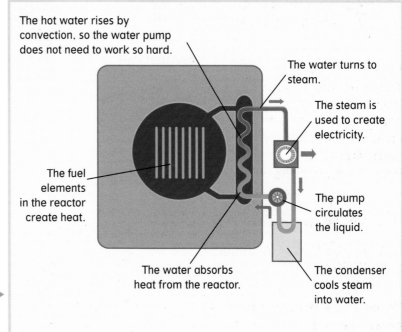

The hot water rises by convection, so the water pump does not need to work so hard.

The water turns to steam.

The steam is used to create electricity.

The fuel elements in the reactor create heat.

The pump circulates the liquid.

The water absorbs heat from the reactor.

The condenser cools steam into water.

A nuclear reactor.   F

6 Look at diagram F. How does convection help a nuclear reactor heat water, creating steam?

7 Explain how a hot air balloon can fly.

8 a) During the day the land is warmer than the sea. Explain why this will cause a breeze to blow from the sea to the land in coastal areas.
   b) At night the land loses heat very quickly but the sea stays relatively warm. What will happen to the direction of the breeze? Explain your answer.

Summary

Write five bullet points to explain convection. Include the words: rise, density, mass and volume.

Radiation

How is heat transferred through space?

Studying volcanoes is hot work! Scientists working near an eruption wear white or silver suits, which reflect the heat from the volcano. This keeps the scientists cool enough to survive.

 1 Why do white clothes help you keep cool?

Hot objects give out heat. They are said to **radiate** heat. Heat radiation is also called **infrared radiation.** The hotter an object is the more heat radiation it will produce.

Radiation travels as waves of energy that can travel through empty space and through transparent things like air or glass. Particles are not involved in the transfer of heat by radiation.

 2 What is another name for heat radiation?

3 How does radiation travel?

A

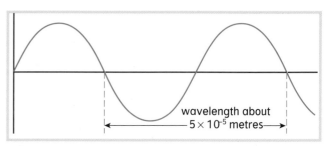

wavelength about 5×10^{-5} metres

B   *Heat radiation is transferred by waves called electromagnetic waves.*

Reflecting radiation

Some colours are better than others at reflecting heat. White and shiny surfaces reflect heat well. Lorries carrying milk or chocolate are often painted white. This **reflects** the Sun's heat so the milk or chocolate inside stays cool.

Giving out heat radiation

Black surfaces are good at radiating heat. The insides of ovens are a dull black colour to help the food cook more quickly.

Silvery and white surfaces do not radiate heat well. A person standing near a white car on a hot day feels less heat radiating from its paintwork than from a black car.

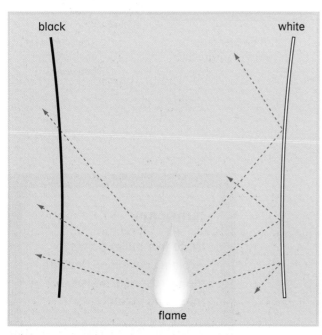

black

white

flame

C   *White surfaces reflect radiated heat so the sheet stays cool to touch. Black surfaces absorb radiated heat which then radiates from the other side.*

Absorbing radiation

Solar panels **absorb** the sun's heat and use it to heat water. They are black because black absorbs heat best.

	Black	Silver
Reflecting heat radiation	worst	best
Giving out heat radiation	best	worst
Absorbing heat radiation	best	worst

4 Why is it not a good idea to wear black clothes on a hot, sunny day?

5 Houses in hot countries often have shutters on the windows. Why do people usually close these shutters during the day?

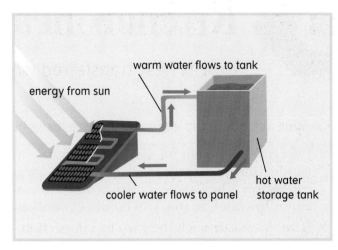

D This solar panel is designed to heat water. Black surfaces absorb the Sun's heat well.

P Most people like their cold drinks to stay cool while they drink them. How would you find out the best colour for a soft drink can?

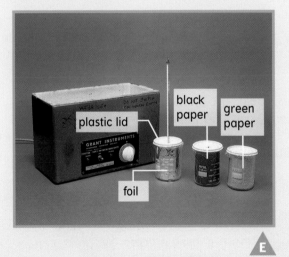

plastic lid • black paper • green paper • foil

E

Summary

Explain how heat is transferred by radiation. Use these key words: radiation, infrared radiation, reflects, absorbs.

6 Look at diagram F. Which cup radiates most heat and cools down quickest? Explain your answer.

F

75°C 75°C 75°C

7 Wrapping food in aluminium foil stops it cooking too fast. How does this work? Choose the correct answer.
  A By stopping heat conduction.
  B By reflecting the heat radiation.
  C By cooling the food.

8 Electric fires usually have a curved reflector behind the heating element. Explain what it does, how it works and why it is shiny.

Kitchen heat transfers

How is heat transferred when cooking a meal?

Cooking a meal of soup and toast involves many heat transfers.

- Heat travels through the solid saucepan base by **conduction**. Saucepans made from metal are good heat conductors. The handle is often covered in plastic, a heat insulator, to stop you burning your hands.

- Heat spreads through the soup by **convection**. Soup is heated from the bottom of the pan. As hot soup rises, the cooler soup falls and is warmed.

- Heat **radiates** from the elements of a toaster to heat the bread. The inside of the toaster is shiny to reflect the heat onto the bread.

 A

1 a) Why are most saucepans made of metal?

    b) Why are their handles often made of plastic?

2 Why won't a pan of soup heat properly under the grill?

Stopping heat losses

Kettles are designed to heat water effectively. The heating element is at the bottom so that convection currents heat the water quickly. A lid stops heat losses by convection. Jug kettles are made of plastic, a heat insulator, to reduce heat losses by conduction.

3 Explain why it takes less heat energy to boil water in a kettle than it does to boil the same volume of water in a saucepan.

In some countries, meals are cooked in earth pits. Meat is heated up, then wrapped and packed tightly into a pit lined with hay (a poor heat conductor). After several hours, the food is unwrapped, still hot and cooked through.

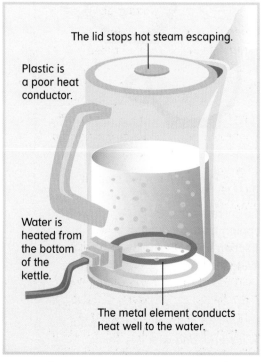

The lid stops hot steam escaping.

Plastic is a poor heat conductor.

Water is heated from the bottom of the kettle.

The metal element conducts heat well to the water.

 B

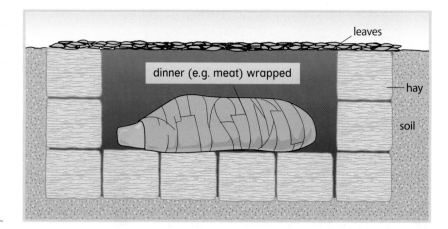

leaves

dinner (e.g. meat) wrapped

hay

soil

C

4 How are heat losses stopped in a cooking pit?

Vacuum flasks keep drinks hot (or cold) for many hours. They are designed to prevent conduction, convection and radiation.

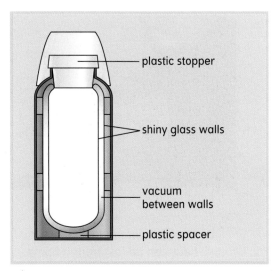

plastic stopper

shiny glass walls

vacuum between walls

plastic spacer

 D *A vacuum flask.*

?

5 Jade is serving stew at a party from two containers. One is an open topped metal dish, the other is a plastic bowl with a lid. Explain which container keeps the stew hottest.

6 Why do kebabs cook quicker using a metal skewer instead of a wooden skewer?

7 Look at diagram D. The labels indicate the design features of a vacuum flask that reduce heat transfer.
  a) What design features reduce heat transfer by conduction?
  b) How is heat transfer by radiation reduced?
  c) Which two design features reduce heat transfer by convection?

8 Will a vacuum flask help keep a cold drink cold? Explain your answer.

Summary

Write down the main methods used to reduce heat transfer in kitchen equipment.

P How would you find out the quickest way to cook a potato?

● Should you cut it up?
● Should you put a lid on the pan?
● Should you put a metal skewer through it?

E

A summary of heat transfer. **F**

Method	Key points	Theory
conduction	Main method of heat transfer through solids. Some solids are good thermal conductors, others are poor thermal conductors.	Thermal energy causes particles to vibrate more vigorously. Collisions with neighbouring particles transfer the thermal energy through the material.
convection	Main method of heat transfer in liquids and gases. Heating the gas or liquid causes it to expand and becomes less dense. The resulting movement of the fluid is called a convection current.	Heat energy is transferred because the particles with most thermal energy move up through the colder liquid or gas.
radiation	Transfer of thermal energy by electromagnetic waves. Black surfaces are good absorbers and good radiators of infrared radiation.	Heat radiation travels as an electromagnetic wave and can transfer heat through a vacuum. No particles are involved.

Stopping heat losses at home

Where is heat lost in the home and how can you stop it?

A lot of the energy used to heat our homes escapes. Cutting heat losses cuts down heating bills. Houses lose heat in several different ways:

- Most heat is lost by **conduction** through solid surfaces like floors, walls and windows.
- Warm air rises by **convection** through the house and is lost through the roof.
- Warm air is also lost in **draughts** through gaps in doors, windows and between floorboards.
- Surfaces like walls and windows **radiate** heat from the outside walls of a house.

Look at the two houses in diagram B.

Insulating the loft saves money.  **A**

? **1** Describe three ways in which heat can be lost from a home.

B *One house is insulated and one is not.*

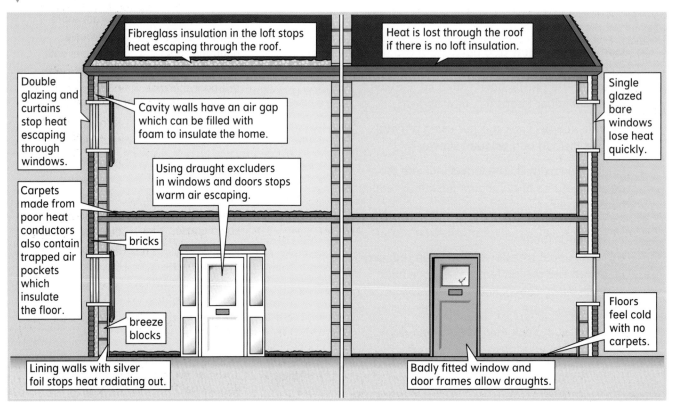

Fibreglass insulation in the loft stops heat escaping through the roof.

Heat is lost through the roof if there is no loft insulation.

Double glazing and curtains stop heat escaping through windows.

Cavity walls have an air gap which can be filled with foam to insulate the home.

Single glazed bare windows lose heat quickly.

Using draught excluders in windows and doors stops warm air escaping.

Carpets made from poor heat conductors also contain trapped air pockets which insulate the floor.

bricks

breeze blocks

Floors feel cold with no carpets.

Lining walls with silver foil stops heat radiating out.

Badly fitted window and door frames allow draughts.

? **2** Copy and complete table C to match each type of heat loss with one of the methods used to prevent it.

C

Type of heat loss	Method used to prevent it
Conduction	
Convection	
Radiation	

3 Look at diagrams D and E.

a) How does injecting a cavity wall with foam help prevent heat loss by conduction and convection?

b) Explain why double glazing helps reduce heat loss by conduction but not by radiation.

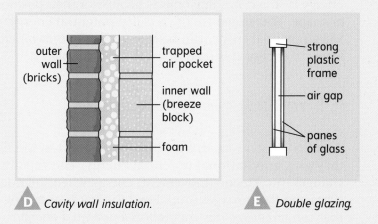

D *Cavity wall insulation.*   **E** *Double glazing.*

Cutting the cost of heating your home

It can be expensive to heat your home. Fitting draught excluders is cheap to do and can cut down heating bills a lot. However, double glazing is very expensive and does not cut fuel bills by much. To choose the best method, you need to find out:

- how much it will cost to fit
- how much money you will save on your heating bills each year.

The best methods are cheap to fit, and save a lot of money each year. To be worthwhile, the amount that you save on heating bills over a few years should be more than you spend insulating your home.

5 Insulating your loft is said to have a shorter payback time than fitting double glazing. What do you think this means?

6 Use your ideas about convection to explain:
a) why central heating boilers are downstairs
b) why hot water tanks are upstairs.

7 Explain why turning up the heating would not stop cold draughts in a poorly insulated house.

P Insulating hot water tanks stops heat escaping into the house. How would you find out the best material to use? How thick should it be to keep the water warm?   **F**

4 Explain whether each person below should fit double glazing or draught excluders.

a) Luca's house has small, badly fitting windows. He will move in 2 years.
b) Asif's house has large, well fitting windows. He plans to live there for 15 years.

! Swedish homes are so well insulated, they use only one third of the energy used to heat British homes.

Summary

Design an information leaflet to explain how to reduce heat loss from the home. Explain how each method works.

Using potential energy

How can we use potential energy?

Energy is stored in some objects because of their position or shape. This stored energy is called **potential energy**. Since potential energy can be changed easily into different forms of energy, it is used in many different places.

? **1** What do we mean by potential energy?

As roller coaster carriages are lifted to the start of the ride, they gain **gravitational potential energy**. This rapidly changes into kinetic (movement) energy when the ride starts and the carriages drop down the track. Anything that can fall down has gravitational potential energy.

Objects have more gravitational potential energy if they are:

- higher up
- heavier (weigh more).

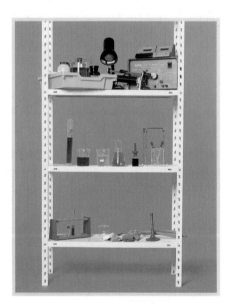

B *Heavy items on the top shelf store more gravitational potential energy than items on lower shelves.*

? **2** A car follows a lorry up a hill. Which would have the most gravitational potential energy when they reached the top of the hill? Explain your answer.

3 What happens to the gravitational potential energy of a bone when a dog buries it in the ground?

4 What happens to the gravitational potential energy of a girl on a trampoline?

E Gravitational potential energy can be calculated if you know:

- the object's weight (in newtons)
- the height it has moved up or down (in metres)

change in gravitational potential energy = **weight** × **change in height**
(in **joules**, **J**) (in **newtons**, **N**) (in **metres**, **m**)

Worked example

Nick weighs 600 newtons. How much gravitational potential energy does he lose when he drops 10 metres on a roller coaster ride?

- Nick's weight is 600 N.
- His change in height is 10 m.
- The gravitational potential energy he loses is

600 N x 10 m
= (600 x 10) J
= 6 000 J

P
How would you use your ideas about gravitational potential energy to make a roller coaster ride faster and more exciting?

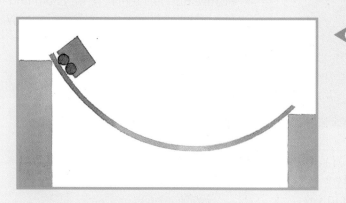

C

Summary

You are in charge of writing a flight manual for a helicopter. Write a short section to explain what gravitational potential energy and kinetic energy are and how they are related. Also explain how the gravitational potential energy lost when the helicopter lands can be calculated.

5 Sue weighs 500 newtons. She dives 4 metres into a swimming pool.
  a) What is Sue's weight?
  b) What is her change in height?
  c) How much gravitational potential energy does she lose?

6 Work out the gravitational potential energy that these objects have:
  a) A bird weighing 1 N, perched at the top of a 20 m high tower.
  b) A football weighing 7 N, kicked 3 m up into the air.

7 As a bungy jumper falls through the air his gravitational potential energy decreases.
  a) Sketch a graph to show how his gravitational potential energy changes into kinetic energy during his first fall.
  Start your graph like this:

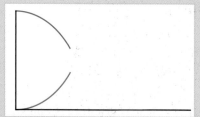

  b) Where does the energy come from to make him bounce back upwards?

E8 Energy transfers

How does energy change from one form to another?

Photograph A shows an electrical goods shop. All the appliances sold here transfer electrical energy into other forms of energy. The mini hi-fi systems at the front of the picture transfer electrical energy into sound energy and they will also produce unwanted thermal energy.

A

A milk float is a large machine that transfers electrical energy into other forms of energy. The electricity needed comes from electrical cells that store chemical energy. This chemical energy is then transferred into electrical energy when it is required.

When the electrical cells start to run out of chemical energy, they can be charged up using the mains electricity supply. While they are charging, electrical energy is being transferred to chemical energy.

! 100 million joules of electrical energy transfers into thermal energy in one bolt of lightning.

C

 1 Name an appliance that transfers electrical energy into:

   a) light energy
   b) thermal energy
   c) kinetic energy.

2 Energy transfers can be shown using **energy flow diagrams** like this:

Hi-fi system:

electrical energy	→	sound energy

   a) Draw energy flow diagrams for these items.
      food mixer   iron   doorbell   lamp
   b) What other forms of energy are given out by these items of equipment?

3 Picture B shows a mini hi-fi system and five other electrical items. Draw energy flow diagrams for two of these appliances.

B

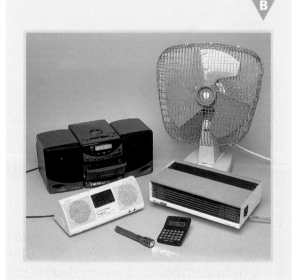

Electrical cells are charged up using electrical energy from the mains.

C

Energy is not destroyed during energy transfers. For example, for every 100 joules of electrical energy supplied to a light bulb, only 6 joules of light energy might be produced. The remaining energy has not been lost, it has been transferred into thermal energy and the bulb gets very hot.

The **law of conservation of energy** states that energy cannot be created or destroyed; it can only be transferred from one form to another.

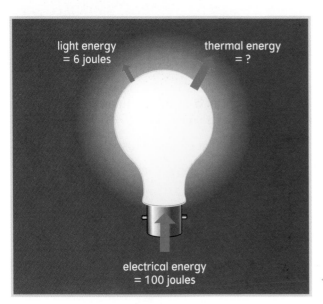

light energy = 6 joules

thermal energy = ?

electrical energy = 100 joules

D

?

4 Where in a milk float is electrical energy transferred into:
   a) kinetic energy
   b) thermal energy
   c) light energy
   d) sound energy?

5 List three different items that often use rechargeable batteries.

6 a) For every 200 joules of electrical energy supplied to the lamp in diagram D, how much thermal energy will be produced?
   b) Draw a diagram to illustrate your answer.

Summary

Write down the law of conservation of energy and explain how it can be applied to the energy transfers in an electric washing machine.

Power

What is power?

Black Rock Desert, Nevada. 15 October 1997. Andy Green breaks the sound barrier, travelling at 1228 kilometres per hour, in his car *ThrustSSC*.

The car is the brainchild of Richard Noble and built to travel faster than most aeroplanes. It uses Rolls Royce jet engines to provide a huge amount of energy every second and allow the car to hurtle along at supersonic speeds.

? 1 Why can *ThrustSSC* travel faster than most aeroplanes?

A

B *Lifting the sugar gave it 1 extra joule of gravitational potential energy.*

Energy is needed before anything can happen. Chemical energy stored in *ThrustSSC's* fuel made it move. The *ThrustSSC* used up the energy from its fuel very quickly because it had very powerful engines. **Energy** is measured in **joules (J)**. One joule is a tiny amount of energy. Lifting a bag of sugar 10 cm uses up 1 joule of energy. *ThrustSSC* used 60 million joules each second!

The **power** of a machine measures how quickly its energy is supplied, or transferred. Power is measured in **watts (W)** or **kilowatts (kW)**. There are 1000 watts in a kilowatt. A watt is a tiny amount of power — a very dim light bulb has a power of 25 watts.

? 2 A machine is supplied with 2400 joules of energy every second. What is the power of this machine in kilowatts?

E The power of a piece of equipment can be worked out if you know:

● the amount of energy used (in joules)

● the time the equipment was on for (in seconds).

$$\text{power} = \text{energy} \div \text{time}$$
(in **watts, W**) (in **joules, J**) (in **seconds, s**)

power = energy *divided by* time

More powerful items use up more energy every second.

A nightlight bulb has a power of 25 watts. It uses 25 joules of energy per second and gives out very dim light.

A bright reading light uses a 100 watt bulb, so it uses up 100 joules every second.

The dim light only uses a quarter of the energy of the bright light each second.

100 watts

25 watts

?

3 Write down the equation we use to calculate power.

4 A light bulb uses 1200 joules of electrical energy in 20 seconds. What is the power of this light bulb?

5 How much energy does a 1.2 kW hairdryer use each second?

P You can find out how powerful you are by measuring how many step-ups you can do in 1 minute.

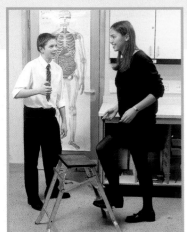
D

C

! The Space Shuttle burns 98 tonnes of fuel in 1 minute and has a power of 17 600 kW.

?

6 Copy and complete table E.

E

Item	Power (watts)	Power (kilowatts)	Energy used in 1 second (joules)
Dishwasher		2	
Electric blanket	100		
Television			300
Vacuum cleaner			1500

7 A 150 watt fridge runs for 60 seconds.
   a) Calculate the energy transferred by the fridge.
   b) How much energy would the fridge transfer in one hour?

8 A family left a 60 W lamp switched on while they were away on holiday for 2 weeks. How much energy will the lamp have used?

9 How much energy will a 2 kW electric fire use in 4.5 hours? Give your answer in kilojoules (kJ).

Summary

Answer the question at the beginning of the topic: What is power? Explain how the power of a machine in kilowatts can be used to calculate the energy transferred in a given time. Include any equations that you would use.

Electrical energy and power

How much energy do electrical devices transfer?

Clubs have powerful loudspeakers to pump out loud music. These loudspeakers use a lot of electrical energy each second, to give out so much sound energy. The equipment is on for a long time so a great deal of electrical energy is used.

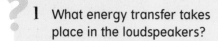

1 What energy transfer takes place in the loudspeakers?

A

E Hi-fi equipment at home is not as powerful as a club's equipment. The amount of electrical energy used at home and at the nightclub can be worked out if you know:

● the power of the equipment (in watts) and
● the time it is on for (in seconds).

> **energy transferred** = **power** × **time**
> (in **joules**, **J**)   (in **watts**, **W**)   (in **seconds**, **s**)

Remember: multiply the number of minutes by 60 to change them into seconds.

Worked example

A radio (power 100 W) is on for 1 minute (or 60 seconds). How much energy is used?

● Its power is 100 W.
● It is on for 60 seconds.
● Energy = power × time
　　　　= 100 W × 60 s
　　　　= 6000 J.

2 A 650 watt microwave oven is on for 30 seconds. How much energy does it use?

Electrical appliances can be powerful and are sometimes left on for a long time.

3 Look at picture B.
　a) What is the power of this microwave oven?
　b) How much energy does it use if it is switched on for 2 minutes?

B

P How would you find out if a kettle transfers the same amount of energy in each second that it is switched on?

E The energy used by more powerful electrical equipment can be measured in **kilowatt-hours**.

You need to know:

- the power of the equipment (in kilowatts)
- the time it is on for (in hours).

energy transferred	=	power	×	time
(in **kilowatt-hours, kWh**)		(in **kilowatts, kW**)		(in hours, **h**)

Remember: Divide the power in watts by 1000 to change it into kilowatts.

D *The radio uses 1 kilowatt-hour of energy in 10 hours. The more powerful heater only takes 1 hour to use 1 kilowatt-hour.*

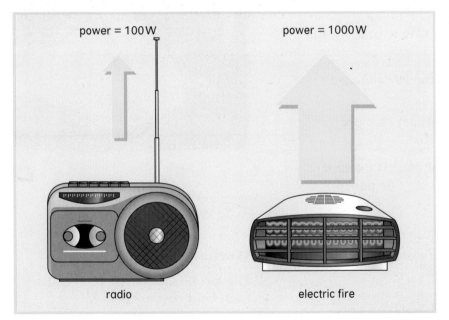

power = 100 W   power = 1000 W

radio   electric fire

Worked example

An iron (power 2 kW) is on for 1 hour. How much energy is used?

- The power of the iron is 2 kW.
- It is on for 1 hour.
- Energy = power × time
  = 2 kW × 1 h
  = 2 kWh.

4 How much energy is used if the iron in the example above is on for 2 hours?

5 The power of an oven is 5 kW.
  a) How much energy (in kWh) does it use in 1 hour?
  b) What is its power in watts?
  c) How much energy (in joules) does it use in 10 seconds?

Summary

A Explain what a kilowatt-hour is.

B Show how an amount of energy given in kilowatt-hours can be converted to joules.

6 Ross watched TV (0.3 kW) for 3 hours one night. His mum used the tumble dryer (4 kW) for half an hour. Who used most energy?

7 a) Write down the equations for calculating **i)** energy transfer in joules, **ii)** energy transfer in kilowatt-hours.
  b) Show how each of these equations can be used to calculate the energy transferred by a 2 kW heater in 3 hours.

Buying electricity

How can you calculate the cost of electricity bills?

The Jacob family's electricity bill in December was much larger than September's bill. Mr Jacob thought that the electricity company had put up its prices. Then he saw that more Units of electricity had been used. The lights were on in the dark evenings and so were the heaters.

 1 Why was Mr Jacob's electricity bill bigger in winter?

The amount of electricity used in homes is measured in **kilowatt-hours**, often just called a **Unit**. More Units are used if:

- more equipment is on
- more powerful equipment is on
- the equipment is on for a longer time.

Remember:
energy (in Units or kWh) = power (in kW) × time (in h).

 The total cost of the electricity used can be calculated if you know:

- the number of Units (or kilowatt-hours) used and
- the cost per Unit (in pence).

total cost = number of Units used × cost per Unit
(in pence) **(in pence)**

 How would you find out which item of electrical equipment increases your electricity bill the most?

B

A

 2 What is a Unit of electricity?

Worked example

The Jacob family used 1280 Units. Each Unit cost 5.9 pence.

The cost of electricity used was:

1280 Units × 5.9 p

= 7552 p (or £75.52).

The electricity meter shows how many Units have been used. Every three months an electricity bill is prepared, showing the last meter reading and the present meter reading. The number of Units to be paid for is the difference between the two readings.

Worked example

The Jacob's bill was prepared using these readings:

- last meter reading: 76885 Units
- present meter reading: 78165 Units
- number of Units used = 78165 – 55542
  = 1280 Units.

3 Look at the electricity bill in picture C.
  a) How many Units were used?
  b) How much did each Unit cost?
  c) What was the total amount to pay?

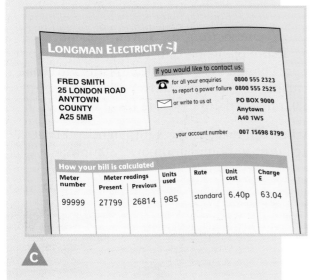

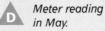

LONGMAN ELECTRICITY

FRED SMITH
25 LONDON ROAD
ANYTOWN
COUNTY
A25 5MB

If you would like to contact us:
☎ for all your enquiries   0800 555 2323
    to report a power failure 0800 555 2525
✉ or write to us at   PO BOX 9000
                              Anytown
                              A40 1WS

your account number   007 15698 8799

How your bill is calculated

Meter number	Meter readings Present	Meter readings Previous	Units used	Rate	Unit cost	Charge £
99999	27799	26814	985	standard	6.40p	63.04

C

Summary

F

Write a set of instructions to explain how someone could calculate the cost of the electricity they use each month.

---

4 Look at the meters in pictures D and E.
  a) What was the reading in May?
  b) What was the reading in August?
  c) How many Units have been used between May and August?

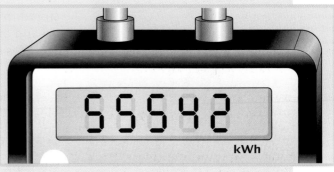

D Meter reading in May.

E Meter reading in August.

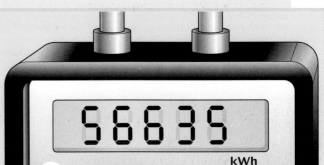

5 Copy and complete table F.

Month	Last reading	Present reading	Units used	Cost (£)
February	52045	53499		
March	53499	54648		

The cost of one Unit is 8.2p.

6 If a Unit of electricity costs 8.2p, how much would it cost to run:
  a) a 1.5 kW fan heater for 5 hours
  b) a 60 W light bulb continuously for one week?

Fuels

What are the different types of fuels?

A

When the Space Shuttle takes off, fuel burns. Chemical energy stored in the fuel is changed into kinetic energy, forcing the rocket up and away from the Earth. The energy needed to launch the rocket is enormous and all the fuel is used up within 2 minutes.

1 What sort of energy is stored in fuels?

Fossil fuels

Growing plants turn light energy from the Sun into chemical energy. After they die, many plants become buried. Over millions of years, heat and pressure change the buried dead plants into **coal**. In the same way, the remains of sea plants and animals change into **oil** and **natural gas**. Coal, oil and natural gas are **fossil fuels**.

The chemical energy in fossil fuels changes into light and heat energy when they are burnt in homes and power stations.

B *From this...* *....to this in 200 million years.*

plants

sea creatures

coal

oil

Oil is used for many things. C

2 a) Name three fossil fuels.
b) Say where each might be used.

P How would you compare the different amounts of energy stored in different fuels?

D

After fossil fuels have been burnt only ashes remain, and these cannot be re-used. Fossil fuels are **non-renewable** energy resources, which means that they cannot be re-used or replaced. It takes millions of years for fossil fuels to form, and we are using up fossil fuels much faster than they are produced. They will run out soon unless we use other ways of providing energy for our everyday needs.

3 Explain why petrol is a non-renewable energy resource.

E *Once it has been burnt, coal cannot be re-used.*

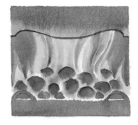

Other fuels

Nuclear power stations use **uranium** and **plutonium** as fuels. Nuclear reactions release energy from these fuels. Supplies of these metals are limited. Once they have been used up, they cannot be replaced. Nuclear fuels are also non-renewable.

Wood is another fuel, although it gives out less energy than fossil fuels when it burns. Fast growing trees planted now can be used for fuel in 10 years time. Wood is a **renewable energy** resource because we can replace the trees that are cut down.

F *Many of the fuels we use will run out.*

4 What are the advantages and disadvantages of using wood as a fuel?

5 Explain the difference between renewable energy resources and non-renewable energy resources.

6 How can using insulation in your home slow down the rate at which we use up fossil fuels?

Summary

Write a magazine advert for a hydrogen-powered car, explaining clearly why this is better than using any of the other fuels mentioned in this section.

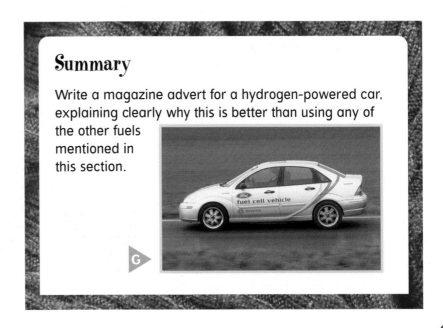

G

Power stations

How is electricity created from energy stored in fuels?

Electricity is generated in power stations. Many power stations change kinetic energy into electrical energy using huge magnets and coils of wire.

 1 Look at diagram A. Why is it better to spin the magnet rather than spin the coil?

Where kinetic energy comes from

Energy stored in fuels is used to heat water until it turns into steam. The steam gains the kinetic energy that is needed to generate electrical energy. Power stations use:

- fossil fuels like coal, natural gas and oil
- the nuclear fuels uranium and plutonium.

horse-shoe magnet — coil of wire — 00.01 — bulb — microammeter — turntable

A

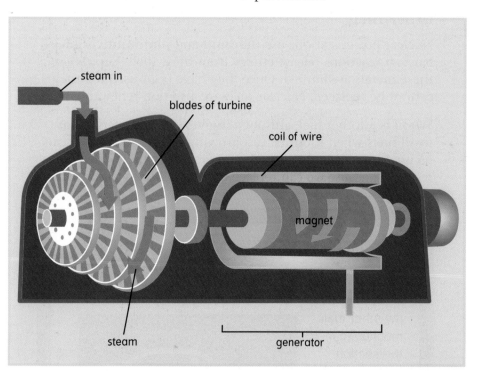

steam in — blades of turbine — coil of wire — magnet — steam — generator

A turbine. **B**

Why steam is needed in power stations

The steam has enough kinetic energy to turn the blades of large **turbines**.

The turbine spins a magnet, which is inside a coil of wire. The magnet and the coil of wire are together called a **generator**.

The kinetic energy of the turbine changes into electrical energy inside the generator.

This makes an electric current flow in the coil of wire.

 2 **a)** Explain how steam is used to generate electricity.
b) What would you expect to happen if the kinetic energy of the magnet in the generator was increased?

P How would you make your own electricity generator from magnets and wire?

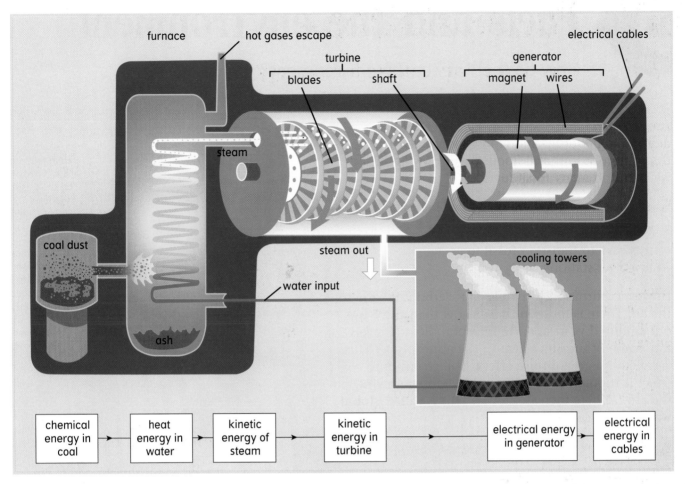

| chemical energy in coal | → | heat energy in water | → | kinetic energy of steam | → | kinetic energy in turbine | → | electrical energy in generator | → | electrical energy in cables |

Diagram C shows what happens inside a coal-fired power station.

An average person in India uses 50 times less energy per day than an average person in the USA.

C

?

3 Draw an energy flow diagram to show the energy changes taking place inside a power station.

4 Why do you think power stations are often built near rivers?

5 a) In a power station there is still a lot of thermal energy in the steam after it has turned the turbine. Suggest how this thermal energy could be used.

b) Why is electricity not used to turn the generator?

D

Summary

Write a bullet point list to explain how coal can be used to generate electricity.

Fuels and the environment

How do fuels affect the environment?

Severe storms and floods can cause deaths and damage to buildings and crops. Some scientists think more storms and floods occur now because we burn too many fossil fuels.

Fossil fuels are a good energy source because:

- their energy is very concentrated
- it is easy to transport fossil fuels to power stations.

However, burning fossil fuels adds carbon dioxide to the air. There is more in the air now than there was one hundred years ago. High carbon dioxide levels trap some of the Sun's heat in the atmosphere. This is called the **greenhouse effect**. The greenhouse effect is thought to be making the temperature of the atmosphere increase slowly. This is called **global warming**.

heat and light from sun

atmosphere

Heat from the Sun is absorbed by the Earth. The Earth radiates this heat.

Carbon dioxide (and other greenhouse gases) absorb some of this heat and so the atmosphere gets warmer.

A *The greenhouse effect.*

? **1** How do power stations add to the greenhouse effect?

! Severe floods in Bangladesh have killed tens of thousands of people. As sea levels rise due to global warming, many more could die in the future.

Burning coal, oil and natural gas releases **pollution** into the air. Sulphur is found in fossil fuels. When it burns it forms sulphur dioxide. This dissolves in the clouds, forming **acid rain**. Acid rain can kill plants, and animals and plants living in lakes and ponds.

The sulphur can be removed from fuels before they are burnt, or sulphur dioxide can be removed from waste gases. However, this makes the fossil fuels more expensive to use.

B *The effects of acid rain.*

In 1989, school children in Mexico City had a month off school because pollution caused such severe smog.

Different fuels release different amounts of carbon dioxide for the same amount of energy released. Natural gas releases the least, then oil, and coal releases the most.

Type of pollution	Effect on environment	Ways to reduce effect
carbon dioxide	It increases the greenhouse effect, causing global warming.	Burn less fuel.
sulphur dioxide	It dissolves in rain making it acidic. Acid rain kills plants, and plants and animals in lakes and ponds.	Remove the sulphur from the fuel before it is burned. Fit filters in power station chimneys to absorb the sulphur dioxide produced.

2 What is the advantage of removing the sulphur from coal before it is burnt at a power station?

3 Why do you think Britain has more coal-fired power stations than natural gas-fired power stations?

Nuclear power

Nuclear power does not cause global warming or acid rain, but it creates **radioactive waste**. Fairly small amounts are produced which are sealed in glass and stored underground. Nuclear waste needs careful storage because it can stay radioactive for thousands of years. A **nuclear accident** can release a lot of radioactivity into the surrounding areas. In Britain, strict controls on reactor design make nuclear accidents very unlikely.

Nuclear power stations are expensive to build but cheap to run. When they reach the end of their useful life they have to be shut down and made safe by an expensive process called **decommissioning**.

4 Why do nuclear power stations not contribute to global warming?

5 How might nuclear power stations pollute the environment?

6 Suggest three ways to reduce the amount of carbon dioxide gas released into the environment by power stations.

D Nuclear waste can be stored in glass then sealed in metal drums.

Summary

Draw a table to outline the advantages and disadvantages of replacing coal-fired power stations with nuclear power stations.

Renewable energy resources

What is a renewable energy resource?

For centuries, grains of corn and wheat have been ground into flour for cooking. Kinetic energy from flowing rivers helped to turned huge stones in watermills. Windmills used kinetic energy from the wind.

The energy from flowing water and the wind are **renewable energy resources**, which will never be used up.

? **1** Why is energy from the wind called a renewable energy resource?

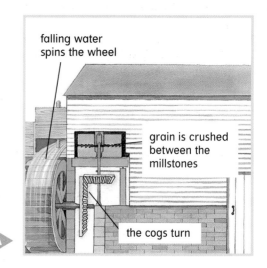

falling water spins the wheel

grain is crushed between the millstones

the cogs turn

A

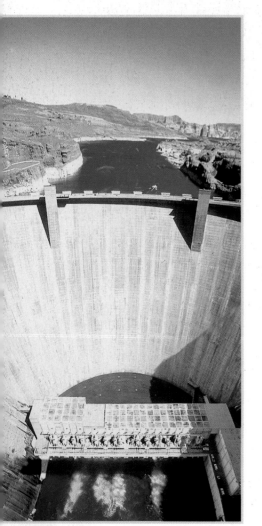

Gravitational potential energy can be stored in reservoirs for later use. **B**

Hydroelectric power

When rivers flow into a lake behind a dam, they fill reservoirs with large amounts of water.

- The water has gravitational potential energy.
- This energy changes into kinetic energy when the water falls through pipes.
- The pipes contain turbines which spin as the water rushes through.
- The turbines spin generators.
- The generators change the kinetic energy into electrical energy.
- This is called **hydroelectric power**.

? **2** Copy this energy flow diagram. Complete the missing energy transfers inside the hydroelectric scheme:

| ____ energy | → | ____ energy | → | ____ energy |

P How would you investigate what is the best design for a waterwheel? Test your idea by using it to lift a small mass.

! Dams can be dangerous. Tens of thousands of people were killed in India when a dam burst in 1979.

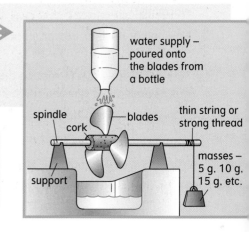

C

water supply – poured onto the blades from a bottle

spindle

cork

blades

thin string or strong thread

support

masses – 5 g, 10 g, 15 g. etc.

Tidal power

Energy is available from moving water in the sea. Twice a day, huge quantities of water flow in and out of the estuaries as **tides** go in and out.

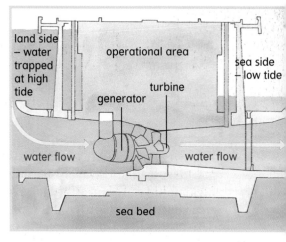

- Dams, called **barrages**, trap water at high tide.
- After the tide goes out, gates in the barrage are opened.
- Water rushes out through pipes, spinning turbines in the pipes.
- These turbines turn the generators, creating electricity.
- When the tide comes in, water rushes in and the turbines spin the other way.

D The gravitational pull of the Moon and Sun provides the energy needed to produce electricity!

3 In a tidal scheme gravitational potential energy is converted to electrical energy. How is this achieved?

Problems

Hydroelectric power and tidal power both use **renewable** energy resources. Although no pollution is produced, there are problems.

In hydroelectric schemes, whole valleys are flooded using large dams, destroying farming and forestry land.

E Tidal barrage in France.

In tidal schemes, huge barrages across river mouths are needed, permanently flooding large areas of river estuaries. This destroys the habitats of wading birds and other wildlife. Very few places have tides that are strong enough for a tidal scheme.

4 In a tidal scheme, describe where:
  a) gravitational potential energy is changed into kinetic energy
  b) kinetic energy is changed into electrical energy.

5 Hydroelectric power stations are usually built in mountainous regions with narrow, deep valleys. Why is this the best place for them?

6 Give one advantage and one disadvantage each for tidal schemes and hydroelectric power.

7 Hydroelectric and tidal schemes do not use fuel. Explain why people still have to pay for the electricity they produce.

8 At a hydroelectric power station in Dinorwic, electricity is used to pump water up a mountain during the night. The stored water is then released to generate electricity during the day or during periods of high demand.

Explain why the electricity company regards this as a sensible thing to do.

Summary

A Explain how energy from the Sun is transferred to electrical energy by a hydroelectric power station.

B Explain how gravitational potential energy is transferred to electrical energy by a tidal power scheme.

Other renewable resources

What other renewable energy resources can we use?

The world's population is increasing. Technology is widespread and travel is easy but fossil and nuclear fuel supplies are running out. We have only used electricity for 100 years, but already billions of people depend on it. Using renewable energy resources like the wind, waves and the Sun will help our fossil and nuclear fuels last longer.

 1 Why do we need to develop renewable energy resources?

Wind power

When a strong wind blows, the fast moving air turns large blades on **wind turbines**. This spins the generator, producing electricity. Groups of wind turbines work best in windy places like hilltops and coastlines so that the wind can turn the blades easily. There are problems though:

- Many people think wind turbines are ugly and they are noisy. They cause visual and noise pollution.
- The amount of electricity produced changes with the amount of wind.
- If it is calm, no electricity is produced.
- Wind turbines must stop in storms to prevent them being damaged.

 2 Wind turbines are described as an unreliable energy source. Why is this?

Geothermal power

In some volcanic areas, steam is produced naturally underground. It is piped when it reaches the surface, and used to turn turbines directly. This renewable energy resource is called geothermal power. The underground rocks are hot because radioactive elements in them, including uranium, produce heat as radioactive decay occurs.

A *A group of wind turbines like this is called a wind farm.*

P How would you find out what is the best design for a wind turbine? The electricity is produced using a small generator (called a dynamo). **B**

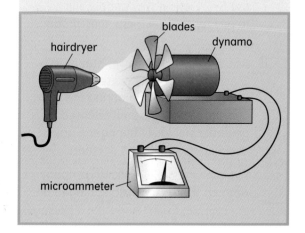

Wave power

It is possible to get energy from **waves**. Small rafts move up and down with the water. This movement can be used to turn small turbines, which generate electricity. However, the amounts of electricity which can be produced at the moment are too small to be useful.

Solar power

When sunlight shines on **solar cells**, they convert energy into electricity. Solar cells are useful:

- in sunny, remote places
- on satellites many miles away from Earth
- if very small amounts of electricity are needed, e.g. in watches or calculators.

3 Why are solar cells more useful than mains electricity in very remote locations?

There are some problems with solar cells:

- Many solar cells are needed to generate reasonable amounts of electricity.
- They are very expensive.
- The amount of electricity produced depends on the amount of sunlight.
- If it is not sunny, little or no electricity is produced.

4 Draw an energy flow diagram for geothermal power.

5 Solar panels can take a long time to repay their installation costs. Give two reasons why this is so.

6 What are the problems with using wave power?

7 The table below gives information about the estimated costs of generating electricity in the UK in the year 2025.

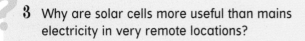

This is the world's first wave power station. It is on the coast of Islay in Scotland. **C**

Solar power is used on Earth and in space. **D**

Summary

List the advantages and disadvantages of generating electricity from: wind power, geothermal power, wave power, solar power.

Energy source	Solar cells in buildings	Offshore wind	Onshore wind	Biomass from crops	Wave
Cost per kWh (pence)	7.0	2.8	3.4	4.0	4.0

a) Draw a bar chart to display this information.
b) Why is there a difference between onshore wind and offshore wind?
c) Why will it not be practical for all the UK's electricity to be generated from the cheapest renewable energy resource in the year 2025?
d) It is estimated that sunnier countries will be able to generate electricity from solar cells for about 2 pence per kilowatt-hour in the year 2025. Why will it be cheaper than in the UK?

Fuels for electricity

What is the best method for producing electricity?

The amount of energy that we use can vary. In summer, less energy is needed for heat and light. However, every evening, many people cook meals, watch TV and put the kettle on. TV schedules and the time of day provide important information for power station engineers so that they can control the amount of electricity available.

 1 Look at graph A. Explain the variations in power output during a typical summer's day.

The best energy resource to use:

- does not pollute or affect the environment
- is plentiful, cheap and local
- provides the energy required when we want it.

The best power stations are:

- cheap to build
- safe to use
- easy and quick to stop and start.

In reality, no energy resource provides all of these. In the UK, we use a variety of energy resources.

 2 Look at the information shown in pie chart B. What percentage of the UK's electricity did non-renewable energy resources provide in 1999?

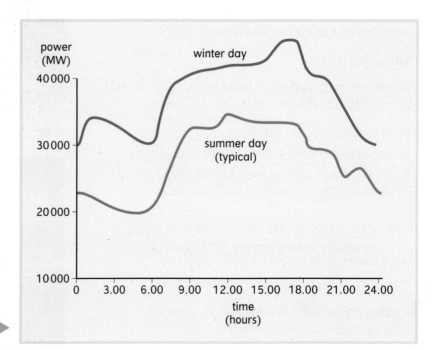

A

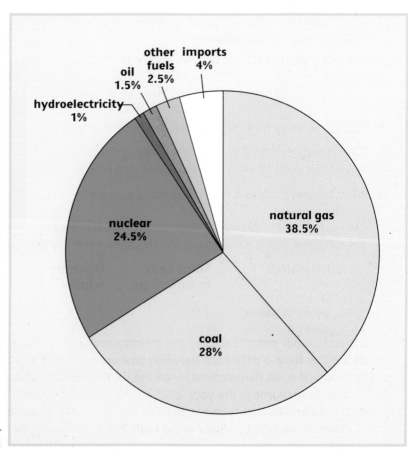

How the UK's electricity was provided in 1999. **B**

Each type has advantages and disadvantages.

Fossil fuel power stations:

- can use coal which is cheap and plentiful.
- can use natural gas efficiently.
- can use oil, but oil is expensive and oil reserves have other important uses so oil is not used much.
- can take hours to start and stop, so they cannot provide extra electricity quickly. Natural gas stations can start the quickest, then oil, and finally coal-fired stations.

Nuclear power stations:

- run all the time because it takes so long to stop and start them (much longer than fossil fuel power stations).

C *The dots in the top right of the screen warn engineers to expect a surge in demand during adverts.*

3 List these power stations in order, starting with the one that is quickest to start generating electricity: nuclear, oil, coal, natural gas, hydroelectric.

Power stations using renewable sources:

- Hydroelectricity provides electricity very quickly. The stations are used for surges in demand, for example during TV adverts when kettles are switched on!
- Hydroelectricity schemes can use spare energy produced by other power stations to pump water back into its reservoirs.
- Tidal schemes can provide energy in minutes if the tide is at the right part of its cycle. This varies with the time of day. The height of the tide varies too, depending on the month and the time of year.

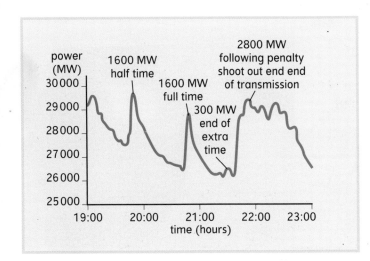

D *The demand for electricity during the 1990 England-Germany World Cup semi-final. Kettles and lights being turned on caused the peaks in demand.*

4 Write down one reason why fossil and nuclear fuels provide most of our energy.

5 Write sentences explaining why:
- **a)** oil is not used much
- **b)** tidal schemes are not used for sudden surges in demand
- **c)** nuclear power is used all the time.

6 Nuclear fuel is cheap but some countries have decided not to replace the nuclear power stations they close down with new ones. What are the economic and safety arguments for and against this decision?

Summary

Draw a table to compare the following ways of producing electricity against the features of a good power station: coal, nuclear, tidal, wind, solar, hydroelectric. Features to use include: little pollution, cheap to run, cheap to build the power station, ability to provide electricity on demand.

Energy losses

How is energy wasted?

Two friends are out for a cycle ride. Josh's bike is brand new and its pedals turn easily, the wheels go round quietly and the chain doesn't rub. Sam's bike is older and much harder to ride. The wheels get hot as they rub against the brake pads, the pedals squeak as they turn, and the chain catches as he rides.

 1 While Sam's bicycle is moving, it releases two other forms of energy. What are they?

 A

Whenever energy is transferred, only part of it ends up in the form that is wanted. Some energy is wasted in the form of unwanted sound or heat. Eventually the **wasted energy** spreads out to the surroundings. It is very hard to re-use wasted energy once it has spread out.

 2 Sam's bike converts 61% of the energy supplied into kinetic energy. For every 100 J of energy that Sam gives to the pedals, how much energy is wasted?

 Water at the bottom of a waterfall is slightly warmer than at the top. However, this heat energy cannot be used as the temperature difference is very small.

B When the balloon pops, its elastic potential energy is lost to the surroundings as sound.

Wasted energy is usually in the form of heat or sound. For example, washing machines and vacuum cleaners make a noise while they are being used.

Other items that make a noise include cars and lorries, squeaky hinges and banging doors. You can feel warmth from computers and lamps when they are switched on. Car engines and tools like saws and drills become hot when they are used.

heat
sound
chemical energy
kinetic energy

C

 3 Draw an energy flow diagram for a motorbike. Include the wasted energy in your flow diagram.

P How many forms of unwanted energy can you identify when these objects are used?

D

E

Summary

A motorbike converts about 90% of the chemical energy from its fuel into heat energy. About 6% of the energy is transferred to kinetic energy and the rest to sound energy. Use this as an example to explain the terms 'useful energy' and 'wasted energy'. Include a Sankey diagram in your notes.

The diagram below shows a Sankey diagram for a light bulb.

F

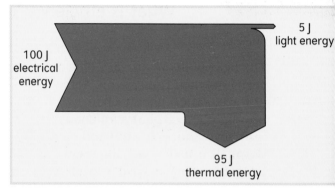

100 J electrical energy

5 J light energy

95 J thermal energy

The width of each arrow is in proportion to the amount of energy it represents. The arrow pointing to the right shows the useful energy produced and the arrow pointing down shows wasted energy.

?

4 Light bulbs are sometimes used to heat small insect houses. Draw a Sankey diagram to represent a light bulb being used for this purpose.

5 Copy and complete table G for the following items: lamp, hairdryer, bicycle, lawnmower, kettle, bus.

G

Item	Forms of energy given out	Wanted energy	Wasted energy

6 Write down two ways to cut down on wasted energy transfers on a bicycle.

7 An electric drill like the one in photograph E might convert 40% of the electrical energy supplied into kinetic energy. 55% of the energy might be wasted as heat energy and the rest wasted as sound energy.

Copy and complete the Sankey diagram below:

H

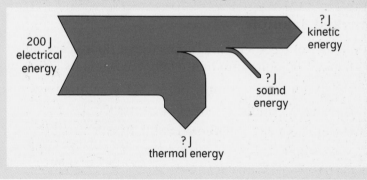

200 J electrical energy

? J kinetic energy

? J sound energy

? J thermal energy

Efficiency

What is efficiency?

A *Fluorescent lights in a supermarket.*

The light bulbs we use at home get very hot when they are on. Some of the electrical energy changes into light energy, but a lot changes into heat. Shops, schools and hospitals usually use fluorescent lights because they cost less to run as less electricity is wasted as heat.

Some equipment transfers energy better than others. **Efficient** equipment transfers a lot of the supplied energy into the forms of energy we want. Fluorescent lights are more efficient than filament bulbs because they change more electricity into light.

B *Filament bulb in a house.*

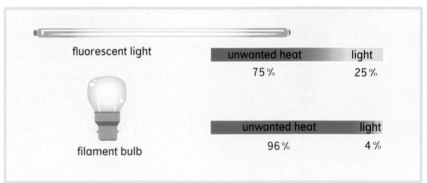

C

fluorescent light	unwanted heat	light
	75%	25%

filament bulb	unwanted heat	light
	96%	4%

? **1** If 500 joules of electrical energy were supplied to the fluorescent light in diagram C, how many joules of light energy would be produced?

E The fraction of energy *usefully* transferred is the equipment's efficiency.

The efficiency can be worked out if you know:

- how much useful energy comes out of the equipment
- how much energy is supplied to the equipment.

efficiency of the equipment = useful energy coming out ÷ total energy supplied
(in **joules**, J)   (in **joules**, J)

Worked example

100 joules of electricity are supplied to a fluorescent light. It changes 25 joules into light energy. What is its **efficiency**?

- The useful energy coming out is 25 J of light energy.
- The energy supplied is 100 J of electricity.
- The efficiency of the fluorescent light is:

25 J ÷ 100 J

= 0.25

! Blackpool illuminations now use energy efficient bulbs, saving thousands of pounds each year.

A 100 W light bulb only changes 4 joules per second into light, so its efficiency is 0.04. More electricity is needed by filament bulbs to provide the same amount of light as fluorescent lights. You can find out which equipment is the most efficient by comparing the amount of energy they use to do the same job.

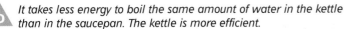

D It takes less energy to boil the same amount of water in the kettle than in the saucepan. The kettle is more efficient.

P

E

? 2 Put these different types of light bulb in order with the most efficient first:

filament bulb, efficiency = 0.04
fluorescent light, efficiency = 0.25
energy efficient bulb, efficiency = 0.16.

3 A petrol engine produces 7 joules of kinetic energy for every 100 joules supplied.
a) Calculate the efficiency of this engine.
b) What other forms of energy will the engine produce?

! Six times more energy is needed to produce an electrical cell than the energy you can get out of it.

How would you compare the efficiency of different kinds of bouncing ball? How high does each ball bounce?

? 4 A food mixer was described as being 35% efficient. What does this mean?

5 The information below shows the energy transfers for a crane lifting a load.

Energy supplied to the crane: 240 kJ
Gravitational potential energy gained by
the load: 72 kJ
Sound energy produced: 18 kJ
Heat energy produced: ?? kJ

a) How much heat energy will be produced?
b) Calculate the efficiency of the crane.

Summary

A Explain what is meant by the term 'efficiency'.

B Explain the importance of making machines as efficient as possible.

Further questions

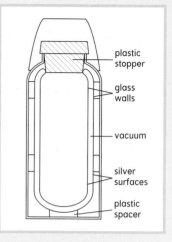

plastic
stopper

glass
walls

vacuum

silver
surfaces

plastic
spacer

1 This diagram shows part of an electricity bill

> **HARLOW ELECTRICITY COMPANY**
>
> Account number: 0164271
> Account date: 15 July 2003
>
> **Charges for electricity**
>
> Date | Reading
> 11 July 2003 | 65128
> 11 April 2003 | 64123
>
> Cost per Unit: 6.4 pence

a) How much did each Unit of electricity cost? (1)

b) How many Units were used in the period from April until July? (1)

c) How much did the electricity used cost? (1)

2 Here are the results of an experiment to find out how to keep a drink warm for the longest.

Exp.	Beaker	Starting temperature	Temperature after 5 min
A	no lid, no foil, no insulation	80 °C	60 °C
B	lid (no foil, no insulation)	80 °C	65 °C
C	foil (no lid, no insulation)	80 °C	68 °C
D	insulation (no lid, no foil)	80 °C	73 °C

a) List *three* things the student should have done to make sure it was a fair test. (3)

b) What type of heat transfer is she stopping in each of experiments B, C and D? (3)

c) In which experiment was the heat loss biggest? (1)

d) Looking at her results, what one thing should she do to keep a drink as warm as possible? (1)

3 This diagram shows a vacuum flask, designed to keep drinks hot.

This table compares the ways that heat is transferred in the flask. Write down what should go in boxes **a)** to **d)**. (4)

Type of heat transfer	Takes place mainly through	Can be stopped in a vacuum flask by using
conduction	a)	b)
convection	c)	d)
radiation	empty space (vacuum)	shiny coating on the glass

e) Use ideas about particles to explain how heat is conducted through solids. (2)

f) Explain how convection can transfer heat through liquids. (2)

4 The table shows ways that a house may be insulated.

Where heat is lost	How heat loss can be reduced	Cost of reducing the heat loss	Amount saved each year
floor	lay carpets	£600	£150
door	draught proofing	£10	£100
roof	install fibreglass loft insulation	£350	£300

a) Explain how fibreglass insulation helps to reduce the heat loss from the roof. (1)

b) Explain which method of insulation would save you money quickest. (2)

c) Copy and complete these sentences using words from the box. You may use each word once, more than once, or not at all.

Gaps underneath doors allow heat to escape by ____. Carpets are made from good ____. They stop heat escaping by ____. (3)

> cold   conductors   conduction
> convection   heat   insulators   radiation

5 Look at these ways of generating electricity:

> hydroelectricity   wind power   oil
> wave power   tidal power

a) Explain why oil is the odd one out. (2)

b) Many people would like us to use renewable energy resources more often. Explain one benefit of this. (1)

c) State *one* reason why each of the energy resources listed below is not used more often:

    i) tidal power   ii) wave power

    iii) solar power. (3)

6 The diagram below shows a power station.

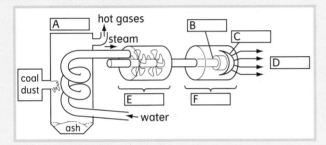

When a fuel is burned in the **furnace**, the heat released is used to change water into steam. The jet of steam forces a **turbine** to spin. The shaft of the turbine is connected to a **generator**, consisting of a **magnet** surrounded by **coils of wire**. The magnet spins. This generates **electrical energy** in the coils which can then be carried to homes and businesses.

a) Which of the bold words in the passage should go in each of the boxes A to F? (6)

b) Energy is changed into different forms in the power station. Copy and complete the table using words from the box. You may use each word once, more than once, or not at all. (4)

Part of the power station	Energy type that the part has
fuel	
heated water	
spinning turbine	
cables	

> chemical   electrical   gravitational
> potential   heat   kinetic   light   sound

7 Look at this table comparing three fridges.

Fridge	Price	Annual running cost	Efficiency rating
A	£120	£30	0.7
B	£109	£38	0.6
C	£170	£24	0.9

a) Explain what is meant by efficiency. (1)

b) Which fridge is most efficient? (1)

c) When you buy a fridge, it is important to compare the running costs as well as the price. Calculate the running costs for each fridge over 3 years. (3)

d) Explain which fridge would be cheapest over 3 years. (2)

8 The power of a hairdryer is 1.6 kW

a) How many joules of energy will it transfer each second? (1)

b) How many joules of energy will it transfer in 5 minutes? (1)

c) How many kilowatt-hours of energy will it use in 5 minutes? (1)

9 A computer monitor has a power rating of 120 W. Calculate how much it would cost to leave the monitor switched on for 12 hours. Assume electricity costs 8 pence per kilowatt-hour. (3)

10 The table below shows the energy transfers for a television when it was switched on for 30 minutes.

electrical energy supplied	300 kJ
light energy produced	20 kJ
sound energy produced	5 kJ
thermal energy produced	275 kJ

a) Calculate the power of the television. (2)

b) Draw a Sankey diagram to show these energy transfers. (2)

c) Calculate the efficiency of the television. (1)

Voltage and current

What are current and voltage?

Electricity plays an important part in our everyday lives. Think what life would be like without electricity: no television, computers, telephones or electric lights. Electricity is one of a number of different types of energy. We often refer to electricity as **electrical energy**. Different components or devices are designed to convert electrical energy from one form into another form. A television converts electrical energy into light and sound as useful forms and heat as a wasted form. Usually, electrical energy is converted into heat, light, sound or kinetic energy.

Everything around us is made up of **atoms**. The nucleus of the atom contains positively charged protons as well as neutrons that have no charge. Negatively charged particles, called **electrons**, surround the nucleus. When electrons move we say that there is an electric **current**. The more electrons flowing per second, the bigger the current. Current is measured in **amperes** (or **amps**). The symbol for amps is A.

 1 In a radio, what type of useful energy is electrical energy changed into?

2 An electric motor converts electrical energy into kinetic energy as a useful form. How is some of the electrical energy wasted by the motor?

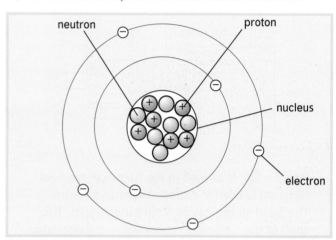

A *An atom has a nucleus at the centre, which contains protons and neutrons. Tiny electrons orbit around the nucleus.*

B *Electrons leave the negative side of the cell and are attracted round to the positive side of the cell.*

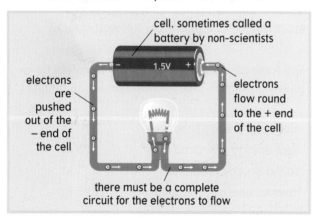

Metals are good **conductors** of electricity because electrons in metals are free to move. Electrons will only flow in a **circuit** when they are given electrical energy. This energy is often provided by an electrical **cell**. The cell provides the electrons with a 'push' to get them going. This push is called a **potential difference** (**p.d.**) or a **voltage**. The bigger the potential difference, the greater the flow of electrons and therefore the bigger the current. Potential difference or voltage is measured in **volts**. The symbol for volts is **V**.

C *Electrons can flow along a metal wire.*

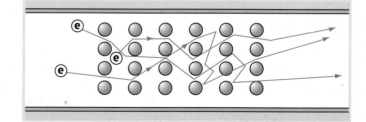

When scientists originally started to look at electricity they thought that it was a flow of positive charges that moved from positive to negative. This is called **conventional current**. We now know that electrons flow from negative to positive.

Scientists use symbols to draw circuit diagrams. Diagram E shows some of the symbols. When all the components are on a single circuit they are said to be in **series**.

3 Draw a circuit diagram containing two bulbs, a battery and an open switch arranged in series.

Cells in series

Different devices need different voltages to work, so more than one cell has to be used. Two or more cells used together are called a **battery**. When connected end to end they are in series.

If two cells are connected so that they push in the same direction then their voltages are added together. If they are pushing in opposite directions then they cancel each other out.

Summary

Explain what all of the words in bold mean on these two pages.

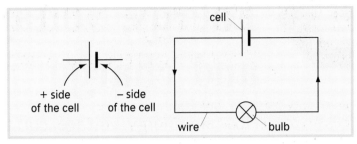

 D A circuit diagram. The arrows show current. Electron flow is actually in the opposite direction to conventional current. Don't get the two mixed up.

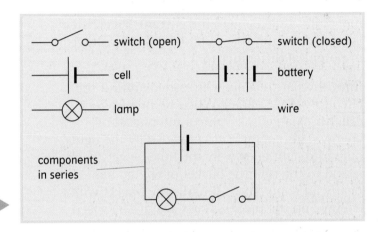

E

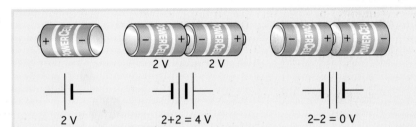

F

4 What are the possible voltages you could get by arranging four 1.5 V cells in series?

5 How many 1.5 V cells would you need to run a 9 V radio?

6 Look at diagram G. Each cell has a voltage of 1.5 V. Work out how much voltage each combination would give you:

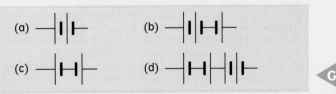

(a)　(b)　(c)　(d)

G

7 You can explain what current and voltage are to a friend by using a simple model of water flowing through a hosepipe. How would you do it?

Energy, voltage, current and charge

How are energy, voltage, current and charge related?

Electrical energy is carried around a circuit by negatively charged electrons. A large 'bundle' of electrons make up the **charge**. When the charge moves it is called an electric **current**. The charge is pushed around the circuit by the cell **voltage** or **potential difference** (**p.d.**).

Imagine that the energy is carried around the circuit by 'Mr Charge'. When he first leaves the cell, Mr Charge is carrying a full bucket of energy. This energy gets converted by the light bulb into light energy. By the time he gets back round to the cell, the bucket of energy has nearly all gone. The cell refills the bucket with energy and the process starts again. The speed at which Mr. Charge moves around the circuit does not depend on the amount of electrical energy that he is carrying, he just moves around at a constant speed and the energy in the bucket gets changed into other forms.

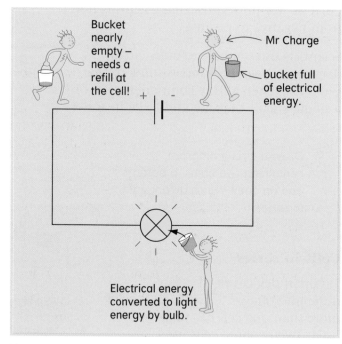

Bucket nearly empty – needs a refill at the cell!

Mr Charge

bucket full of electrical energy.

Electrical energy converted to light energy by bulb.

A

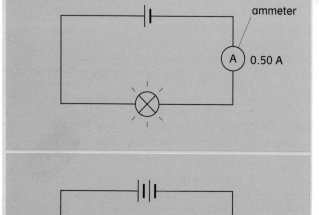

ammeter

A 0.50 A

A 1.00 A

We measure current with an **ammeter**. The ammeter is arranged in the main part of the circuit in **series**. The *more charge* that flows through the ammeter each second, the *bigger* the current. The unit of electrical charge is the **coulomb** (**C**).

B

1 a) What instrument is used to measure current?

b) How is it connected in the circuit?

2 a) What is the unit of electrical charge?

b) What is its symbol?

E The charge in a circuit can be worked out if you know:

- the current (in amps)
- the time the current flows for (in seconds).

charge	=	current	×	time
(in **coulombs**, **C**)		(in **amps**, **A**)		(in **seconds**, **s**)

Note: Q is often used as a shorthand way of writing 'charge'. I is used to represent current.

The amount of energy that is carried around a circuit depends on the amount of charge flowing and the voltage. With a greater voltage and greater amount of charge, more energy can be transferred. We use a **voltmeter** to measure voltage or potential difference. The voltmeter is always arranged in **parallel**, across the component.

E You can work out the energy in a circuit if you know:

- the charge (in coulombs)
- the voltage (in volts).

energy	=	charge	×	voltage
(in **joules**, **J**)		(in **coulombs**, **C**)		(in **volts**, **V**)

3 a) How much charge will pass a point in a circuit if 2.5 A flows for 5 seconds?

b) What is the current flowing if 35 C of charge flows in 7 seconds?

4 How long would it take for 48 000 C to pass through an ammeter if 4.2 A is flowing in the circuit? Give your answer in seconds.

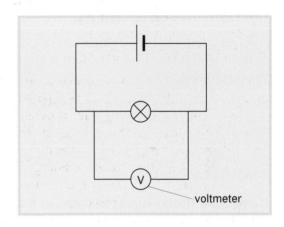

C We say that the voltmeter is in parallel as it is in its own branch of the circuit.

5 How much energy does a motor receive if a voltage of 12 V pushes 8.5 C of charge through it?

6 A radio receives 350 J of electrical energy and it uses four 1.5 V cells. How much charge has passed through the radio?

7 You want to find the current through a bulb and the voltage across it. What apparatus would you use? Draw a circuit diagram to show how you would set it up.

8 A current of 0.5 A flows through a bulb. The current is left on for 8 seconds and the voltage across the bulb is 6 V. Calculate:
a) the charge that has passed through the bulb
b) the energy that the bulb has converted.

9 Why does an electric oven require such a large current compared to other household appliances?

Summary

Before electrical goods can leave a factory they are tested to make sure they are working properly. Write a set of instructions for testing a CD player, explaining how the current and voltage should be tested. Explain how the amount of charge and energy can be worked out from these measurements.

Series circuits

What happens to voltage and current in a series circuit?

All electrical circuits can be divided into two main groups:

- **series** circuits
- **parallel** circuits.

Currents in series circuits

A series circuit has only one route for the current to travel round. Diagram A shows two examples.

In each circuit the current must travel through all of the components. If a current of 3 A leaves the cell, then a current of 3 A will travel through the light bulb, wires and ammeter back to the cell.

If one bulb in the circuit in diagram B breaks then there will be a gap in the circuit, so the current cannot flow. We call this an **open circuit**. Any other bulbs in the circuit will go out.

> **Rule 1:** *In a series circuit the current is the same all the way round the circuit.*

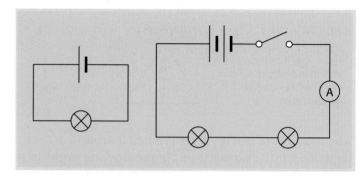

A

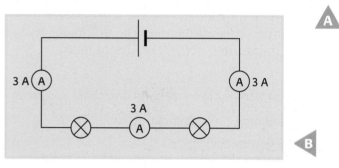

B

1 If the current leaving one end of a cell is 5 A, what will the current be when it is returning to the other end of the cell?

2 If there are two bulbs in a series circuit and one of them breaks, what will happen to the other bulb?

Voltage in a series circuit

The potential difference provided by the cell gives the electrons energy. The moving electrons transfer this energy to the other components in the circuit. The electrons transfer some energy to each component as they pass through, so that by the time they return to the cell they have given up all of their energy.

Look at diagram C. In circuit X, a voltage of 6 V is provided by the cell. The current delivers half of its energy to each bulb, as they are identical. Each bulb will have 3 V across it.

In circuit Y there are three identical bulbs so the 6 V will be divided equally between the three. Each bulb will have a voltage of 2 V across it.

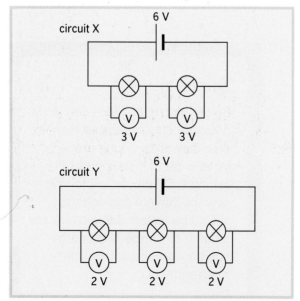

C

Rule 2: *In a series circuit the potential difference (voltage) is shared between the components in the circuit.*

In the examples in diagram C the bulbs are identical, so the voltage is shared equally between them. In some circuits the components are different and the voltage may not be shared out equally.

D

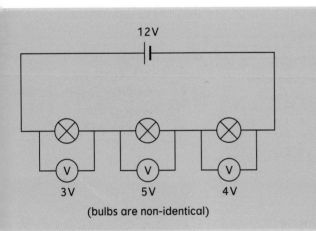

(bulbs are non-identical)

Summary
Draw fully labelled circuit diagrams to show how voltage and current behave in a series circuit.

How can you show that the two series circuit rules are correct?

3 A cell in a series circuit has a potential difference of 3 V. If there are two identical bulbs in the circuit, what is the voltage across each bulb?

4 Look at diagram E. Work out the correct currents and voltages where there are question marks. (All the bulbs are identical.)

E

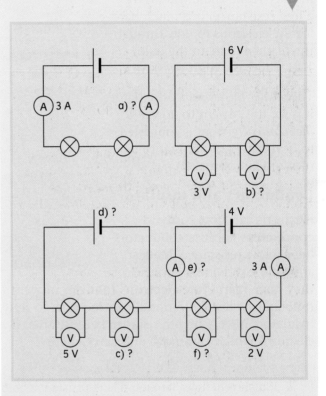

5 A 6 V cell operates two bulbs in a series circuit. The first bulb uses twice as much energy as the second bulb. Draw the circuit, showing the value of the voltage across each bulb.

Resistance

Why do electrons need energy to move around a circuit?

Electrons need energy to move around a circuit.

Resistance is a way of saying how easy or difficult it is for electrons to flow through something. Look at diagram A. It is easy for electrons to flow along the connecting wires in the circuit. These wires have a **low resistance**. It is much harder for the electrons to flow through the filament wire in the bulb. This wire has a **high resistance**.

The *greater the resistance* the harder it is for the current to flow and *the more energy* that is converted to heat and light. Resistance is measured in **ohms** (Ω).

Conductors and insulators

Electrons can flow easily in **conductors** because conductors have a low resistance. Metals are good conductors because they have many **free electrons** that can move. **Insulators**, such as rubber and plastic, do not allow electrons to flow through them. Insulators have a high resistance because they do not have any free electrons which can move and carry energy.

 A

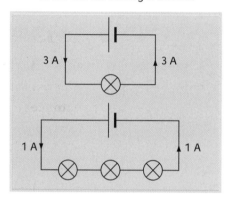

The current has only a small amount of energy left to travel back to the cell.

Current leaves the cell with plenty of energy.

A small amount of energy is changed to heat energy as electrons flow through the wires.

The thin filament wire in the bulb is much harder for electrons to travel through. The electrons change nearly all their energy into heat and light travelling through the bulb.

B *The three-bulb circuit has more resistance so the current flowing is smaller.*

? **1** Where do the electrons get their energy from in a circuit?

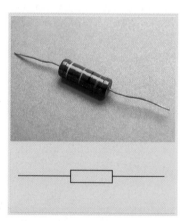

 C *A resistor and its symbol.*

? **2** If a current flows through a high resistance bulb and then through a low resistance buzzer, where will the electrons give up most of their energy?

Resistors in series

Every component has a resistance. Look at diagram B. There are three times as many bulbs in the second circuit, so there is three times the resistance.

A **resistor** is a component that decreases the current in a circuit. When electricity flows through a resistor, some of the electrical energy is transferred as heat energy.

When resistors are connected in series their resistances can be *added* together to give the total resistance in the circuit.

D *The total resistance in this circuit is 6 Ω.*

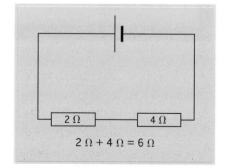

$2\,\Omega + 4\,\Omega = 6\,\Omega$

3 What is a resistor?

4 If each bulb has a resistance of 20 Ω, what is the total resistance of a series circuit with:

  a) 2 bulbs in it

  b) 4 bulbs in it?

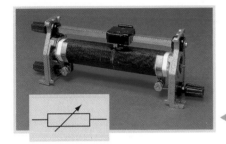

A variable resistor is used in circuits when you want to change the resistance in the circuit easily.

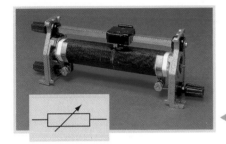

E

P How would you find out whether different lengths of wire have different resistances?

5 What is the voltage across a 10 Ω resistor with a 2 A current flowing through it?

6 True or false? A piece of nylon thread has a higher resistance than a piece of copper wire. Explain your answer.

7 A current of 2.5 A flows through a resistor when the voltage across its ends is 12 V. What is the resistance of the resistor?

Summary

You are asked to work out the resistance of a coin. Make a list of any apparatus you would need and draw the circuit diagram. State which equation you will need.

Changing currents

A component with a large resistance needs a bigger voltage to push a certain current through it. If the voltage is not increased then the current will be smaller. Look at diagram F.

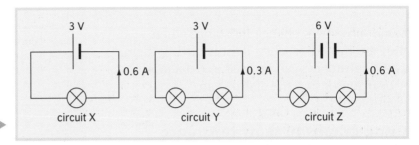

F

Circuit Y has twice the resistance of circuit X. However, there is no extra cell voltage and so the current is halved.

Circuit Z has twice the resistance of circuit X and also has twice the cell voltage so the current stays the same.

E The resistance (R) can be worked out if you know:

● the voltage (V) across the component (in volts)

● the current (I) flowing through the component (in amps).

$$\text{resistance (in ohms, } \Omega) = \frac{\text{voltage (in volts, V)}}{\text{current (in amps, A)}}$$

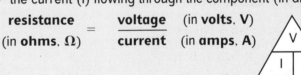

If the voltage across a resistor doubles, the current through the resistor will double. If the voltage becomes three times as big, the current must be three times as big. This means the current flowing through the resistor is said to be **proportional** to the voltage across it.

8 When the voltage across a particular resistor is 15 V, the current flowing through it is 3A. What will the size of the current be if the voltage is now increased to 20 V?

9 Resistance depends on a number of variables. One variable is the length of the wire that is being used in the circuit. When the length of a wire is 20 cm, its resistance is 12 Ω. What do you think the resistance will be when the length of the wire is increased to 50 cm? Explain your answer.

10 Resistors with very high values (1000 Ω or more) are often used in electronic circuits to protect very delicate components like transistors. How do they do this?

Current-voltage graphs

What happens when the current in a component changes?

Some substances change resistance when they are heated or when light is hitting them. These substances can be used as detectors. A heat sensor in a fire alarm is an example of this.

Using graphs to show resistance

We can use graphs to see how much resistance a component has.

Graph A shows what happens to the current through two resistors X and Y as the voltage across them changes. The *slope* of the line represents their *resistance*. The *steeper* the line the *lower* the resistance.

 1 Look at graph A. Which resistor, X or Y, has the greatest resistance?

The lines on graph A are straight, which shows that the resistance of a resistor stays the same (constant). The temperature of the resistor must also stay the same.

Current–voltage graph for a light bulb

Most components do not have a constant resistance. As the current going through them increases, the resistance changes. On a graph of current against voltage, the line will not be straight. If the resistance is *decreasing* the line will become *steeper* (curve upwards). If the resistance is *increasing* the line will become *less steep* (become flatter).

The thin wire in a light bulb is called the **filament**. As the voltage and current get bigger the filament wire becomes hot. The heat energy makes the particles in the wire vibrate more, making it harder for the electrons to travel through the wire. This makes the resistance increase, so the line becomes *less steep*. The hotter the filament gets the higher its resistance.

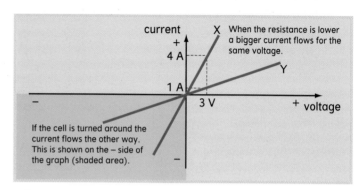

A *Resistors at constant temperature.*

B *Decreasing resistance.*   *Increasing resistance.* **C**

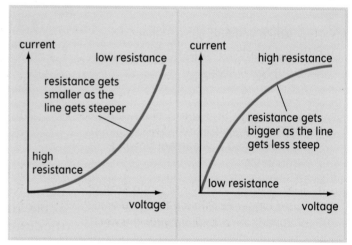

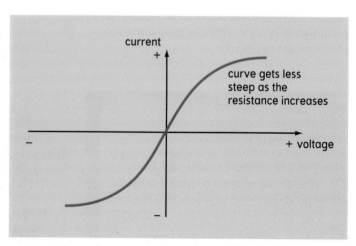

D *A current–voltage graph for a light bulb.*

Current–voltage graph for a diode

A diode is a special component that only lets current flow through it in one direction. When the current is in this direction the diode behaves just like a resistor. If the current tries to flow the other way the diode's resistance becomes extremely high so the current cannot flow.

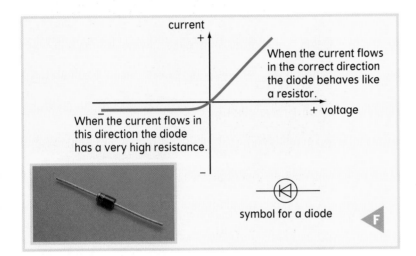

When the current flows in the correct direction the diode behaves like a resistor.

When the current flows in this direction the diode has a very high resistance.

symbol for a diode

F

Some components change resistance for other reasons:

- The resistance of a light dependent resistor decreases if the amount of light shining on it increases. It is affected by the intensity of light.
- The resistance of a thermistor decreases if it gets hotter. It is affected by temperature.

P How would you draw the current–voltage graph for a piece of wire? What circuit would you need to set up to find the measurements you need?

4 The resistance of a metal increases when the current increases. Explain why this happens in a metal using ideas about particle theory.

5 Draw a graph of resistance against temperature for a thermistor.

6 The resistance of a metal wire increases as it gets hotter but the resistance of a thermistor decreases as it gets hotter. Why does this happen? (*Hint:* What does the heat energy do to the electrons in the thermistor?)

7 The resistance of an L.D.R. decreases as the light intensity increases. Why does this happen?

2 Graph E shows the current–voltage relationship for an electric heater.

  a) Is the resistance getting higher or lower as the voltage increases?

  b) Up to what voltage does the resistance remain constant?

E

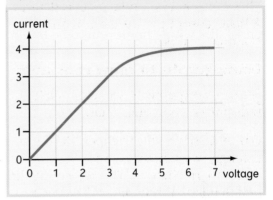

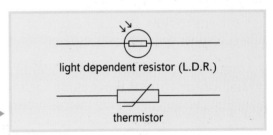

light dependent resistor (L.D.R.)

thermistor

G

3 Name one component that normally has a constant resistance, and two components where the resistance changes when the current changes.

Summary

A Draw a labelled graph to show how the voltage affects the resistance of a resistor, a light bulb and a diode.

B The resistance of components can be affected by temperature and light intensity. Explain how this is true for a bulb, a thermistor and an L.D.R.

Parallel circuits

What happens to voltage and current in a parallel circuit?

A

Parallel circuits are more useful than series circuits. If there are two bulbs in a series circuit they both have to be switched on and off at the same time. This would not be very useful at home. If one bulb broke, the whole house would be left in darkness! Parallel circuits solve problems like these.

 1 **a)** Are most Christmas tree lights in series or in parallel?

     b) How do you know?

Current in parallel circuits

In a parallel circuit there is more than one route for current to flow along. The current leaving the cell splits up and takes different routes.

In diagram B the circuit has two identical routes, so half of the current flows along each route.

$$2\ A + 2\ A = 4\ A$$

B

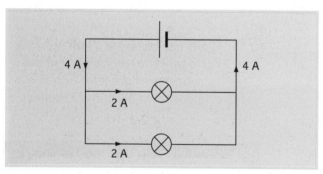

Rule 1: *The current in a parallel circuit splits to go down different routes. The total current through the cell is the sum of all the separate currents.*

 2 A parallel circuit has two identical routes. A total current of 10 A flows through the cell. How much current will flow along each route?

In diagram C the circuit has three identical routes so a third of the current flows along each route.

$$1\ A + 1\ A + 1\ A = 3\ A$$

C

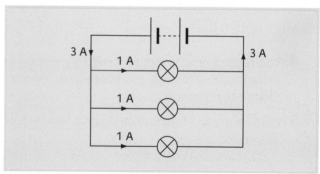

P How would you investigate what happens to the brightness of the bulbs as more are added in parallel to a circuit?

Voltage in parallel circuits

Electrons leaving the cell transfer all of their energy to the circuit before returning. It does not matter which route they take. This means that the voltage must be the same across each route. This is shown in diagram D.

> **Rule 2:** *In a parallel circuit the voltage is the same across each route.*

Routes with different resistances

Circuit E has two routes, with 6 V across each route. Now look at the currents. The top route has a bigger resistance, so a smaller current will flow through it than the bottom route. The current does not divide equally.

> **Rule 3:** *In a parallel circuit the current through a route depends on the resistance. If it has a big resistance only a small current will flow along it.*

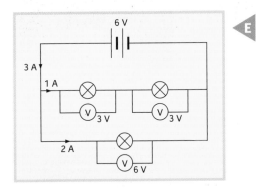

E

Summary

A Draw a table to compare the rules for current and voltage in parallel circuits with the rules for series circuits.

B Draw a table showing the advantages and disadvantages of parallel circuits compared with series circuits.

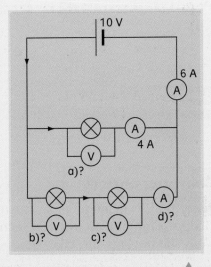

D

The current delivers 4 V to this lamp.

The current delivers 4 V to this lamp.

3 If a 4 V cell is placed in a parallel circuit with three routes, what is the voltage across each route?

4 Look at diagram F. Work out the correct currents and voltages where there are question marks. (All the bulbs are identical.)

5 Design a circuit that can switch on three bulbs separately. Your circuit must also be able to switch all the bulbs off with one switch.

F

6 Explain why a 6 V battery connected to one bulb will last longer than the same 6 V battery connected to three similar bulbs arranged in parallel. Refer to the words voltage, current, charge and energy in your answer.

7 What happens to the brightness of bulbs X and Y when bulb Z is unscrewed? Explain your answer.

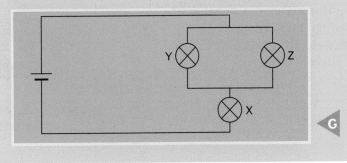

G

Static electricity

What is static electricity?

The first evidence for electrons and electric charge was discovered over 2500 years ago! When people talk about static electricity they tend to think about getting small electric shocks when they touch something. Clothes made from man-made (synthetic) substances, like nylon, often produce small crackling sounds when you take them off. This is caused by static electricity.

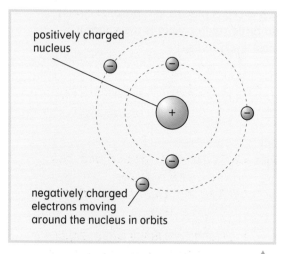

positively charged nucleus

negatively charged electrons moving around the nucleus in orbits

An atom.

P How could you make a stream of water bend, or make your hair stand on end?

? 1 When you take off clothing and hear the crackle of static electricity, what do you sometimes see? Picture A may help you answer this.

Charging objects

Everything is made up of atoms. The atom has a nucleus with electrons moving around it. **Electrons** can sometimes move away from the nucleus and take their negative charge with them.

Normally, objects have equal amounts of positive and negative charge. These charges cancel each other out, so the objects are **neutral**. When two surfaces are rubbed together, the friction can rub electrons off one surface onto the other. This leaves one surface with fewer electrons and the other with extra electrons.

Electrons have a negative charge, so an object that gains electrons becomes negatively charged and an object that loses electrons becomes positively charged.

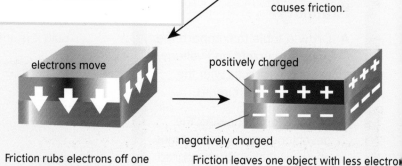

Rubbing surfaces causes friction.

electrons move

Friction rubs electrons off one surface onto the other.

positively charged

negatively charged

Friction leaves one object with less electron (positively charged) and the other object w extra electrons (negatively charged).

2 a) A balloon is rubbed on a jumper, and it becomes negatively charged. What charge is left on the jumper?

b) Have the electrons moved from the jumper onto the balloon, or from the balloon onto the jumper?

Attraction and repulsion

There are two types of charge, positive and negative. Two charged objects near each other will have a force between them. This force can be either attractive or repulsive.

Two positively charged objects will **repel** each other. Two negatively charged objects will repel each other. However, a positively charged object will **attract** a negatively charged object.

3 Copy the sets of spheres in diagram E, and draw arrows to show if they are attracting or repelling each other.

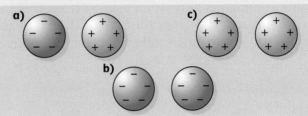

Rule: *Unlike charges attract. Like charges repel.*

Attracting objects with no charge

When a balloon is rubbed with a cloth, electrons can move from the cloth onto the balloon, giving the balloon a negative charge. If the balloon is now placed near to an uncharged wall, the electrons on the balloon will repel the electrons that are at the surface of the wall, leaving an overall positive charge at the surface of the wall. Since opposite charges attract, the balloon will now stick to the wall. This is an example of **electrostatic induction**.

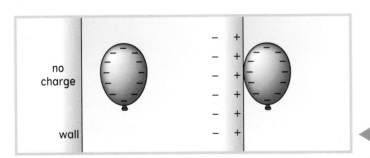

F

4 a) Explain how combing your hair can give it a charge.

b) Why does charged hair always 'stand on end'?

5 Explain how a tiny piece of paper can be picked up with a plastic rod. Refer to the movement of electrons in your answer.

6 David has a balloon that is positively charged and John has a balloon that is negatively charged. Tara says that she has a balloon that can repel both of their balloons. Is she right? Explain your answer. Would Tara be right if she said her balloon could attract the other balloons? Explain your answer.

Summary

Explain how you can make a balloon stick to a wall just by rubbing it. You must refer to the movement of electrons in your answer.

Using static electricity

How can static electricity be used safely?

There are about 100 lightning strikes per second on Earth! Lightning happens when clouds become charged with static electricity. The voltage this makes between the cloud and the ground can make a current flow through the air. The lightning produced can kill humans or animals that it hits.

Lightning conductors provide an easy path for charge to travel down to reach the Earth. This stops the current from damaging buildings. Diagram B shows how sparks like lightning can occur.

A *Charge builds up on clouds. If the amount of charge gets large enough, the charge will jump from the cloud to the Earth as lightning.*

B

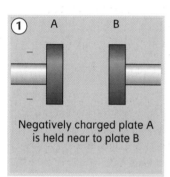

① Negatively charged plate A is held near to plate B

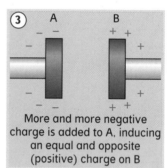

② A *positive* charge is induced on plate B

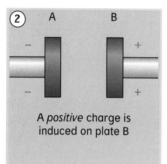

③ More and more negative charge is added to A, inducing an equal and opposite (positive) charge on B

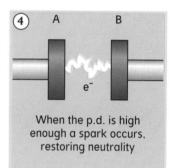

④ When the p.d. is high enough a spark occurs, restoring neutrality

Uses of static electricity

C

An inkjet printer uses static electricity. Droplets of ink are given a charge as they leave the nozzle. As the charged droplets pass between the plates they are attracted to the plate with the opposite charge. This means they are **deflected** (change direction). The bigger the voltage across the plates the bigger the deflection, so the positions where the droplets land can be controlled. Each droplet makes a dot where it hits the paper. A group of dots in the right shape produces a letter.

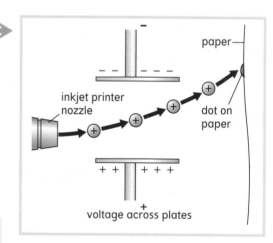

paper

inkjet printer nozzle

dot on paper

voltage across plates

1 a) Lightning is dangerous. Explain how this is true by referring to charge, energy, voltage and current.
b) Lightning is caused because of electrostatic induction. Explain how a large negative charge on the lower surface of the cloud leads to a lightning strike.

2 a) When droplets of ink leave the nozzle of the inkjet printer they get a positive charge. How do they become positively charged?
b) Explain how the direction of the ink droplets can be controlled as they pass through the plates. Draw diagrams to help you explain your answer.

! Glowing balls, the size of footballs, have been seen during thunderstorms. They are called ball lightning. A hissing sound is heard and they melt nearby objects. Nobody knows what causes them.

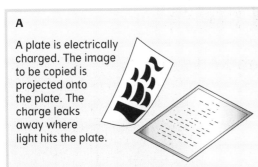

A

A plate is electrically charged. The image to be copied is projected onto the plate. The charge leaks away where light hits the plate.

B

Black powder is blown across the plate, and sticks to the charged parts of the plate.

C

The plate is pressed against a sheet of paper. It is heated, the powder sticks to it, and you have a copy of the original page.

Static electricity is also used in photocopiers. Diagram D explains how they work.

D *Static electricity is also used in photocopiers.*

Discharging objects

When a charged object loses its charge we say that it has been **discharged**. Charged objects can only be discharged if the charge can flow away from the object. The charge normally flows to the Earth down a wire or other conductor. For high voltages, humans or even the air (in lightning) can be the conducting path.

An object that is always connected to the Earth by a conductor cannot become electrically charged, because any charge on the object will flow along the conductor to the Earth.

When an aeroplane flies through the air, friction between the air and the plane charges up the aeroplane. When the plane lands, it remains charged because the electrical charge on the aeroplane cannot be conducted through the rubber tyres to the ground. When the aeroplane is refuelled, the static charge may cause a spark which could ignite the fuel and cause a fire or an explosion. To overcome this problem, a metal wire called a **bonding line** is used to discharge the plane. This allows all of the charge on the outer surface of the aeroplane to be taken to earth, giving it zero overall charge.

E

?

3 Find an example on these two pages, where the air is the conducting path for charge to flow through.

4 In which of the following situations is static electricity useful? Explain your answers.

   a) inkjet printers
   b) nylon clothing making sparks
   c) photocopiers
   d) lightning

5 Helicopters often need to airlift people off mountains. How could static electricity be dangerous in this situation?

6 You can use static electricity to spray-paint a bicycle frame. Explain how this process works and state the advantages of doing it this way.

Summary

Design a leaflet to explain the uses and dangers of static electricity.

Electrolysis

What is electrolysis and how does it work?

Metals conduct electricity because tiny charged particles called electrons can move through the metal. Liquids can conduct electricity if they contain charged particles that can move about.

Pure water can only conduct electricity if the voltage is high enough. Sea water is a much better conductor than pure water because it has salt dissolved in it. Different liquids have different amounts of resistance.

When electricity flows through sea water some of the chemicals in the water are changed into other substances. This process is called electrolysis. Liquids used in **electrolysis** are called **electrolytes**.

Conducting electricity

Substances like common salt (sodium chloride) are made of tiny particles called ions. Ions are atoms with a positive or negative charge. These ions can be separated. When we dissolve an ionic compound in water the positive and negative ions become separated and are free to move. In the solid state the ions are not free to move because they are held together by strong bonds.

Sodium chloride (common salt, NaCl) exists as sodium ions, Na^+, and chloride ions, Cl^-. Copper chloride, $CuCl_2$, exists as copper ions, Cu^{2+}, and chloride ions, Cl^-.

Types of electrolytes

Salt water (sodium chloride solution) conducts electricity because the ions can move about in the solution. This means that charge is flowing through the liquid, so there is a current flowing. Any liquid that has ions moving in it will conduct electricity. This means that some substances that have been melted will also be able to conduct electricity.

Moving ions in liquids

The ions in an electrolyte solution have charges so they can be attracted to charged objects. In electrolysis the ions are attracted to **electrodes**.

Positive charges are attracted to the negative electrode; negative charges are attracted to the positive electrode.

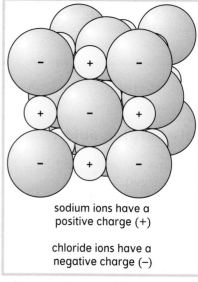

sodium ions have a positive charge (+)

chloride ions have a negative charge (−)

A Solid sodium chloride – the ions cannot move around.

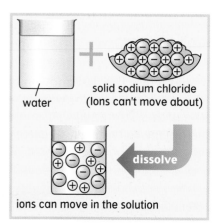

water   solid sodium chloride (ions can't move about)

dissolve

ions can move in the solution

B When an ionic solid is dissolved, the ions are free to move around in the solution.

1 Explain why seawater is a better conductor of electricity than tap water.

2 State whether the following particles are negatively or positively charged:
   a) sodium ion **b)** chloride ion **c)** electron **d)** copper ion.

3 Would a copper ion be attracted to a negative or a positive electrode?

When copper chloride is dissolved in water, the copper chloride splits into free copper ions and chloride ions. These ions conduct electricity.

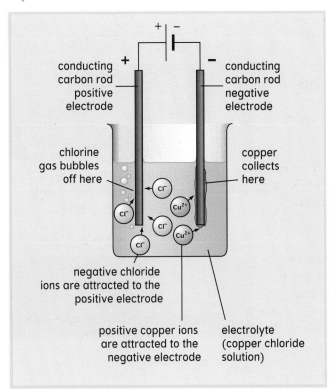

conducting carbon rod positive electrode

conducting carbon rod negative electrode

chlorine gas bubbles off here

copper collects here

negative chloride ions are attracted to the positive electrode

positive copper ions are attracted to the negative electrode

electrolyte (copper chloride solution)

How can you get pure copper from copper chloride solution?

copper chloride solution

4 Look at diagram C. If the cell is turned round:
   a) will the positive electrode be on the left or the right?
   b) where will the chlorine now form?

5 What two elements are produced when copper chloride solution is the electrolyte in an electrolysis experiment?

Factors that affect electrolysis

The volume of gas that is released at the positive electrode and the mass of metal deposited at the negative electrode are affected by:

- the size of the current
- the time the current flows for.

The bigger the current and the longer the time the current flows for, the greater the amount of products. If the size of the current doubles, then the volume of gas produced will also double. If the time for which the current flows doubles, then the volume of gas produced will also double.

6 A current of 2 A flows in copper chloride solution for 10 minutes. At the end of this time, the volume of gas produced is measured and the mass of the copper deposited is also measured. What changes to the volume of gas produced and the mass of copper deposited would you expect to find if:

   a) the current was 4 A instead of 2 A and the time was 10 minutes
   b) the current was 2 A but the time was changed to 5 minutes
   c) the current was 1 A and the time was 20 minutes?

7 a) Why doesn't solid sodium chloride conduct electricity?
   b) Describe two things that you could do to make solid sodium chloride conduct electricity. Explain your answer.

Summary

Write a method for an experiment which would show that electrolysis only occurs in some solutions – those containing ions. State what you would observe and explain these observations.

F10 Magnetism and electromagnetism

What are magnetism and electromagnetism?

You can't touch or see magnetic fields, but they can produce forces that make motors turn, or generate electricity. Magnetic substances were found naturally, hundreds of years ago, in rocks. Humans first used these magnetic materials and the Earth's magnetism for navigation.

A The needle can turn freely. The red end points north. It is the north-seeking pole of the compass 'needle.'

 1 Give three uses for magnetism.

Magnetic materials

A **magnet** is something that can attract a **magnetic material**. There are only three natural magnetic elements: **iron**, **nickel**, and **cobalt**. Other magnetic materials can be made by mixing these elements with other materials. Steel is made from iron that has been mixed with carbon, so steel is also a magnetic material.

Only magnetic materials can be made into magnets.

The rules of magnetism

A magnet can attract *or* repel another magnet, but can *only* attract a magnetic material. You can only prove something is a magnet by seeing if it will repel another magnet.

Magnetic fields and poles

Magnets have **magnetic fields** around them. This is the space around the magnet where it can attract magnetic materials. The magnetic field is strongest at the ends of a magnet. These are called the **poles** of the magnet.

The Earth has a magnetic field. If a magnet can move, it will turn around until it is lined up with the north-south direction of the Earth.

The end of a freely suspended magnet that points north is called the **north-seeking pole** of the magnet. The end of the magnet pointing south is called the **south-seeking pole**.

The name north-seeking pole is often shortened to **north pole**. South-seeking pole is often shortened to **south pole**.

B A bar magnet.

Rules:
Unlike poles will attract each other (i.e. N–S).

Like poles will repel each other. (i.e. N–N or S–S).

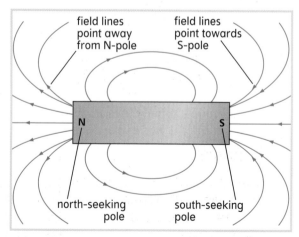

field lines point away from N-pole

field lines point towards S-pole

north-seeking pole

south-seeking pole

 C Magnetic fields can be drawn with arrows, which always point from the north-seeking pole towards the south-seeking pole.

Electromagnetism

Whenever a current flows in a circuit a magnetic field is produced. This is called **electromagnetism**. The field can be made stronger by coiling up a piece of wire through which a current is flowing. This makes an **electromagnet**.

The magnetic field around an electromagnet is the same shape as the field around a bar magnet. Reversing the direction of the current reverses the position of the poles.

Electromagnets are called **temporary magnets** because their magnetism can be switched on and off. This is different from **permanent magnets** which always stay magnetic.

Electromagnets are used in industry. For example old cars are picked up by electromagnets to move them around in scrap yards. To put the car down again the electromagnet is switched off.

F An electromagnet being used in a scrap yard.

P How could you use iron filings and a compass to find the shape of a magnetic field around a magnet? **D**

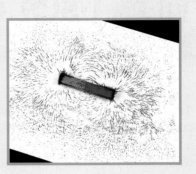

E The magnetic field around an electromagnet.

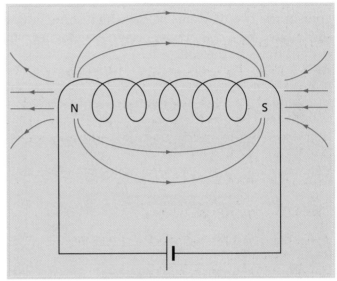

4 Name the three magnetic elements found in the Earth's crust.

5 Where is the magnetic field strongest on a magnet or an electromagnet?

6 What can you do to an electromagnet that you cannot do to a permanent magnet?

7 The Earth has a magnetic field as shown in diagram G. Look carefully at the directions of the magnetic field lines. What does this tell you about the magnetic poles of the Earth?

8 Find out what causes some materials to be magnetic and others to be non-magnetic.

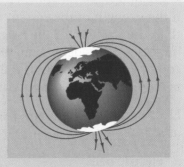

G

Summary

Construct a table that states the similarities and differences between magnets and electromagnets.

Uses of electromagnetism

What are the uses of electromagnetism?

An electromagnet can be switched on and off by an electric current. Usually, an electromagnet consists of a cell, a coil of wire, a switch and a **soft iron core**. The coil of wire is wrapped round the core.

A *soft* magnetic material, such as iron, can be easily magnetised and demagnetised by an electric current. A *hard* magnetic material like steel will remain magnetised once the current is switched off.

Look at the two diagrams below which show how a soft iron bar surrounded by a coil of wire becomes a magnet when an electric current flows in the coil.

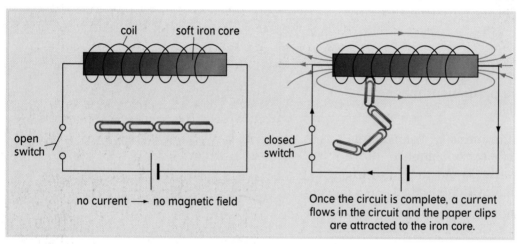

coil   soft iron core

open switch

no current → no magnetic field

closed switch

Once the circuit is complete, a current flows in the circuit and the paper clips are attracted to the iron core.

The strength of an electromagnet can be increased by changing the following:

- the *current* in the coil of wire
- the *number* of turns of wire on the coil
- the *material* used as the core.

If the strength of the current or the number of coils is increased, then the strength of the magnetic field around the coil also increases. If a magnetic material such as iron is placed inside the coil, then the strength of the magnetic field will also increase because the iron helps to 'concentrate' the field, making it stronger.

Electromagnets are useful in a number of devices. They can be used in:

- electric bells
- relays
- lifting devices in scrap metal yards.

1 An electromagnet can pick up 50 paper clips when it is switched on. What changes could be made to allow it to:
   a) pick up 80 paper clips
   b) pick up 20 paper clips?

2 Why is it important to use a 'soft' magnetic material in an electromagnet rather than a 'hard' magnetic material such as steel?

Most flats and houses have their own electric doorbell, which uses an electromagnet.

When the bell switch is pushed a current flows in the circuit, causing a magnetic field to be produced around the electromagnet. When this happens, the armature is attracted towards the electromagnet, causing the hammer to hit the gong and ring the bell. At the same time, this movement breaks the circuit and the hammer and armature move back to their original positions. This recloses the circuit and starts the whole cycle again, providing the switch is still being pushed.

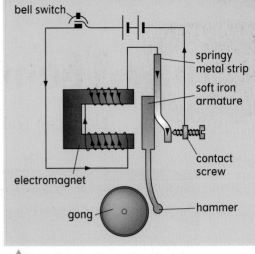

B *An electric doorbell.*

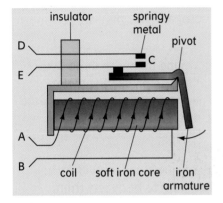

 A relay.

A **relay** is a switch that is worked by an electromagnet. It is useful if we want to control one circuit with another circuit. A relay is shown in diagram C.

When the current flows from A to B in the coil, the soft iron core becomes magnetised. The iron armature is attracted towards the electromagnet. As the armature moves about the pivot, the contacts at C are pushed together, completing a second circuit so that a current flows from D to E.

P How could you show that the magnetic field around an electromagnet increases as the number of coils increases?

?

3 Give an example of where a relay might be useful.

4 What will happen to lamps A, B and C in circuit E once the switch has been closed?

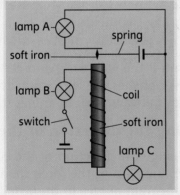

E

5 If the number of coils in an electromagnet is doubled and the current is also doubled, what will happen to the strength of the magnetic field?

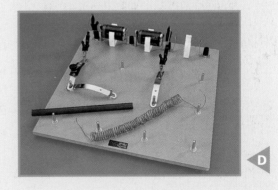

D

6 Find out how a loudspeaker makes use of electromagnetism.

7 Design a simple circuit that uses an electromagnet to unlock a door when somebody presses the correct combination into a keypad. Do not design the workings of the keypad, it is just necessary to realise that it is an input device.

Summary

An electrical goods shop needs a new member of its technical support staff. One of the interview questions is: 'How is electromagnetism useful in everyday life?' What would your answer be, in no more than 200 words?

The motor effect

How can the field around a current be used to turn motors?

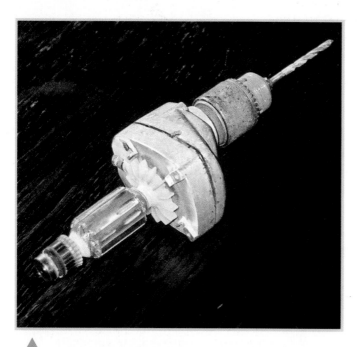

After scientists had discovered that currents had magnetic fields around them, they invented devices that made use of this new discovery. One of the most useful of these devices is the electric motor. Many of the objects that we use at home have motors inside, for example, hairdryers and compact disc players.

1 a) Write down the names of three other devices that use an electric motor.
 b) What energy changes take place in the electric motor?

When two magnets are near to each other they will produce a force between them. This is because the two magnetic fields affect each other.

A *The motor of an electric drill.*

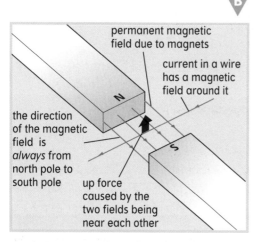

permanent magnetic field due to magnets

current in a wire has a magnetic field around it

the direction of the magnetic field is *always* from north pole to south pole

up force caused by the two fields being near each other

Anything with a current flowing through it has a magnetic field around it. If this magnetic field is placed near another magnetic field, it is similar to putting two magnets close together. The two fields affect each other and produce a force. This is called the **motor effect**.

In diagram B the wire will be forced to move upwards. The force never pushes the wire towards the magnet. The force produced is always at right angles to the wire.

Changing the direction of the force

If you change the direction of the current or the magnetic field, the direction of the force changes. The force produced is *always* at right angles to the wire. Look carefully at diagrams C, D and E.

D *The direction of the current is changed.*

E *The direction of the magnetic field between the magnets is changed.*

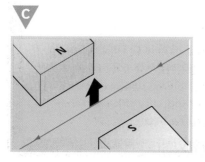

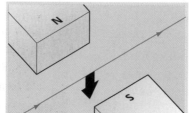

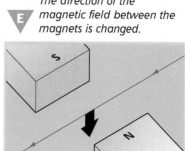

Electric motors

Look at diagram F. The current in the wire loop has its own magnetic field, which is inside the magnetic field of the permanent magnets. This produces a force. On one side of the coil the current is flowing from left to right and the force is upwards. Along the other side of the coil the current flows the opposite way so the force is downwards.
This makes the loop turn.

There are three ways to make a motor produce more force:

- wind more coils onto the loop
- use stronger magnets
- increase the current in the wire loop.

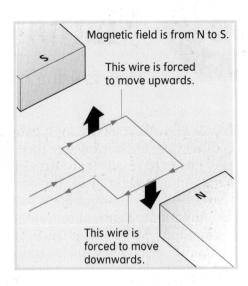

Magnetic field is from N to S.

This wire is forced to move upwards.

This wire is forced to move downwards.

F

2 In diagram G the current and the magnetic field between the magnets are both changed to the opposite directions. What direction will the new force be in?

3 Many electric motors use electromagnets instead of permanent magnets. How can the magnetic field be made stronger using an electromagnet?

4 There are two magnetic fields in diagram G. Where does each one come from?

5 Copy table H and tick the statements that will make the motor spin faster.

6 Which of the following statements about the motor effect is true? Choose the correct answer.
   A Using a bigger current will make the force smaller.
   B Changing the current direction will not change the direction of the force.
   C Changing the direction of the magnetic field will change the direction of the force.

7 Find out about 'Fleming's left hand rule'. Use the rule to show that the direction of movement of the wire in each of the examples on these two pages is correct.

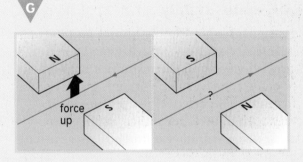

G

force up

H

a) Use weaker magnets in the motor.	
b) Wind more coils onto the loop.	
c) Use a smaller current in the coil.	
d) Use a higher voltage cell to power the motor.	

Summary

You have been asked to alter the motor for a toy car to make it move faster. Explain what you would do to the motor. What could you do to make the car move forwards and backwards?

Mains electricity

How is using mains electricity different from using batteries?

People know that electricity is dangerous but because they use it every day they forget how easy it is to have accidents. An electric shock can burn you or even kill you. You can get an electric shock when your body becomes the easiest path for a current to travel down into the Earth. Faulty plugs or appliances can give you an electric shock. Water can also conduct electricity at high voltage, so you must never use electrical equipment with wet hands.

The UK mains supply

Electricity companies supply houses and flats with electricity at 230 V. The size of the current that flows depends on the resistance of the device being used. A radio with a high resistance will have a small current flowing through it. A device with a lower resistance, such as an electric shower, will have a much higher current flowing through it.

Humans have quite a high resistance, but a voltage of 230 V will make a current of around 2 A flow through a human body. This is a large enough current to cause severe injury or death.

> **1** Why should you dry your hands before using electrical equipment in the kitchen?
>
> **2** What is the voltage of the UK mains supply?
>
> **3** The light switch in a bathroom is usually a pull cord rather than a wall switch. Explain why.

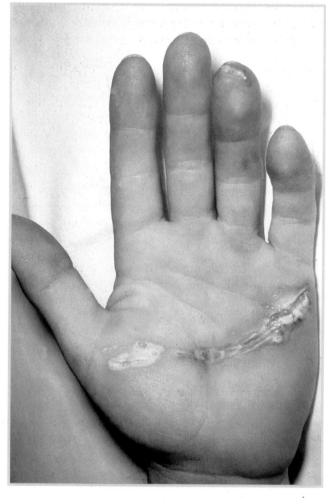

A

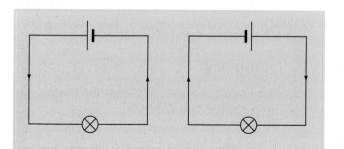

B *Direct current always flows one way around the circuit. You can only change it by taking out the cell and replacing it the other way round.*

Direct current and alternating current

The electricity you get from a cell is not the same as the electricity from the mains supply. The voltage of the mains supply is much higher, but also the current from the mains supply is constantly changing direction.

A cell supplies a current that always flows in one direction. This is called **direct current** (d.c.).

The mains electricity supplies current that is constantly changing direction. In fact it changes direction 100 times per second. (It has a frequency of 50 hertz or 50 cycles per second.) One cycle is one change in direction followed by a second change in direction. This would be like changing the direction of a battery 100 times in a second to make the current go backwards and forwards. This is called **alternating current** (a.c.).

Diagram D compares d.c. and a.c. supplies by showing the traces as they appear on an oscilloscope. The d.c. voltage (like that supplied by a cell) remains relatively constant. The a.c. voltage alternates rapidly (every 1/100 of a second) from + to −.

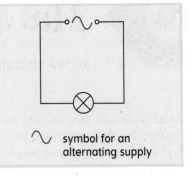

The direction of the current in an alternating current supply is constantly changing. An alternating current supply has a different symbol.

∿ symbol for an alternating supply

D

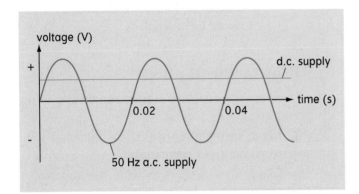

Summary

A tourist office needs a set of instructions explaining how the electricity supply in the UK works. Explain whether people from Portugal can use their electrical appliances in the UK.

F *A plug socket in the UK ...* **G** *... and one in Portugal.*

4 Write down whether each of the following appliances uses direct current or alternating current. Explain your answers.
   a) battery operated calculator
   b) washing machine
   c) television
   d) mobile phone

5 Why don't you get an electric shock from a 1.5 V battery?

6 a) The a.c. supply in the UK has a frequency of 50 Hz. Explain what this means.
   b) How long would it take for this a.c. supply to perform 100 cycles?

7 Look at the following trace of an a.c. voltage. Work out:
   a) the peak voltage
   b) the time for one complete cycle
   c) the frequency of this a.c. voltage.

E

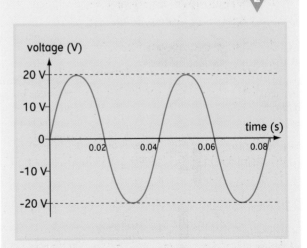

8 Find out how it is possible to convert an a.c. signal into a d.c. signal.

The plug

How should a plug be wired?

Electric appliances are now sold with plugs fitted, and some of these have plastic moulded round them so they cannot be removed. This was done to reduce the number of accidents in the home, because many people do not know how to wire a plug properly. A plug is needed to allow the electricity to get from the mains socket into the appliance. The current enters the appliance through the live wire which is connected to a **fuse**. The fuse is a thin piece of metal that melts if too much current flows through the appliance. This creates a gap in the circuit so no more current flows.

The plug and the cable.

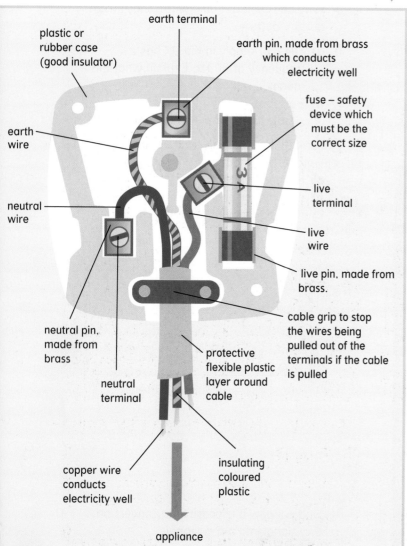

- earth terminal
- plastic or rubber case (good insulator)
- earth pin, made from brass which conducts electricity well
- fuse – safety device which must be the correct size
- earth wire
- 3 A
- live terminal
- neutral wire
- live wire
- live pin, made from brass.
- neutral pin, made from brass
- cable grip to stop the wires being pulled out of the terminals if the cable is pulled
- protective flexible plastic layer around cable
- neutral terminal
- copper wire conducts electricity well
- insulating coloured plastic
- appliance

1 How many wires are there inside a cable?

2 What are the colours used on the insulating cover of each wire?

3 Which terminal on the plug is connected to the fuse?

4 **a)** What is the cable grip for?
   b) Write down an example of a situation where the cable grip would be needed.

How to wire a plug

Here are the main things to remember when you are wiring a plug.

- Make sure you connect the coloured wires to the correct **terminals**.
- Make sure the copper wires are tightly screwed into the terminals.
- Make sure the wires are not sticking up in the plug. The top must fit on easily.
- Have the outer plastic coating of the cable right under the **cable grip**.
- Make sure the cable grip is screwed down tightly.
- Make sure the fuse is the correct size for the appliance (see pages 234–235).
- Don't have strands of copper wire that aren't screwed into a terminal.

5 Which parts of a plug need to be metal and which parts need to be plastic or rubber? Explain your answer.

There are three holes in the electric wall sockets. If you poke anything into just one hole you can be electrocuted, it doesn't take two, as many people think!

The three wires

The **live** and **neutral** wires carry the electricity for the appliance. The third **earth** wire is for safety and usually no current travels down it. Appliances that have a metal case have the earth wire connected to the case. If the case accidentally becomes charged, there is an easy path for the electricity to travel down to the ground, instead of it travelling through a person who touches the case. Appliances that have an earth wire attached to them are said to be **earthed**.

The earth wire has a low resistance. If a fault in the appliance connects the metal case to the live wire, a large current flows which breaks the fuse in the plug. This stops the current flowing. It also means that someone touching the case will not get an electric shock.

Earthing

Look at diagrams C and D below and follow the sequence of events through as they happen.

6 How many problems can you spot in this incorrectly wired plug? Make a list. **B**

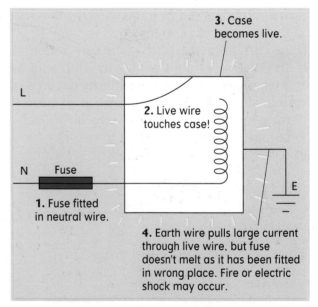

C *Correct earthing.*

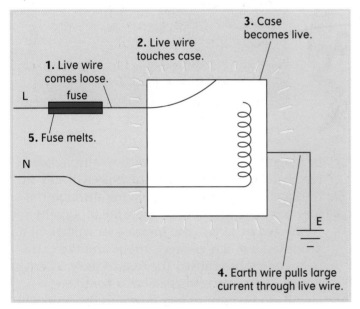

1. Live wire comes loose.
2. Live wire touches case.
3. Case becomes live.
5. Fuse melts.
4. Earth wire pulls large current through live wire.

L   fuse
N
E

D *Incorrect earthing.*

3. Case becomes live.
2. Live wire touches case!
1. Fuse fitted in neutral wire.
4. Earth wire pulls large current through live wire, but fuse doesn't melt as it has been fitted in wrong place. Fire or electric shock may occur.

L
N   Fuse
E

7 Look at diagrams C and D. Explain why it is not safe to connect the fuse to the neutral wire.

8 Explain, in detail, why devices with plastic cases do not need an earth wire.

Summary

Write a set of step-by-step instructions on how to wire a plug. Explain the reasons for each step.

233

Fuses and circuit breakers

How do fuses and circuit breakers work?

Imagine buying a new stereo system or a computer. You plug it into the mains supply and it works perfectly. Suddenly, because of a fault, there is a surge of current from the mains which flows into the new equipment, melts the wires and components inside it and breaks it.

This could easily happen. The only way to prevent this is to use a safety device that stops the current flowing if the current gets too big. These devices also protect people from electrical shocks.

There are two safety devices that are used to stop the current flowing when it becomes too large:

- a **fuse** (found in plugs)
- a **circuit breaker** (made from an electromagnet).

Fuse

A fuse is a very thin piece of wire held in a glass container. It is fitted in series with the live wire so that the electric current flows through it. If the current increases, the wire gets hotter. If the current becomes too big the thin wire melts and breaks. This puts a gap into the circuit so the current stops flowing. Since there is no current flowing in the circuit it is not possible for the device to become damaged, for a fire to occur or for the user to receive an electric shock.

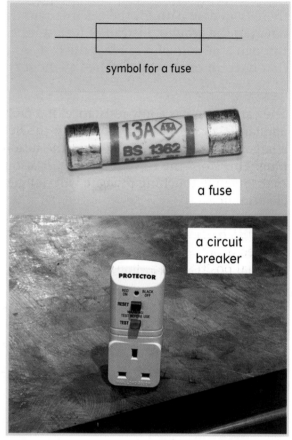

symbol for a fuse

a fuse

a circuit breaker

A

In diagram B, the current can flow through the fuse without melting it, so the bulb will stay lit. In diagram C, the current flowing through the fuse has increased because there are more cells connected in series. The increase in voltage has produced a much greater current and the extra heat energy has caused the fuse to melt. There is now an open circuit instead of a complete circuit, so no current can flow and the bulb will not be lit.

The *thicker* the fuse wire the *higher* the current needed to melt it. The **fuse rating** (size) must be correct for each appliance. If the appliance only needs 4·5 A to run then the fuse needs to melt at a current just above 4·5 A. A fuse is **overloaded** when the current becomes too large and it melts.

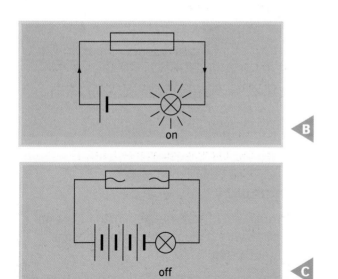

on

B

off

C

For an appliance that takes a current of 4.5 A, a 5 A fuse rather than a 3 A or 13 A fuse should be used. The 3 A fuse would simply melt each time the appliance was used whereas the 13 A fuse would only melt once more than 13 A of current was flowing. This would be unsafe as it could cause the appliance to overheat or even catch fire!

Circuit breakers

A **circuit breaker** also stops current flowing if the current gets too large. The current flows into the device as shown in diagram D. If the current is not too high, then the magnetic field around the electromagnet will not be strong enough to break the circuit. The bigger the current, the greater the strength of the electromagnet's magnetic field. When the current exceeds a particular value, the magnetic field becomes strong enough to attract the iron armature, breaking the circuit (diagram E). Once the fault has been corrected, the reset button can be pressed down, resetting the iron armature back to its original position and allowing current to flow again.

3 a) What happens to the coil when a current flows through it?

b) When the current gets bigger, why does the armature rotate?

c) Why does this stop the current flowing?

d) What does the reset button do?

4 a) What advantage do fuses have over circuit breakers?

b) What two advantages do circuit breakers have over fuses?

Advantages and disadvantages

Fuses are cheaper to use than circuit breakers. Circuit breakers are more sensitive to increases in current and will break a circuit faster than a fuse. Therefore circuit breakers give greater protection to equipment.

Summary

Write an article for an electrical supplies magazine explaining the advantages and disadvantages of using circuit breakers instead of fuses.

1 How does a fuse work?

2 a) If a heater needs 12 A to run properly, what size fuse would it need? Choose the correct answer.
A 5 A   **B** 13 A   **C** 25 A.

b) Explain your choice.

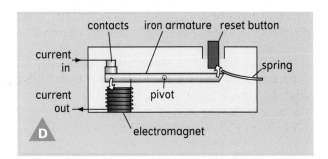

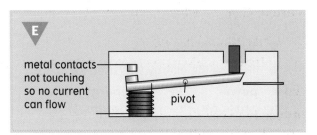

5 Explain the function of these parts of a circuit breaker:
a) the reset button
b) the coil
c) the iron armature.

6 Here are three fuse wires. Their values are 1 A, 3 A and 13 A.

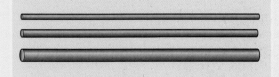

a) Which is which?
b) Explain how you worked out your answer.

7 A circuit breaker has been made, but the core of the electromagnet has been accidentally left out. Explain, in detail, why this makes the circuit breaker dangerous.

Electrical power

How do we work out how much energy appliances use?

The words power and powerful have many different meanings. A person is said to be powerful if they can lift heavy objects. A car is powerful if it can do 0–100 kilometres per hour in less than 5 seconds, and so on. In electricity, **power** is a measure of how quickly something transfers energy.

Power is measured in **watts (W)**. This is the amount of energy transferred in one second. Energy is measured in **joules (J)**, and so:

1 watt = 1 joule of energy transferred per second
1 W = (1 J/s)

 Power can be worked out if you know:

- the energy used
- the time the energy was used for.

power	=	**energy**	÷	**time**
(in **watts, W**)		(in **joules, J**)		(in **seconds, s**)

A 120 watt light bulb is twice as powerful as a 60 watt light bulb, as it produces about twice as much visible light energy per second. This is why it looks brighter.

 1 What is the unit of power?

2 How many times more powerful is a 240 watt light bulb than a 60 watt light bulb?

As many electrical appliances convert large amounts of energy per second, we often have to work in kilowatts (kW), where 1 kW = 1000 W.

 The power of an electrical appliance can also be worked out if you know:

- the voltage it uses
- the current it uses.

Note: The letter 'I' is used as a shorthand way of writing 'current'.

power	=	**voltage**	×	**current**
(in **watts, W**)		(in **volts, V**)		(in **amps, A**)

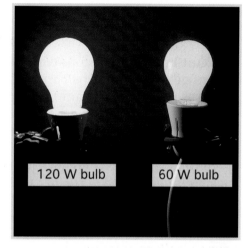

120 W bulb   60 W bulb

 This electric fire is using 1 kW of power. When the second bar is switched on it uses 2 kW.

 3 a) How many watts of power are there in 5 kW?

b) How many watts of power are there in 0.5 kW?

c) What is the power of a hairdryer if it uses a voltage of 240 V and a current of 5 A?

d) How much energy does a 60 W bulb convert if it is used continuously for 20 minutes?

Appliances that have high power ratings convert more energy per second than appliances with low power ratings. Electrical appliances that are used to heat things generally have higher power ratings than other appliances, like televisions or radios.

Worked examples

An electric motor needs a voltage of 4 V to operate normally with a current of 0.1 A. What is the power of the motor?

power = voltage × current

$= 4 × 0.1$

$= 0.4$ W

An electric shower is supplied by mains electricity (230 V). If a current of 20 A flows through it, how powerful is the shower? Put your answer in kW.

power = voltage × current

$= 230 × 20$

$= 4600$ W

$= 4.6$ kW

P How can you find the power of an electric motor when it is lifting different loads? **D**

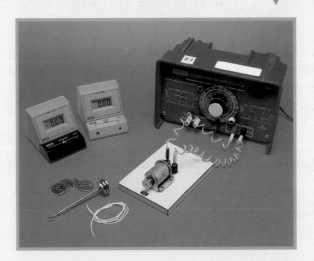

We can use the power equation to work out how much current a device needs to operate properly. We have to rearrange the power equation. This equation is useful because if we can calculate how much current a device needs then we can also work out the rating of the fuse that needs to be put in the plug.

Worked example

A kettle has a power rating of 2800 W and uses mains electricity. What size fuse needs to be fitted to the plug? Commonly available fuses are 1A, 3A, 5A, 13A.

power   = voltage × current

so current = power ÷ voltage

$= 2800 ÷ 230$

$= 12.2$ A

A 13 A fuse is needed.

4 a) What current would a device take if its power rating was 115 W and the voltage it used was 230 V?

b) Copy and complete the following table. **E**

Power (watts)	Voltage (volts)	Current (amps)	Correct fuse rating (amps)
	10	12	
20	5		
	4	10	
60		3	
	20	2.5	

5 An electric shower is supplied by the mains at 230 V and has a current of 25 A flowing through it. What is the power of the shower?

6 Electrical items in the home have labels with the power rating stamped on them. Find out the power rating of as many items as possible. Use the equation P = VI to work out the current that each item uses when working properly. For each item, state the correct size fuse needed.

Summary

Design a poster for an electrical goods shop that explains how to work out the correct fuse to use in an appliance if you know its power rating. You should include a worked example and explain why the correct fuse is needed.

Generating electricity

How is electricity generated?

Scientists are constantly looking for new, cheaper ways to produce electricity. Their methods use magnetism to make electric currents.

There are two ways to produce a current.

P How can you induce a current in a wire? How can you make the current bigger?

Method 1: Move a magnet in a coil of wire

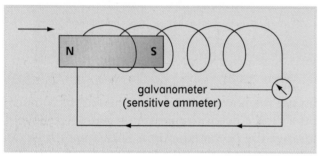

galvanometer (sensitive ammeter)

A

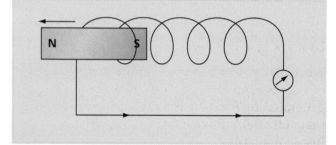

B

As the magnet is moved into the coil of wire a voltage is produced. If there is a complete circuit a current will flow in the wire. We say that current is **induced** in the wire.

If the south pole of the magnet is now moved *out* of the coil of wire, it causes the current to move in the opposite direction. This is shown by the needle on the galvanometer, which is now pointing to the right.

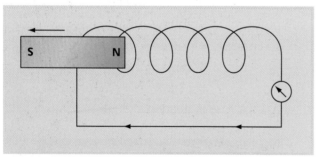

C

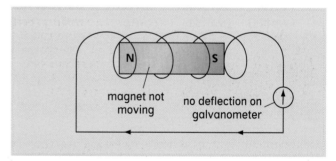

magnet not moving   no deflection on galvanometer

D

If the poles of the magnet are reversed, the current is induced in the opposite direction.

If the magnet is simply left inside the coil and not moved, no current will be induced. The magnetic field must be *constantly changing* in order to induce a current, and this can only be made to happen by moving the magnet (or moving the coil).

? 1 What is an induced current?

2 What are the two ways to change the direction of the induced current?

Method 2: Move a wire through a magnetic field

If a wire moves through a magnetic field a voltage is induced. If there is a complete circuit a current can flow.

If the wire moves in the opposite direction the current will flow in the opposite direction.

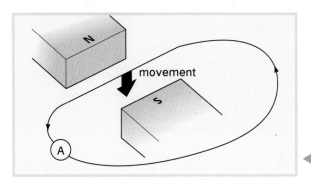

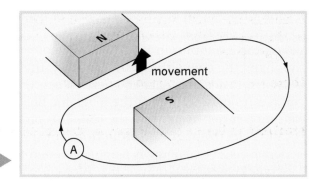

Electricity generators

Electricity generators use a very long piece of wire wound into a coil. Electricity can be generated by rotating the coil of wire in a magnetic field or by rotating a magnet inside the coil.

There are four ways to increase the size of the induced voltage and current:

- move the coil or magnet faster
- use a stronger magnetic field
- wrap more turns (loops) on the coil
- make the area of the coil bigger.

 These torches contain small generators. 60 turns of the handle produces enough electricity to keep the bulb lit for 10 minutes.

Summary

Your school science club is running a competition. The task you have been set involves designing a way to make a bulb light up as bright as possible using a magnet, a coil of wire and a bulb. What would your design be? Explain your reasons.

3 What will happen to the current if the wire moves faster through the magnetic field?

4 How can you change the direction of the current?

5 How can you increase the induced voltage in a generator?

6 A bicycle dynamo works like a generator. It provides the electricity for the lights. Explain why this is not useful when stopped at traffic lights.

7 Why must the magnet or the coil of wire be moving in order to constantly induce an electrical current in a circuit?

8 A generator produces an alternating current. Sketch a graph showing how this type of current changes with time and explain which factors affect the size of the induced current.

9 Find out about Fleming's right hand rule. How is this rule important when dealing with electrical generators?

Generators

What are generators?

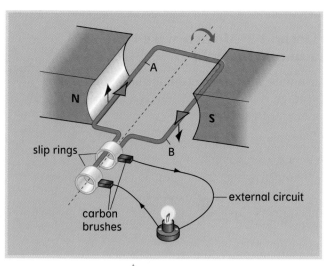

A

A motor uses a coil of wire and a pair of magnets to convert electrical energy into kinetic energy. A **generator** is a motor in reverse. Instead of supplying the coil with electrical energy, the coil is rotated inside the magnetic field. When the coil rotates it cuts through the magnetic field, causing a current to flow in the coil. This process is called **electromagnetic induction**. For the generator, kinetic energy is being converted to electrical energy. The type of electrical output that is produced is called a.c. or alternating current because it is constantly changing direction.

Diagram A shows the most important parts of an a.c. generator.

The electrical current is conducted in and out of the coil by means of the metal **slip rings** and the carbon **brushes**. Every half turn the current flowing in the part of the coil that is connected to each slip ring changes direction. In the diagram, the part of the coil labelled A is moving up and B is moving down. This causes the current to flow in a clockwise direction in the coil.

1 How could a motor be changed into a generator?

2 An a.c. generator produces a.c current because of the slip rings. Draw diagrams to show why this is true.

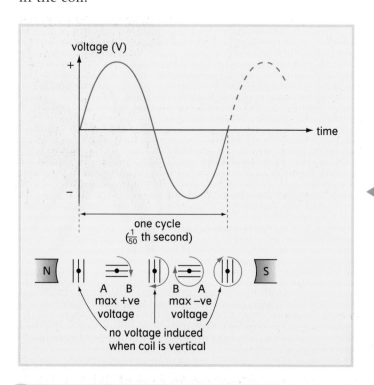

B

When the coil rotates through half a turn, the positions of A and B are swapped over which causes the current in the external circuit to flow in the opposite direction. The brushes touch the slip rings as they rotate and establish electrical contact with the external circuit.

Graph **B** shows how the size of the induced voltage changes as the coil rotates through one complete cycle (360 degrees).

Changing the size of the voltage and current produced

The voltage and current can be increased by:

- using a coil with more turns of wire
- using a stronger magnet
- rotating the coil faster
- using a coil or magnet with a greater area.

3 Name four ways in which the size of the current or voltage produced by an a.c. generator could be reduced.

The a.c. current that we use in our homes has a **frequency** of 50 Hz (hertz). This means that there are 50 complete cycles every second. In other words, it takes 1/50 of a second for each cycle. The frequency of the a.c. supply can be increased by rotating the coil faster. This also increases the output voltage as shown in diagram C.

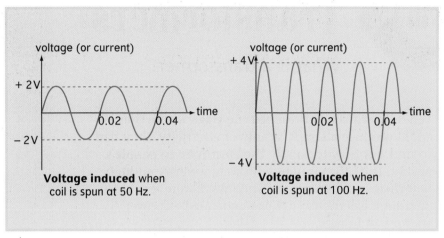

voltage (or current)

+ 2V

− 2V

0.02 0.04

time

Voltage induced when coil is spun at 50 Hz.

voltage (or current)

+ 4 V

− 4 V

0.02 0.04

time

Voltage induced when coil is spun at 100 Hz.

4 What would the frequency of the a.c. supply be in our homes if the magnets in power stations were rotated at 4 times the present rate?

The electrical energy that enters our homes comes from power stations. Fuels such as coal, oil, natural gas or nuclear fuel are used to heat water and make steam. The steam is blown onto turbines at high pressure. The turbines are connected to a large magnet called a stator which rotates inside a coil of wire. The magnet and coil arrangement is known as the generator or alternator. The stator makes 50 complete rotations each second inside the coil, hence an a.c. supply of 50 Hz!

A generator (alternator) in a power station.

5 Explain why no voltage or current is produced by a generator when the coil and magnet are not moving relative to each other.

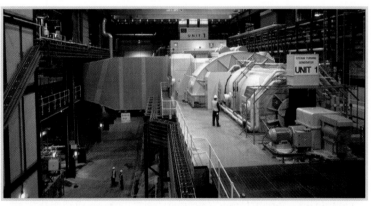

6 Find out how a d.c. generator is different in design to an a.c. generator and explain why it produces a d.c. voltage instead of an a.c. voltage.

7 An a.c. generator produces an a.c. voltage of 6 V with a frequency of 50 Hz. How could you change the design of the a.c. generator so that it produced:
   a) a bigger output voltage at the same frequency
   b) a bigger output voltage at a higher frequency
   c) a smaller output voltage at the same frequency
   d) a smaller output voltage at a higher frequency
   e) a smaller output voltage at a lower frequency?

Summary

Draw a concept map to show how an a.c. generator works and how it can be used to produce different types of a.c. signal. Use the following words and any others you wish to use:

faster, higher, slip rings, smaller, lower, brushes, voltage, frequency, induced, coils, magnet, generator.

Transformers

What is a transformer?

When scientists had reached the stage where they could produce a steady supply of electricity, they had to find out how to supply the electricity to people's homes. Initially, families who were wealthy enough had their own generators. Then ways were found to distribute electricity that was generated at power stations to homes.

> ! An electric eel can produce voltages up to 650 V. It can generate currents large enough to stun a horse or a man.

A *Early generators were unreliable and very noisy.*

The National Grid

Power stations produce electricity, which is **transmitted** along cables called **power lines**. Many of these are supported by tall **pylons**. This network of power lines is called the **National Grid**. It connects almost every home in the UK to an electricity supply.

? 1 What voltage is the electricity in the power lines?

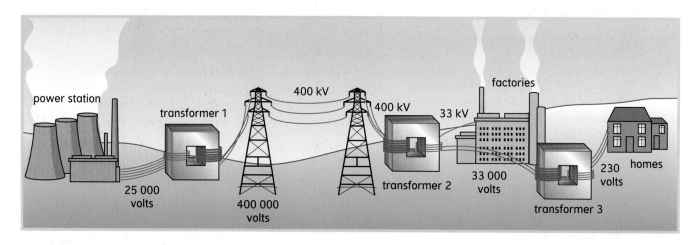

power station

transformer 1

25 000 volts

400 000 volts

400 kV

400 kV

33 kV

factories

33 000 volts

transformer 2

230 volts

homes

transformer 3

B

Electricity has to flow along many miles of wire before it reaches people's homes. The current heats up the wire, so some of the electrical energy is wasted as heat energy as it travels. If the electricity is transmitted at high voltages and low currents, less energy is wasted. This makes the National Grid more **efficient**.

It would be far too dangerous to have the same high voltages in the home so the voltage is reduced to 230 V.

? 2 a) What would happen to the electric currents in the home if the voltage from the National Grid increased from 230 V to 275 000 V?

b) What could this size of current do to the wires in electrical equipment?

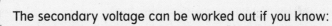

Transformers

Transformers are used to increase and decrease the voltage. A **step-up transformer** increases the voltage. A **step-down transformer** decreases the voltage.

Transformers are used to step-up the voltage from the power station to the power lines, and then local transformers step-down the voltage from the power lines to factories and homes. Transformers only work with alternating currents and voltages, which is why the mains supply is an alternating supply.

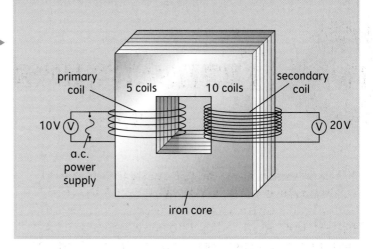

?

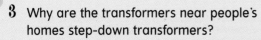

3 Why are the transformers near people's homes step-down transformers?

4 Write down whether a step-up or a step-down transformer is used:
   a) at a power station to change the voltage before it goes along power lines
   b) to change the mains supply to a smaller voltage for a model racing car.

5 Explain why it is dangerous to fly kites near power lines.

6 Calculate the voltage in a secondary coil if: $N_S = 29$; $N_P = 24\,375$; $V_P = 275\,000$.

7 1 000 000 W of electrical power could be transmitted by using a current of 100 000 A and a voltage of 10 V, or the same amount of power could be transmitted by using 10 A and a voltage of 100 000 V. Which is best and why?

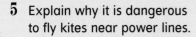

8 We can use the equation $P = I^2R$ (power = current squared times resistance) to calculate the power lost as heat in the National Grid. Use this equation to explain why a small current is preferable to a large current when transmitting electrical power in the National Grid. Make up your own values to put into the equation.

When an alternating voltage is applied across the primary coil, an alternating current flows in the primary coil. This creates a *constantly changing* magnetic field in the primary coil. The magnetic iron core helps to concentrate this field, causing a constantly changing magnetic field to be produced through the secondary coil. This changing magnetic field causes an alternating voltage to be induced across the secondary coil. If there are more turns of the wire on the secondary coil than on the primary coil there will be a bigger voltage across the secondary coil; if there are fewer, the voltage will be less.

The voltages across the primary and secondary coils are related by the equation shown here:

E The secondary voltage can be worked out if you know:
- the primary voltage
- the number of turns on the primary coil
- the number of turns on the secondary coil.

$$\frac{\text{voltage across primary } (V_P)}{\text{voltage across secondary } (V_S)} = \frac{\text{number of turns on the primary } (N_P)}{\text{number of turns on the secondary } (N_S)}$$

This can be arranged to give $V_S = \dfrac{N_S \times V_P}{N_P}$

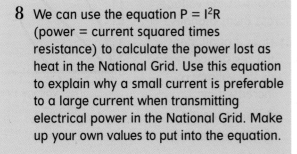

Summary

An electricity company wants to explain to people living near a transformer what it is for. Design a leaflet for the company explaining what the National Grid is, why transformers are used and how they work.

Further questions

1 Name the electrical symbols shown in this table. (4)

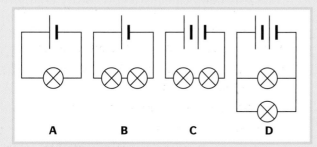

2 Circuits A to D have identical cells and bulbs.

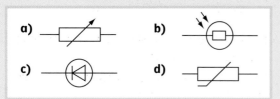

a) Which circuit has:

i) the brightest bulb(s)
ii) the dimmest bulb(s)? (2)

b) Which *two* circuits have bulbs with equal brightness? (1)

c) If each of the cells above has a voltage of 1.5 V and each bulb has a resistance of 5 Ω then find the current flowing in each of the bulbs in circuits A, B, C and D. (4)

3 a) What kind of charge will attract a negative charge? (1)

b) i) Explain how the positively charged sphere will attract unchanged sphere X if it is placed close to it. (2)

ii) What do we call this process? (1)

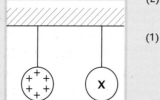

c) Describe *two* uses of static electricity and two potential hazards. (4)

d) How is it possible to avoid an explosion when refuelling a plane? (2)

4 The bulbs in this circuit are identical.

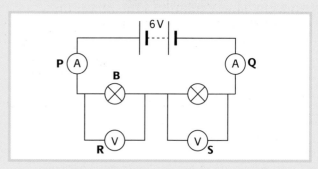

a) Ammeter P reads 0.5 A. What is the reading on ammeter Q? (1)

b) The battery supplies a voltage of 6 V to the circuit. What is the reading on:

i) voltmeter R
ii) voltmeter S? (2)

c) Each bulb in the circuit has a resistance of 6 Ω.

i) What is the total resistance of the two bulbs in the circuit?
ii) A current of 0.2 A now flows through one of the bulbs. Calculate the voltage across the bulb.
iii) Calculate how much charge flows through each bulb in five minutes. (2)
iv) How much energy is converted by each bulb during this time? (2)

d) Bulb B is unscrewed. What are the new readings on each of the meters, P and Q? (2)

5 This graph shows how the current in three components, A, B and C, changes as the voltage across them changes.

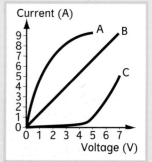

a) How, if at all, does the resistance change as the voltage is increased in:

i) component A
ii) component B? (2)

b) i) What is component A?
ii) What is component B? (2)

6 This diagram shows two carbon electrodes in a beaker of copper chloride solution. The ammeter shows there is a current flowing.

a) Copy the diagram and label:

   i) the negative electrode

   ii) the positive electrode.   (2)

b) Explain how the current flows:

   i) in the solution

   ii) in the wires.   (2)

7 This diagram shows a coil of wire with a current flowing through it. A magnetic field is formed around the coil.

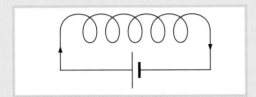

a) Copy the diagram and draw the magnetic field around the coil.   (2)

b) Describe *three* ways of increasing the strength of the magnetic field.   (3)

c) Explain what would happen to the magnetic field if the cell were reversed.   (2)

8 This diagram shows a relay circuit. The circuit is used to start the motor in a machine.

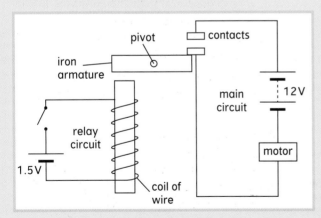

a) Explain how pressing the switch makes current flow in the motor. Include each of the labelled parts in your explanation.   (5)

b) Give *three* other uses of an electromagnet.   (3)

9 The diagram shows the major parts of a transformer.

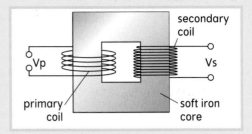

a) Is this a step-up or a step-down transformer? Explain your answer.   (2)

b) How could a step-down transformer be turned into a step-up transformer?   (1)

c) There are 20 turns on the primary coil and 440 turns on the secondary coil. If the input voltage is 12 V, what will the size of the output voltage be?   (3)

d) Why do transformers only work with a.c.?   (2)

e) Where in the National Grid would you find:
  i) step up transformers

  ii) step down transformers?

  Explain your answers.   (4)

f) Why is electrical energy transmitted at a high voltage in the National Grid?   (3)

10 This diagram shows an electricity generator. When the coil rotates a current is induced in the wire.

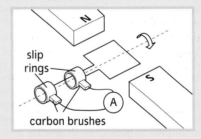

a) Name *three* ways to increase the size of the induced current.   (3)

b) The mains supply voltage is 230 V. A telephone answering machine only needs 9 V to work properly. What component is used to reduce the mains supply voltage to a smaller voltage?   (1)

c) Explain the role of the slip rings and the carbon brushes in the circuit above.   (2)

d) Sketch a voltage–time graph to show the electrical output that will be produced when the generator is rotated with a frequency of 20 Hz.   (4)

Glossary

abdomen Part of the body between the chest and hip, containing organs like the stomach, liver and intestines.

absorb Soaking something up from the surroundings. A sponge absorbs water.

acid A liquid with a pH of less than 7.

acid rain Rain containing sulphuric acid and nitric acid. Acid rain has a pH of less than 5.6.

adapted When a cell or an organism has certain features to help it do a particular job.

addictive A drug that causes the user to become dependent on it.

aerobic respiration The main respiration reaction in cells. It uses oxygen from the air and glucose from food to release energy. The waste products are carbon dioxide and water.

alcohol One of a group of chemicals with similar properties. Ethanol is the scientific name for the chemical found in alcoholic drinks.

alcoholic Someone who is dependent on alcoholic drinks.

alkali A liquid with a pH of more than 7.

alkaline With a pH of more than 7.

alternating current An electrical current that flows one way then the other. Generators and the mains supply alternating current.

alveoli Tiny pockets in the lungs at the ends of the bronchioles, where oxygen diffuses into the blood and carbon dioxide diffuses out.

amino acids The molecules that proteins are made of.

ammeter Piece of equipment used to measure electrical current.

ampère or **amp (A)** The unit for measuring electrical current.

anaerobe A living thing that survives without oxygen.

anaerobic respiration Respiration without oxygen.

anode Positive electrode in electrolysis.

antibodies Proteins that destroy particular microbes. They are made by white blood cells.

antitoxins Chemicals that destroy toxins. They are made by white blood cells.

anus Where unwanted remains of food leave the body as faeces when you go to the toilet.

aqueous solution A solution of something in water.

armature The turning part of a motor or generator.

artery A blood vessel that carries blood away from the heart.

atom The smallest particle of an element. It has no overall electric charge.

atomic mass The relative mass of an atom. Roughly how many times heavier it is than an atom of hydrogen.

atomic number The number of protons in an element's atoms.

atrium (plural **atria**) The upper space on each side of the heart. It receives blood from the veins.

attract Pull something closer.

auxin Plant growth hormone. It is found in the tips of shoots and roots.

bacterium (plural **bacteria**) A single-celled microbe without a nucleus.

barrage Large dam across a river to control the flow of the tides.

base A substance that reacts with an acid to form a salt. Some bases are alkalis.

battery Two or more electrical cells used together.

bauxite Rock containing aluminium oxide.

bile An alkaline liquid made by the liver. It helps to emulsify fats in the small intestine and neutralises acid from the stomach.

biodegradable Something that will decay naturally.

bladder The organ that stores urine.

blast furnace A large industrial furnace for extracting iron from iron ore.

blood clot A plug formed by blood to seal a cut and stop microbes getting into the body. Often dries to form a scab.

blood vessel A tube that carries blood around the body.

boiling point When a liquid is at its boiling point it is as hot as it can get. It is evaporating as fast as it can.

breathing Using the lungs to take in and blow out air.

bronchi Pair of large air tubes from the trachea to the lungs.

bronchioles Small air tubes that branch out from the bronchi inside the lungs.

bronchitis When mucus in the lungs is infected by bacteria.

by-product A substance produced by a chemical reaction but is not needed.

calcium carbonate Compound of calcium, carbon and oxygen. The chemical name for limestone and marble.

calcium hydroxide Compound of calcium, hydrogen and oxygen. The chemical name for slaked lime.

calcium oxide Compound of calcium and oxygen. The chemical name for quicklime.

cancer When some of the body's cells divide too quickly. The lump of cells that forms (a tumour) can stop other cells doing their job.

capillaries Tiny blood vessels that link arteries and veins.

carbohydrates A group of foods used for energy, e.g. starch and sugars.

carbon dioxide A colourless gas. It is produced by respiration and used up in photosynthesis.

carbon monoxide Very poisonous colourless gas. It stops red blood cells carrying enough oxygen around the body.

catalyse Speed up a chemical reaction.

catalyst Something that speeds up a chemical reaction without being changed at the end of it.

cathode Negative electrode in electrolysis.

cell (in biology) The basic unit which living things are made of.

cell (in chemistry) Apparatus for electrolysis.

cell (in physics) The scientific name for a battery.

cellulose The substance that plant cell walls are made of.

cement A mixture of powdered limestone and powdered clay which is heated in a rotary kiln.

cementing When sediments are compressed, water is squeezed out from between the particles. Some of the dissolved minerals get left behind and form crystals which stick the particles together to make rock.

chemical energy The kind of energy stored in chemicals.

chemical formula Shorthand way of describing a substance using symbols.

chemical reaction A change that forms new substances.

chlorophyll The green substance found inside chloroplasts.

chloroplast A green disc containing chlorophyll. Found in plant cells and used to make glucose by photosynthesis.

cholesterol A fatty substance found in some foods. It can clog up arteries and lead to heart disease.

chromosome A thread-like strand found in the nucleus of a cell. Chromosomes are made of DNA and contain the 'instructions' for a living thing.

cilia Small hairs on the surface of some cells.

ciliary muscle A part of the eye. It works with the suspensory ligaments to hold the lens in place and change its shape.

ciliated epithelial cells Cells found in the lungs. Their hairs sweep dirty mucus out of the lungs.

circuit breaker An electromagnetic switch that breaks a circuit if the current gets too big.

circuit diagram Shorthand way of showing an electric circuit using symbols.

circulation system The set of organs that carry oxygen and food around the body in the blood.

coal A fossil fuel made from the remains of plants.

coke A fuel made from coal. It is almost pure carbon.

compress Make something smaller by squashing it.

concentrated A solution that contains a lot of the solute.

concentration gradient When a substance is more concentrated in one place than another.

concrete A mixture of cement, water, sand and crushed rock, which reacts together to form a hard substance used in building.

condense Turning from a gas into a liquid.

conduction The way that heat or electricity travels through solids by passing from particle to particle.

conductor A material that lets energy travel through it easily.

contract Muscle cells contract by getting shorter and fatter.

convection The way that heat travels through liquids and gases as the particles in them move about.

convection current A flow of liquid or gas caused by part of it being heated or cooled more than the rest.

core The innermost section of the Earth.

cornea The clear part of the sclera at the front of the eye. It helps to focus light on the retina.

corrode, corrosion When a substance is 'eaten' away by a chemical reaction.

crack, cracking Breaking long hydrocarbon molecules into shorter ones.

crude oil Oil as it comes out of the ground. It is mainly a mixture of hydrocarbons.

crust The rocky outer layer of the Earth.

cryolite A compound of aluminium, sodium and fluorine. It is added to bauxite to help lower the melting point when extracting aluminium.

cuticle Waterproof top surface of a leaf.

cutting A side stem taken off a plant. It is allowed to sprout roots to make a new plant.

decay When microbes eat the remains of a dead organism and it rots away.

decommission To put something out of use, for example nuclear power stations are very expensive to decommission because the reactor core must be carefully sealed.

decompose (in chemistry) Splitting up a substance by a chemical reaction.

deflect Change something's direction.

density The mass of one gram of a substance. e.g. gold has a density of 18.9 grams per cm^3.

dependent When someone feels that they have to carry on taking a drug to survive.

deposit A layer of particles that settles at the bottom of a liquid.

depressant A drug that slows down the nervous system.

diabetes When the pancreas produces too little insulin.

diabetic Someone who has diabetes.

diaphragm A sheet of muscle that separates the thorax from the abdomen. It moves to help you breathe.

diet Everything an animal eats and drinks.

diffuse, diffusion When particles mix together without anything moving them. They move from an area where there are lots of them to where there are fewer of them.

digest, digestion Breaking down food into smaller units that the body can use.

digestive juices Secretions that help break down foods in the digestive system.

digestive system Organ system used to break down food and change it into a form the body can use.

dilute A solution that does not contain much of the solute.

direct current An electrical current that flows in the same direction all the time. Electrical cells make direct current.

discharge Remove the electrical charge from something.

discontinuous deposition When the sedimentary rocks found at a place were not laid down continuously, but at different times.

displace Replacing one element in a compound with a more reactive one.

displacement reaction 'Competition' reaction between elements. A more reactive element displaces a less reactive one from it's compound.

DNA Complicated chemical that contains the 'instructions' for a living thing.

dormant When a volcano has not erupted for many years.

drug A chemical that changes the way the body works in some way.

earth Safety wire fitted to an appliance to stop anyone getting an electric shock by touching its metal case.

effector A part of the body that carries out a response to a stimulus.

efficiency The fraction of energy that is usefully transferred.

efficient When not much energy is wasted.

elastic potential energy The kind of energy stored in something that has been stretched or squashed and which can bounce back to its original shape.

electrical component Something that can be part of an electric circuit (e.g. cell, lamp).

electrical current A flow of electrical charges.

electrical energy The kind of energy carried by electricity.

electrode The place where electricity enters an electrolyte.

electrolysis Splitting up a substance by electricity.

electrolyte A liquid that conducts electricity.

electromagnet A magnet made by electricity.

electron A tiny negatively charged particle.

electroplating Using electrolysis to coat a metal object with a thin layer of another metal.

emphysema When parts of the lungs develop holes filled with liquid.

emulsification Breaking down large droplets into smaller ones to make an emulsion.

emulsion A mixture of tiny droplets of one liquid blended throughout another liquid.

energy Something that is needed to make things happen.

energy flow diagram A diagram to show energy changes.

enzyme Substance that speeds up a chemical reaction in the body (a biological catalyst).

epidermis tissue Layer of cells that covers the surfaces of a leaf.

epithelial tissue Layers of cells that cover different body surfaces.

erosion When bits of weathered rock are moved by gravity, water, wind or ice.

ethanol The chemical name for the alcohol in alcoholic drinks.

ethene A hydrocarbon gas.

excretion Getting rid of the waste substances that have been made by chemical reactions in the body.

extrusive Igneous rock formed from lava cooling quickly on the Earth's surface (e.g. basalt). It has small crystals.

faeces The undigested and unabsorbed remains of food.

fats A group of foods used as a food reserve and to keep the body warm.

fault A break in rock layers.

fetus A developing baby inside a pregnant woman's body.

fibre The part of foods from plants that cannot be broken down by the body.

filament (in Physics) A thin wire that glows inside a light bulb.

flammable Something that burns very easily.

flowering plant A plant that reproduces using seeds found in fruits.

fluid A substance which can flow (a gas or a liquid).

fold A bend in rock layers.

food poisoning When harmful microbes in food cause illness.

fossil The ancient remains or traces of a plant or animal, preserved in rocks.

fossil fuel A fuel formed from the remains of plants or animals that died millions of years ago.

fraction A separated part from a mixture of liquids. It contains compounds that boil at nearly the same temperature.

fractional distillation A process for separating a mixture of liquids with different boiling points.

fractionating column The apparatus used to separate the different fractions in a mixture of liquids.

fruit An organ that carries the seeds of flowering plants. Can be fleshy or dry.

function The job that something does.

fuse A thin wire that melts and breaks if the current in a circuit gets too big.

fuse rating The maximum current that a fuse will conduct without melting.

gall bladder The organ that stores bile.

gastric juice Digestive juice made by glands in the stomach lining. It is very acidic and contains enzymes to break down proteins.

gene Part of a chromosome. It contains the 'instructions' for a particular feature (e.g. eye colour).

generator Large coil of wire with a magnet inside. When the magnet is turned, electricity is produced in the coil of wire.

gland cells Cells that make and release fluids.

glandular tissue Many gland cells grouped together.

glass A transparent solid which is made by heating limestone, sand and sodium carbonate together.

global warming Gradual heating of the Earth's atmosphere. It is caused by the 'greenhouse effect'.

glucagon A hormone that makes the amount of glucose in the blood go up.

glucose The sugar that plants make by photosynthesis, and that carbohydrates break down into in digestion.

gravitational potential energy The kind of energy stored by anything that can fall to the ground.

greenhouse effect When the Earth warms up more than it should because heat is trapped in its atmosphere and cannot escape into space.

greenhouse gas A gas that traps heat in the Earth's atmosphere (e.g. carbon dioxide).

group Column of elements with similar properties in the Periodic Table.

guard cells Cells on the underside of a leaf, which control the opening and closing of stomata.

gullet The tube from the back of the mouth to the stomach.

heart The organ that pumps blood around the body.

heart beat One complete pumping action of the heart.

heart beat rate How many times the heart beats in a minute.

heart disease When some of the heart muscle has not received enough oxygen and has died.

heart valves Valves in the heart to stop blood flowing backwards.

heat conductor A material that lets heat energy flow through it easily.

heat energy The hotter something is, the more heat energy it has.

heat insulator A material that does not let heat energy flow through it easily.

heat radiation The waves of energy given off by something hot.

homeostasis The way the body keeps the conditions inside it (e.g. temperature) constant.

hormone A chemical 'messenger' that makes a body process happen. Hormones are secreted by glands.

hydrocarbon A compound made of only hydrogen and carbon.

hydroelectric power Making electricity by letting falling water (usually from a reservoir) turn turbines and generators.

hydrogen A light colourless gas. It is very flammable.

hydroxide A compound containing the elements hydrogen and oxygen, as well as another element, e.g. sodium hydroxide.

hydroxide ion Ion formed when a hydroxide dissolves in water (OH^-).

igneous Rock formed when hot molten magma from deep inside the Earth cools and becomes solid.

immune Protected against catching a disease because the body has already made the right antibodies.

immune system The body's ways of defending itself against disease.

immunised Protected against catching a disease by vaccination.

impulse The electrical 'message' that travels along a nerve cell.

inactive volcano One that has not erupted for many years.

indicator A dye that will change colour in acids and alkalis.

induced A current produced in a loop of wire by a changing magnetic field.

infected Having a disease caused by a microbe.

infrared radiation Another term for heat radiation.

ingest Eat. We ingest (eat) food. Some white blood cells ingest microbes by surrounding them.

insoluble Something that will not dissolve.

insulated Covered with an electrical insulator.

insulator A material that does not let energy or electricity flow through it.

insulin A hormone that makes the amount of glucose in the blood go down.

intensity The amount of light energy.

intrusive An igneous rock formed underground from magma cooling slowly inside the Earth's crust (e.g. granite). It has large crystals.

ion An atom or group of atoms with an electrical charge.

iris The coloured part of the eye. It is a muscle that opens and closes the pupil.

iron core The iron rod placed inside an electromagnet's coil to make the electromagnet stronger.

iron ore Rock containing iron oxides.

joule (J) The unit for measuring energy.

kidneys A pair of organs used to clean the blood. They remove the urea in the blood and make it into urine.

kilowatt (kW) A unit for measuring power. 1 kW = 1000 W.

kilowatt-hour (kWh) The amount of energy transferred in an hour by an appliance.

kinetic energy The kind of energy in moving things.

lactic acid The waste product of anaerobic respiration.

large intestine The organ used to remove water from undigested food.

lava Magma that has erupted from a volcano.

leaf A plant organ used to make food using photosynthesis.

leaf mosaic Non-overlapping arrangement of a plant's leaves.

leaf stalk The part of a leaf that joins it to the stem.

lens The part of the eye which changes shape to focus light on the retina.

limestone A sedimentary rock made mainly of calcium carbonate.

limiting factor The factor that controls how fast a chemical reaction can go.

lithosphere A layer in the Earth made up of the crust and the top part of the mantle.

litmus A simple kind of indicator. It is red in acids and blue in alkalis.

live One of the wires that carries electricity in a plug.

liver The organ used to make and destroy substances in our bodies.

magma Hot liquid rock in the Earth's mantle or crust.

magnet Something that attracts iron.

magnetic field The space around a magnet where its effects are felt.

magnetic material Substance that is attracted to a magnet. Contains iron, nickel or cobalt.

mantle The layer of the Earth between the crust and the core.

medicine A substance used to prevent or cure illness. It may contain a drug.

metal A strong shiny element that can be hammered into shape. Metals are good conductors of heat and electricity.

metal hydroxide A compound of oxygen, hydrogen and a metal (e.g. sodium hydroxide).

metal ion An metal atom that has lost at least one electron to form a particle with a positive charge.

metal oxide A compound of a metal and oxygen.

metamorphic A rock that has been changed by great heat or pressure.

metre (m) A unit for measuring length.

microbe A tiny organism that can only be seen with a microscope.

micro-organism Another name for a microbe.

microscope Instrument used to look at very small things.

minerals (in biology) Chemical ions that are essential in small amounts for living things to stay healthy.

minerals (in geology) The chemicals that form rocks.

monomer The building blocks of polymers. Many monomers join together to make a polymer.

motor effect Movement caused by the magnetic field around a current-carrying wire coming near the magnetic field around another magnet.

mucus A thick slippery secretion.

muscle tissue Cells that can change their length and so help us to move.

National Grid System of overhead and underground cables that carry electricity around the country.

native When something occurs in nature as the element itself, not as a compound.

natural gas A fossil fuel made from the remains of animals.

naturally immune When you become immune to a disease because you have already had it.

nerve Bundle of nerve cells.

nerve cell A cell that carries messages to other nerve cells.

nerve ending A receptor in the skin which is sensitive to temperature or touch.

nervous system The organ system that carries messages around the body.

neurone Another name for a nerve cell.

neutral (in chemistry) A liquid that is not an acid or an alkali. Has a pH of 7.

neutral (in physics) i) One of the wires that carries electricity in an appliance. ii) Something with equal amounts of positive and negative charge.

neutralisation The reaction between an acid and a base. A salt and water are produced.

neutralise Making something neutral.

newton (N) The unit for force.

nicotine A poisonous, addictive drug in tobacco.

non-metal Element that is not a metal.

non-renewable Resources that cannot be replaced once they have been used. Eventually they will run out.

north pole, north-seeking pole The end of a freely suspended bar magnet that points north.

nuclear reaction A change inside atoms. A different element is produced and huge amounts of energy are released.

nutrient A substance that a living thing needs so that it can grow healthily.

ohm (Ω) The unit for measuring electrical resistance.

oil A fossil fuel made from the remains of animals.

optic nerve The nerve that carries messages from the retina to the brain.

ore A rock that contains useful minerals.

organ A group of different tissues working together.

organ system A collection of organs working together.

organism Any living thing. An organism must do all seven of the 'life processes'.

osmosis When water flows through a semi-permeable membrane so that the concentrations on either side become more equal.

overload A fuse is overloaded if the currents gets too big and melts it.

oxide A compound of an element and oxygen.

oxidise, oxidation Adding oxygen to a chemical, in a chemical reaction.

oxygen A colourless gas that makes up about 20% of the air.

oxygen debt The amount of oxygen needed to remove the lactic acid left from anaerobic respiration.

palisade cell A cell found in leaves, which contains many chloroplasts.

pancreas The gland that secretes digestive juices and hormones.

parallel (electricity) When the current in an electrical circuit can flow along different routes.

period Horizontal row of elements in the Periodic Table.

Periodic Table Chart with the chemical elements arranged in order of atomic number.

permanent magnet Something that attracts iron all the time.

phloem tissue Living cells grouped together to carry dissolved food substances from the leaves to other parts of the plant.

photosynthesis Process that plants use to make their own food. It needs light to work. Carbon dioxide and water are used up. A sugar called glucose, and oxygen are produced.

photosynthesise Making food by photosynthesis.

plant hormone Chemical that controls the way a plant grows.

plasma The liquid part of the blood, which is mainly water.

platelets Tiny pieces of cells in the blood that release chemicals to help blood to clot.

plutonium A fuel used in nuclear power stations.

pole The ends of a magnet, where its effects are strongest.

polyethene The chemical name for polythene. It is a polymer of ethene.

polymer A long molecule made from thousands of smaller ones (monomers). Plastics are polymers.

potential difference Another name for voltage.

potential energy The scientific word for 'stored' energy.

power How quickly something transfers energy.

power line Overhead or underground cables that carry electricity.

process Sort out information.

product A substance formed by a chemical reaction.

property A way that a substance behaves.

proportional Two quantities are proportional to each other if doubling one of them makes the other one double too.

protein coat Outer coating of a virus.

proteins Important substances used for growth and repair.

proton Tiny positively charged particle in an atom's nucleus.

pupil Gap in the middle of the iris of the eye.

pure A single substance, not mixed with anything else.

pus The remains after many microbes have been ingested by white blood cells at a spot or cut.

pylon A tall tower holding up overhead power cables.

quarry A place where useful rocks are dug out of the ground.

quicklime Substance made by heating limestone. Its chemical name is calcium oxide.

radiate Give off waves of energy. A candle radiates light and heat energy.

radiation The way heat travels as waves of energy through space or transparent materials.

radioactive waste Dangerous waste from nuclear power stations.

rate The speed of a chemical reaction.

raw material Another term for a reactant.

reactant A substance used up in a chemical reaction.

reactive A substance that is likely to react.

Reactivity Series List of metals arranged in order of how reactive they are.

receptors Cells that detect changes in the body or its surroundings.

rectum The last part of the large intestine, leading to the anus. It stores faeces.

red blood cells Cells that contain haemoglobin, which carries oxygen around the body.

reduce, reduction Taking oxygen away from a compound in a chemical reaction.

reducing agent A chemical that will reduce other substances.

refinery Place where the chemicals in crude oil are separated and purified.

reflect Bouncing something back from a surface.

reflex action An automatic response to a stimulus, often to protect the body from harm.

relax When a muscle relaxes after contracting it goes back to its original shape.

relay An electromagnetic switch for turning large currents on safely.

renewable An energy source that can be replaced or used again and again, and will never run out (e.g. solar power).

repel Push something away.

resistance How difficult it is for an electrical current to flow through something.

resistor An electrical component that decreases the current in a circuit.

respiration Chemical reaction inside cells to release energy from glucose.

response How the body reacts to a stimulus that has been detected.

retina The back of the eye. It contains receptors that are sensitive to light.

ripple mark Patterns left behind in sedimentary rock from the time when the sediment was under water.

rock cycle Cycle showing how rocks are being formed and changed all the time.

root Plant organ used to hold the plant in the ground and take water and mineral salts out of the soil.

root hair cell Cell found in roots. It has a large surface area to help the cell absorb water quickly.

root hair tissue Many root hair cells grouped together.

rusting Corrosion of iron by water and oxygen.

sacrificial protection Allowing a piece of reactive metal to corrode so that an object made of a less reactive metal does not.

saliva Secretion from the salivary glands. It contains enzymes to break down starch, and mucus to help food pass smoothly down the gullet.

salt A compound formed when an acid reacts with a base.

Sankey diagram A diagram which shows how much energy goes into a system and the forms that the energy is given out as.

scab Hard protective covering over a cut that forms when a blood clot dries.

sclera Protective outer layer of the eye.

secretion Useful substance (e.g. saliva) made by gland cells.

sediment Tiny particles that settle to the bottom of a liquid.

sedimentary Rock formed by the compression and cementing of material that has settled at the bottom of the sea.

seed Grows into a new plant. Made by flowering plants and conifers.

semi-permeable A membrane that will let small particles, like water, through it but not large ones.

sensory neurone A nerve cell that carries messages from a receptor to the brain or spinal cord.

series Electrical components connected 'in line' so that all of an electric current flows through each one, one after another.

sex organ The stamen (male) and carpel (female) in a flower. They make the male and female sex cells.

slaked lime A base made from limestone. Its chemical name is calcium hydroxide.

small intestine The organ used to digest and absorb food.

solar cell A kind of battery that generates electricity using energy from the Sun.

soluble Something that can dissolve in a liquid.

solution A substance dissolved in a solute.

solvent A chemical used to dissolve something.

solvent abuse Breathing in solvent fumes on purpose.

south pole, south-seeking pole The end of a freely suspended bar magnet that points south.

spinal cord Large bundle of nerve cells that carries messages to and from the brain. It runs down the back, inside the spine.

stain Dye used to colour parts of a cell to make them easier to see.

stainless steel Mixture of iron with chromium, carbon and other elements. It does not rust.

starch Carbohydrate that plants use as a store of food.

stem Plant organ used to support a plant and take water and mineral salts to the leaves.

stimulus (plural **stimuli**) Change within the body or in its surroundings that a receptor senses.

stomach Organ used to help break down food. It secretes digestive juices.

stomata (singular **stoma**) Small holes on the underside of leaves which let gases into and out of the leaf.

storage organ Part of a plant where food substances can be stored.

sucrose The chemical name for the sugar used in cooking. Some plants (e.g. sugar beet) make it from glucose.

sugars Group of carbohydrates that dissolve in water and taste sweet.

sulphur dioxide A gas that is produced in small quantities when fossil fuels are burnt.

surface area The total area of all the surfaces of a shape.

suspensory ligaments Part of the eye. They work with the ciliary muscle to hold the lens in place and change its shape.

symbol equation Shorthand way of showing what happens in a chemical reaction using symbols.

symptom Sign that the body has a disease.

target cell A cell that is affected by a hormone.

target organ An organ that is affected by a hormone.

taste bud Receptor on the tongue which is sensitive to flavours.

tectonic plate A section of the Earth's lithosphere.

temporary magnet Something that can be made to attract iron when needed.

terminal Where an electrical connection is made.

thermal decomposition Breaking a compound down by heating it.

thermal energy Another name for heat energy.

thorax The chest, containing the lungs and heart.

tides Twice-daily rising and falling of sea levels, caused by the pull of the Moon.

tissue A group of the same cells all doing the same job.

toxin Poisonous substance made by a living thing.

trachea The main air tube to the lungs.

transfer The word used for heat or energy moving from place to place.

transformer Piece of equipment that increases or decreases voltage. A step-up transformer increases voltage and a step-down transformer decreases voltage.

transmit Getting electricity from one place to another.

transpiration Loss of water from a plant's leaves.

transpiration stream The flow of water up through a plant's roots and stem to its leaves.

transport (in Earth science) When eroded fragments are moved away from their 'parent rock' by wind or water.

turbine A machine that is turned by a moving fluid.

Unit A unit for measuring the amount of electrical energy transferred. 1 Unit is the same as 1 kilowatt-hour.

universal indicator A mixture of indicators used to tell how weak or strong an acid or an alkali is.

uranium A fuel used in nuclear power stations.

urea Waste product from the breakdown of unwanted amino acids by the liver.

urinate Getting rid of urine when you go to the toilet.

urine Solution of the body's waste products, which are removed from the blood by the kidneys.

useful energy Energy that is in a form that can be used, e.g. in a power station the energy produced as electricity is useful energy – the energy lost as heat is not.

vaccination Being given an injection of a vaccine to help the body protect itself against a disease.

vaccine Weak or dead disease-causing microbes put into the body on purpose. White blood cells make the right antibodies and the person becomes immune.

valve Part of a vein or the heart that stops the blood in it from flowing the wrong way.

vapour Another name for a gas.

vein (in a plant) Bundle of tubes that carry water and food substances into and out of a leaf.

vein (in the body) Blood vessel that carries blood towards the heart.

ventilation The movement of air into and out of the lungs.

ventricle The lower space on each side of the heart. It pumps blood into arteries.

villus (plural **villi**) Projections on the lining of the small intestine. They increase its surface area and speed up absorption of nutrients into the blood.

violent A reaction that is very quick.

virus Tiny protein-coated particle that causes disease. It enters a living cell where it reproduces, damaging the cell.

viscous A liquid that is thick and 'treacly', not runny.

vitamin Chemical from a living thing that is essential in tiny amounts for the body to stay healthy.

volcano An opening in the Earth's crust where magma can flow out (erupt) onto the surface.

volt (**V**) The unit for measuring voltage, or potential difference.

voltage The amount of 'pushing' that an electrical cell does.

voltmeter Piece of equipment used to measure voltage.

wasted energy Energy that cannot be used.

watt (**W**) The unit for measuring power.

weathering The breaking down of rocks by rain or ice.

white blood cells Various types of cells in the blood that help to protect the body from disease.

wilt When a plant has not had enough water and goes 'floppy'.

wind turbine A kind of windmill that generates electricity using energy from the wind.

withdrawal symptom The unpleasant side-effects when someone stops taking an addictive drug.

word equation Way of showing what happens in a chemical reaction using words.

xylem cells Dead cells found in the stems and roots of plants. They are hollow.

xylem tissue Xylem cells grouped together in tubes that carry water and mineral salts up from the plant's roots to the leaves.

Index

Pearson Educational
Edinburgh Gate
Harlow
Essex

© Pearson Education Limited 2002

The right of Mark Levesley, Jackie Hardie, Richard O'Regan, Sarah Pitt, Nicky Thomas, Bob Wakefield, Richard Grime, Penny Johnson, Silvia Newton, Mike O'Neill and Gary Philpott to be identified as the authors of this Work has been asserted by them in accordance with the Copyright, Designs and Patents Act of 1988.

Third impression 2004

ISBN 0582 776120

Designed by Pentacor and produced by IFADesign Ltd

Printed in China SWTC/03

The publisher's policy is to use paper manufactured from sustainable forests.

Acknowledgments

The publisher would like to thank many people for their help, support and encouragement in the production of this book. In particular: Susan Anderson, Gary Baker, Patricia Baker, Graham Barney, John Brierley, Malcolm Burns, David Kirkby, Janet Murray, Alastair Sandiforth, and Chris Shipley: Davenant Foundation School, Loughton; Burnt Mill School, Harlow.

We are grateful to the following for permission to reproduce copyright photographs:

Ace Photo Agency pages 80 *top left* (Graham Young), 94 *top* (Ian Sabell), 108 *top left* (P & M Walton), 159 (Peter Adams), 162 *top right* (PLI); Adams Picture Library page 166; John Adds page 48; Agripicture.com page 161; Alton Towers page 178 *left*; Ardea page 122 *top*; Art Directors &: TRIP pages 10 *bottom left* (Eric Smith), 73 (H Rogers), 94 *middle left* (A Lambert), 94 *middle right* (A Lambert), 181 (H Rogers), 199 (H Rogers); Associated Press page 117 *bottom* (Kevork Djansezian); Auto Express Picture Library page 48 *top*; Biophoto Associates pages 8 *top right*; Gareth Boden pages 11, 15, 20 *bottom*, 31 *bottom left*, 31 *top*, 32 *bottom*, 37, 42 *bottom*, 55, 67, 68, 72 *bottom*, 88, 93, 94 *bottom*, 96, 97,100, 107, 110, 112 *top left*, 112 *bottom* 117 *top*. 119, 121, 122 *bottom*, 123 *right*, 127, 128 *top*, 129 *middle*, 129 *bottom*, 131 *bottom 1eft*, 147 *bottom*, 163 *bottom*, 166 *bottom*, 167 *bottom*, 171, 173, 174,175, 177, 178 *right*, 180 *right*, 183 *left*, 184 *bottom*, 185, 186 *bottom*, 189, 200 *top*, 201 *top*, 203 *bottom*, 212, 213, 215, 223, 237 *bottom*, 239; Professor W J Broughton page 61 *right*; Trevor Clifford pages 13, 25, 92 *top*, 130 *top right*, 132 *bottom right*, 147 168 *top*, 166, 183 *top*, 225, 227; Corbis page 242; Custom Medical Stock Photo pages 80 (V Zuber), 83 *bottom right* (OJ Staats); Dorling Kindersley pages 43 *top right* (Ian O'Leary), 54 *top* (Neil Fletcher), 64 *top* (Max Alexander), 87 *top left* (Dave King), 129 *top* (Harry Taylor), 134 *top left*, 134 *top middle* (Colin Keates), 134 *top right* (Harry Taylor), 134 *bottom left* (Colin Keates), 134 *top midd1e* (Colin Keates), 134 *bottom right*, 201 *bottom* (Tim Ridley), 224 *top* (Susannah Price); Greg Evans International pages 10 *top right* (Greg Balfour Evans), 91 *bottom left*; Mary Evans Picture Library page 142; www.freeplay.net page 239;Ford Motor Company page 189;Geophotos pages 130 *bottom right*, 137, 191; GeoScience Picture Library pages, 48 *bottom*, 87 *bottom left*, 92 *bottom*, 102 *bottom right*, 131 *top*, 132 *bottom left*, 139 *bottom*, 156, 160 to, 162 *top left*, 162 *bottom*; Robert Harding Picture Library pages 6 *bottom right* (Jay Thomas), 27 *top* (Dr Dennis Kunkel/Phototake NYC);C Hoseason pages 114 *top right*, 114 *middle left*, 117 *middle*, 153 *middle top*, 234 *bottom*, 236 *bottom*; Holt Studios International pages 61 *middle left*, 61 *bottom left*, 62 *bottom*, 64 *middle left* & 64 *middle right* (Nigel Cattlin);Hutchinson Picture Library pages 89 (Robert Francis), 163 *top* (Tony Souter);Penny Johnson pages 3 *top middle*, 132 *top*; Frank Lane Picture Agency pages 6 *top right below top right* (D Maslowski), 6 *middle* (Marineland), 6 *bottom left* (Silvestris), 46 *top*, 56 (M J Thomas), 58 *top* (A Wharton), 196 (Celtic Picture Library), 22O (H Binz); Mark Levesley pages 4 *bottom*, 43 *top left*, 46 *top right*, 46 *bottom left*, 48 *bottom middle*, 51 *top*, 51 *bottom*, 52, 62 *top*, 64 *bottom*, 65 *left*, 69 *right*, 80 *top right*, 90 *bottom*, 91 *top*, 103, 114 *middle*, 116, 118 *top*, 118 *bottom*, 120 *top*, 120 *bottom left*, 120 *bottom right*, 152, 153 *middle*, 182 *right*, 186 *top*, 200 *bottom*, 202 *top*, 216, 234 *top*, 236 *top*; Miller Pattison Ltd page 176; NHPA pages 6 *above bottom* (Joe Blossom), 120 *middle left* (Stephen Dalton), 131 *middle right* (N A Callow), 160 *bottom* (David Woodfall); Natural Science Photos page 60 *left* (C Williams); Oxford Scientific Films pages 10 *middle* (NASA), 65 *right* (Chris Sharp), 120 *middle right* (Larry Crowhurst), 126 (NASA), 128 *bottom* (Andrew Plumptire), 140 (Doug Alan), 195 (Ronald Toms); PA News page 40; PYMCA page 184 *top* (Richard Braine); Panos Pictures page 105 (Rob Huibers); Pictor International pages 42 *top*, 42 *middle*, 91 *bottom right*, 197 *left*; Popperfoto pages 38 *left*, 139 *top* (Reuters/Simon Kwong), 182 *left* (Reuters/Gary Caskey); Powergen page 241;Powerstock Zefa pages 4 *top left*, 6 *middle left* (Kelly Mooney), 75, 167 *top left, top*; Rex Features pages 43 *bottom*, 102 *top*, 108 *bottom*, 114 *top left*, 141, 180, 193; Coral Rogers page 32 *top*; Keisude Saito page 58 *bottom right*; Science Museum/Science & Society Picture Library page 86 *right*; Science Photo Library pages 2 *bottom middle left bottom right*, 6 (Dr Gopal Murti), 7 (K R Porter), 8 *bottom* (Secchi Lecaque/Roussel-Uclaf/CNRI), 9 (Prof P Mottia/Dept of Anatomy/University "La Sapienza", Rome), 16 (Alfred Pasieka), 19 (Eye of Science), 22 (NASA), 26 (Juergen Berger, Max-Planck Institute), 27 *bottom* (Andrew Syred), 31 *bottom right* (BSIP VEM), 34 *top* (Mark Clarke), 34 *middle* (Dr P Marazzi), 34 *bottom left* (Dept of Medicall Photography, St Stephens Hospital, London), 34 *bottom right* (Scott Camazine), 38 *right* (Dee Breger), 39 *right* (Biology Media), 39 *left* (Dr Jeremy Burgess), 47 (Andrew Syred), 50 (David Frazier/Agstock), 53 (Andrew Syred), 54 *top left* (Dr Jeremy Burgess), 54 *bottom left* (Dr Jeremy Burgess), 60 *right* (Martyn F Chillmaid), 72, 78 *top* (Saturn Stills), 78 *bottom* (Saturn Stills), 81 (A Glauberman), 83 *bottom left*, 131 *left* (Sinclair Stammers), 143 (Dr Ken MacDonald), 146 (Jeremy Walker), 150 (John Kaprielian), 151 *right* (Andrew Lambert Photography), 153 (Simon Fraser/Northumbrian Environmental Management Ltd), 197 *top right* (Martin Bond), 197 *right bottom*, 218 (Peter Menzel) 225 *left* (Laguna Design); E.F. Smith Collection, Rare Books &. Manuscript Library, University of Pennsylvania, Philadelphia page 86 *left*; www.shoutpictures.com page 224 *bottom*; Still Pictures page 104 *top right* (John Maier), 104 *bottom right* (John Maier); The Stock Market page 102 *left*; Telegraph Colour Library pages 3 *bottom right*, 10 *top left* (Megumi Miyake), 10 *bottom right* (F.P.G ©Spencer Jones), 33 (F.P.G. © J Cummins), 158 (David Noton), 172 (I & V Krafft/HoaQui), 188 (NASA), 192 (V.C.L.), 194 (L Lefkowitz), 221 (V.C.L.); Topham Picture point pages 69 *left*, 108 *top right*, 114 *bottom*; Vitax page 80 *middle right*; Simon Watts pages 3 *bottom right*, 74 *top*, 83 *top*, 87 *top*, 87 *bottom right*, 90 *top*, 90 *middle*, 123 *left*, 202 *bottom*, 203 *top*, 228, 231; Wellcome Trust Medical Photographic Library pages 20 *top* (Mike Kayser), 29 *right* (National Medical Slide Bank), 46 *bottom right*, 230;

Cover Photos: PhotoDisc

Every effort has been made to trace, and acknowledge ownership of copyright. If you have been overlooked, the publisher will be pleased to make the necessary changes at the earliest opportunity.